Health Care UK 1996/97

The King's Fund review of health policy

Health Care UK 1996/97

The King's Fund review of health policy

Published by
King's Fund Publishing
11–13 Cavendish Square
London W1M 0AN

First published 1997

ISBN 1 85717 167 5

A CIP catalogue record for this book is available from the British Library

Distributed by Grantham Book Services Limited
Isaac Newton Way
Alma Park Industrial Estate
GRANTHAM
Lincolnshire
NG31 9SD

Tel: 01476 541 080
Fax: 01476 541 061

Printed and bound in Great Britain

Cover illustration: Minuche Mazumdar Farrar

Contents

Contributors

Gifford Batstone
Postgraduate Dean for mid-Trent and Professor of Postgraduate and Continuing Medical Education, Nottingham University

Mary Edwards
Director of Nursing and Patient Services, North Hampshire Hospitals NHS Trust

Anthony Harrison
Fellow in Health Policy Analysis, King's Fund Policy Institute

Bob Hudson
Senior Research Fellow, Community Care Division, Nuffield Institute for Health, University of Leeds

Ken Judge
Formerly Director, King's Fund Policy Institute, now Professor of Social Policy, University of Kent

Thomas Judge
Atlantic Fellow in Public Policy '96-'97, Capital Ambulance Service, Maine, USA

Robert J Maxwell
Chief Executive, King's Fund

Nicholas Mays
Director, Health Services Research, and Acting Director, King's Fund Policy Institute

Martin McKee
Professor of European Public Health, London School of Hygiene and Tropical Medicine

Elias Mossialos
Senior Lecturer in European Health Policy, London School of Economics and Political Science, and Director, LSE Health

Jo Ann Mulligan
Research Officer, King's Fund Policy Institute

Bill New
Senior Research Officer, King's Fund Policy Institute

HEALTH POLICY REVIEW

Part 1 Main Events

As it turned out, this year's Review covers the final year of Conservative responsibility for the NHS. The first section records the final stages of the transformation of the NHS following the NHS and Community Care Act 1990. That transformation from 'old' to 'new' NHS with its introduction of the distinction between providers and purchasers, together with the contracting structure which that entailed, appeared at the time to represent the most radical change that the NHS had ever experienced. But Labour in Opposition had already indicated before coming to office that it did not intend a wholesale elimination of the measures that comprised the 'new' NHS. Thus what was once a radical change is now an established part of the policy environment.

As in previous Reviews, Part 1 goes on to consider the measures the Conservative Government took in the four other main policy areas which together with the introduction of the 1990 Act comprise their attempt to transform the provision of health and social care: community care, public health strategy, serving the consumer and clinical knowledge. Part 2 appraises these and other developments against the three broad criteria of efficiency, equity and accountability. Finally, Part 3 of the Review offers a brief overview of health policy developments in the 1990s.

1.1 Creating the New NHS

The changes in the regional structure and the formation of combined health authorities covering hospital, community and family health services foreshadowed in last year's Review, came formally into effect on 1 April 1996 but had already been anticipated in many districts. This measure was part of a broader programme of slimming down the management costs of running the Service, within the Department of Health and the NHS Executive and among purchasers and providers.

This programme was itself a response to the charge that Labour in Opposition were vigorous in making, that the 1991 reforms had led to a massive increase in the number of managers. Although definitions have changed several times, there is little doubt that numbers have increased as a result of the 1991 reforms, but according to King's Fund Policy Institute estimates, perhaps only some 15-20 per cent of the recorded figures can be accounted for in this way. Administrative costs appear to have risen by about 3 percentage points of total spending on health and community health services during the 1990s.

In August 1996, the Executive published *Planned Management Costs in NHS Trusts* covering the financial years 1995/96 and 1996/97. This showed that spending on management was set to fall by 5 per cent in cash terms in line with the target that had been set in October 1995. Management costs for health authorities were also planned to fall: see Table 1.

The changes in the regional structure and the formation of combined health authorities covering hospital, community and family health services were expected to save some £100 million and cuts within the Department of Health a further £55 million. Taken together a reduction of some £300 million of management costs was claimed. [PR 96/269]

The Executive's booklet acknowledges that the data presented do not give any indication of what the figures 'should' be:

> *The actual cost of management is not a very useful value on its own.* (p5)

That in itself is a recognition of the arbitrary nature of the targeted reductions which are explicable only in terms of the Government's desire to see the figures reduced rather than as genuine improvements to the efficiency of the Service.

Getting management costs to the 'right' level is a much trickier and slower operation than target-setting. Last year's Review referred to the scrutiny of bureaucracy in general practice. In May 1996, the NHS Executive published a similar report, *Seeing the Wood, Sparing the Trees*, which tried to identify how bureaucracy might be reduced within health authorities and trusts. In the foreword, the team responsible for it ingenuously – and ungrammatically – record that they began their review expecting 'some simple, instant answers to cutting bureaucracy' but found instead that 'developing more mature relationships, based on openness and trust' would be the single most important move towards minimising bureaucracy. Achieving such trust, as they acknowledge, 'takes time.' Mindful of the need for immediate savings, they made a series of recommendations – see Box on p. 4 – which they estimated would save some £40 million – only a fraction of the reduction the Executive was looking for.

A substantial part of the identified savings was to come from the proposals in relation to extra-contractual referrals. The report estimates that £22 million is currently spent on administering the system plus the time of clinical and senior managers. In EL (96)94, the Executive removed the requirement on NHS trusts to obtain prior approval for elective referrals. As a result, the Department claimed, some 175,000 forms would

Table 1 Health authority and NHS trust management costs, England,1995–96 to 1997–98

	1995–96 planned (£ million)	*1995–96 actual (£ million)*	*1996–97 planned (£ million)*	*1997–98 planned (£ million)*
Health Authorities	477	497	450	447
NHS Trusts	1,299	1,275	1,232	1,224
Total	1,776	1,773	1,683	1,671

Source: Health Authority Costs and Management Costs in NHS Trusts, NHS Executive, 1996

Table 2 Management and professional letters sent to the NHS

Management letters	*1994*	*1995*
Executive Letters	102	145
Health Service Guidelines	56	67
Finance Director Letters	76	64
Family Health Services Letters	67	76
Professional letters from:	*1994*	*1995*
Chief Medical Officer	13	6
Chief Nursing Officer	17	3
Chief Dental Officer	0	6
Chief Pharmacist	2	0
Chief Officer (usually a Senior Medical Officer)	7	5

Source: *Seeing the Wood, Sparing the Trees,* Department of Health 1966

be abolished, saving £12 million a year. Whether the Department and the Executive will respond to the proposal that the number of management letters is halved remains to be seen. As Table 2 shows, they were issued in 1995 at the rate of more than 1 per working day. In addition, health authorities were sent some 400 other publications and trusts 200.

The growth of management, transaction or bureaucratic costs stems in part from the introduction of the purchaser/provider split in general and the creation of fundholding in particular. The number of fundholders continued to grow. In August 1996, it was announced that a further 1,672 GPs had applied to join as from April 1997, bringing the total to more than 56 per cent of all GPs in England.

1996/67 was also the first year of full piloting of the total purchasing variant of fundholding. Unlike the initial fundholding scheme, the Department has commissioned research – co-ordinated by the King's Fund – designed to monitor its progress from the outset. The research team's first report, *Total Purchasing: a profile of national pilot projects*, was published in January 1997. It found that total purchasing was developing in a number of forms, partly as a reflection of the fact that they were total purchasers in name only. Formally, for services outside the standard fundholding scheme, responsibility continues to remain with health authorities and in practice 'total' purchasers had chosen to 'purchase' only a part of the total spectrum of care. Table 3 sets out the areas where they reported they were seeking to make changes in service delivery.

This report, and another carried out by the Universities of Keele and Birmingham for the NHS Executive West Midlands, *Beyond Fundholding: a mosaic of primary care led commissioning and provision*, confirm the growing diversity of local purchasing arrangements, in terms both of organisational structures and the roles played by different professionals. They also identify the potential, in the absence of measures to prevent it, of even more diversity developing.

Despite its vigorous development, however, the impact of purchasing as a distinct function is hard to determine. Nick Goodwin's assessment of the evidence relating to GP fundholding in *Health Care UK 1995/96* was unable to reach a clear-cut conclusion. Similarly, *Beyond Fundholding* points out that the merits and demerits of the different forms of purchasing remain moot. By its very title, *Small Steps: Big Goals*, Sharon Redmayne's 1996 report on purchasing policies in the NHS indicates that progress in making purchasing effective has been slow. She concludes:

> *It is perhaps inevitable that the purchasing process should only develop slowly: given the*

Cutting back on bureaucracy

The following set of proposals is taken from the executive summary of *Seeing the Wood: Sparing the Trees*. The report contains 54 more specific recommendations.

Central communications:

- Cut in half the number of management letters and newsletters.
- Establish a 'gatekeeper' to control distribution.
- Use electronic links for management communications by April 1997.

The processes for contracting:

Extra-contractual referrals (ECRs)

- Abolish Trust role in seeking approval for elective ECRs.
- Abolish notification of tertiary and emergency ECRs.

Relations between Trusts and GP fundholders

- Automate invoicing.
- Improve relationships through training.
- Practical steps for Trusts and fundholders to take now include:

  reduce the level of queries;

  reduce the number of invoices.

Longer-term contracts and information for contracting

- Encourage use of longer-term (over one year) contracts.
- Standardise formats for contracting information.

Central information requirements:

- Immediate cuts to central monitoring on activity, waiting times, Patient's Charter, and workforce.
- A series of fundamental reviews by June 1997.
- A major drive to improve data quality in the NHS.

Information management and technology:

- Launch initiative to link Trusts and Health Authorities to NHS-wide network.
- Greater commitment to IT investment.

Ideas for the future:

- Streamline approval process for private finance.
- Routine assessments of impact of policy on administration.
- Trusts and health authorities to look at scope for streamlining internal procedures, pool resources

nature of the services provided, commissioners cannot afford to take unnecessary risks. The move to more local, primary care-led services with less emphasis on acute hospital services is taking place at a gradual and steady pace with most purchasing plans identifying specific pilot initiatives designed to shift the focus of care. This reorganisation of the pattern of services also highlights a further and perhaps unexpected change in purchasing policy since the introduction of the purchaser/provider split: the role of the internal market and competition as revealed by the purchasing plans is not developing in the way it was originally envisaged. Health authorities are not leaving the market to determine the level and pattern of services. The purchasing plans, and the five year strategic plans, have revealed that commissioners are seeking to control the market, using competition where necessary to improve quality, but to manage it so that services are adapted to their long term objectives. Relationships with providers are to become more long term and mutually bene-

Table 3 Total purchasing sites: priority service areas for purchasing 1996/97

Service area	*No. of sites*
Emergency admissions and accident and emergency attendances	33
Community/continuing care	32
Mental health care	29
Maternity care	28
Care of the elderly	14
Early discharge/reduced length of stay in acute medical and surgical beds	12
Other accident and emergency (e.g. ambulances, data gathering)	12
Oncology	5
Palliative and terminal care	3
Cardiology	2
Other priority service areas	9

Source: *Total Purchasing: a profile of national pilot projects*, King's Fund 1997

> *ficial, rather than focussed around an annual 'free-for-all' in the market place*. (p 32)

The notion that health authorities could make an independent assessment of the needs of their population, free from the taint of provider interest, was one of the fundamental justifications of the purchaser/provider split. A report prepared for the King's Fund London Commission by Naomi Fulop and colleagues at the London Health Economics Consortium examined the process of needs assessment and its impact on purchasing policies.

The study did find some evidence of impact – at least in terms of people's perceptions: see Table 4. It also found that most needs studies were small-scale:

> *The mean estimated cost per study was £13,783; the median estimated study cost, however, was £7,500. The range of values lay between £160 (a couple of days' work on alcohol consumption levels) and £55,000 (a major project of 18 months duration examining the needs of residents in a particular locality in some detail). Other examples include a mental health needs assessment which cost £6,400; a review of ethnic minority health needs costing £2,760; and a study of the needs for continuing care of the frail elderly which cost £12,000. Cumulatively, the equivalent of some £800,000 was identified as having been committed to the production of these 58 studies*. (p15/16)

Table 4 Influence of needs assessment

	No. of studies	*% total*
Very influential	28	39
Positive but not vital	15	21
Little or no impact	5	7
No needs information	21	30

Source: N Fulop *et al*, *A survey of needs assessment activities in London health authorities*, King's Fund 1997

The modest scale of this work reflects the limited role of needs assessment in practice: whereas initially needs assessment was seen as the first step in the process of defining the mix of services to be provided, it has become one of a large number of health authority functions, which have crowded out this apparently core process. As one director of public health, Philip Milner, has put it:

> *Health authorities have been working hard on developing health strategies and health programmes. Much of this work has come to naught. Towards the end of the financial year the contracting process takes over. Large sums of money are exchanged between purchasers and providers without explicit cognisance of the health strategy or programmes.* (*Journal of Public Health Medicine*, vol 18 no 4 p 379)

Another insight into the effectiveness of purchasing emerges from the Audit Commission study of maternity care *First Class Delivery*. This found that 8 of the 12 authorities studied did not have a strategy for maternity services as a whole; six included maternity care in large block contracts for 'acute' or for 'women's services. It adds:

> *In the absence of a clear lead from purchasers, trusts – and sometimes individual clinicians within trusts – have taken responsibility for key decisions about services, such as what antenatal screening and testing services they will provide or the extent to which they involve GPs in shared care protocols. Health authorities must take responsibility for decisions about the levels and types of service that they commission and improve the specifications in contracts.* (p 68)

Thus, even for this readily definable service, which recent government policy in the form of the *Changing Childbirth* initiative has drawn attention to, the purchasing role is only partly developed. A theme report from the Health Advisory Service, *Mental Health Services*, (which covers Huntington's Disease, acquired brain injury and early onset dementia) reaches very similar conclusions for a different set of patients.

> *Most health authorities and social services departments had no member of staff with any specialist knowledge of the needs of people who form the subject client groups of this report. One health authority that is responsible for the population of a major city even lacked a member of staff with specialist knowledge of mental health. Also, it appeared that specialist skills, where they existed, were not always used effectively.* (p 57)

The report also points out that where change had occurred, the prime movers had been provider clinicians:

> *Visiting teams found that the most dynamic force for change was the existence of a clinical team with a special interest in one or more of the client groups and a commitment to develop a more comprehensive array of services to meet its needs. Where this was the case, the district had a single focus for:*
>
> - *gathering information about need;*
> - *providing advice and support to families and carers;*

- *providing advice and support to primary care teams;*
- *building links with other relevant specialist services (such as neurology, genetics and the psychiatry of old age); and*
- *developing new services in alliance with charities and the independent sector.* (p60)

The report goes on to point out that while services had benefited from a strong provider lead, there were drawbacks:

> *... provider-led autonomous local development of this kind can result in individual service providers defining their own operational policies unilaterally and, as a result, there is a risk that key groups of clients can be excluded or overlooked. In some areas, this has had a combined effect of producing service underlapping.*
>
> *The visiting teams found that, in the absence of a clinical team with a special interest, the health and social services had often come to rely on the local branches of the major charities (eg the Alzheimer's Disease Association, the Huntington's Disease Association and Headway) as the main sources of local expertise, services, equipment and even funds for specialist provision.* (p60)

London's Mental Health, another report for the King's Fund London Commission, also concluded that purchasers found it difficult to define the pattern of service provision they wanted, in part because they had insufficient expertise to do so. Echoing the London Health Consortium findings, it found that:

> *Many health authorities . . . seem simply to have insufficient people working on mental health issue to make any real impact on local services.* (p352)

Similar conclusions were reached by a parallel study into care of the elderly.

In some areas, the need for local knowledge has been removed by central intervention. In the case of emergency care, for example, the Department of Health issued a stream of papers during 1996/97 bearing on how services could be improved and also issued guidance with EL (96)35 in respect of renal services and breast cancer services with EL (97)33. In the case of ambulance services, it went further and set out a new set of performance criteria including a new categorisation of 999 calls, which are to apply nationally, leaving local purchasers little discretion as to the standards to which ambulance services should aim. The recommendation of the *Review of Ambulance Performance Standards: final report of steering group July 1996* that a category of non-urgent calls should be defined which would allow local flexibility as to how they were dealt with was not accepted.

In general, the structure of purchasing has developed more rapidly than providing. Only a few trusts have merged – less than 20 trusts were formed as a result of merger between 1994 and 1996 – and trusts have continued to dominate the provision of NHS care, both overall and in their respective areas. Furthermore, they have also been successful in gaining additional income from the private sector. In 1995, the NHS earned well over £200 million from the provision of private medical care and now holds some 16 per cent of the market. As far as the provision of most hospital and community health services is concerned, there has been no development

Table 5 Structure of GP practices: England

No of Principals	*1985*	*1995*
1	2,915	2,794
2	3,880	3,612
3	4,986	4,041
4	4,352	4,784
5	3,610	4,345
6 +	4,292	7,126

Source: Health and Personal Social Service Statistics

which parallels the growth of locality purchasing in its various forms.

Within primary care, the average 'size of firm', ie the practice, has risen slightly; this is mainly due to larger practices getting larger than the elimination of smaller ones: see Table 5. These figures understate, however, the extent to which general practice has changed and the effective size of the organisations within which general medical services are provided. Not only has the number of practice-based staff continued to rise – between 1989 and 1995, the number of practice nurses doubled to over 10,000 – but co-operation in different forms between practices has continued to develop. In some cases, practices have grouped together specifically so as to become fundholders, as Table 6 shows. In 1991 the number of practices and number of funds was almost the same. By 1995 there was a large difference, implying that groupings were more common.

Co-operation has also become particularly important in out-of-hours services. The number of out-of-hours co-operatives registered with the National Association of General Practice Co-operatives rose from six in 1990 to 124 in October 1996.

The policy rhetoric throughout the 1990s has stressed the development of primary care, be it through a 'shift in the balance of care' from hospital to community or through the creation of a 'primary-care led NHS' within which purchasing decisions were shifted into primary care through fundholding. As noted already, the shift in purchasing has occurred but the parallel shift in provision has been much less noticeable. One reason for this is that the Government failed to match their rhetoric with a financial framework which would encourage shifts to take place. The rigid division between finance for general medical services and hospital and community health services has been largely maintained and as a consequence GPs have had no financial incentive to take on more work from the acute hospital. Transfers have taken place, eg in care for diabetics, but these have been 'uncompensated': the scope of general medical services has been undefined.

These and other issues were identified in the course of a 'listening exercise', a round-the-country tour by Gerry Malone, the then Minister for Health. The problems identified in that process – see Table 7 – were addressed in two White Papers, *Choice and Opportunity* and *Primary Care: delivering the future*.

Subsequently the NHS (Primary Care) Act 1997 which embodied most of their proposals was passed just before Parliament was dissolved. In particular, the Act provides for:

- a salaried option for GPs
- practice-contracts
- a single budget for all health services.

Table 6 New fundholders: England

	1991	*1995*
No of practices	305	524
No of funds	293	325

Source: Royal College of General Practitioners

Table 7 Common problems in NHS primary care identified through the 'listening exercise'

- Variations in quality of care;
- Co-ordination failures between different agencies and professional groups;
- Weaknesses in team working;
- Lack of responsiveness of services to local needs;
- Gaps in the provision of information for patients;
- Barriers to developing the roles of nurses and other non-medical primary care professionals;
- Inequitable distribution of primary care resources;
- Poor quality premises and infrastructure in some areas, particularly inner cities;
- Low morale and recruitment difficulties, particularly in inner cities;
- Inflexibility in service provision due to rigid national practitioner contracts;
- Limited opportunities for research and career development;
- Lack of systemic incentives to shift resources and services out of hospitals;

Source: NHS Executive. *Primary Care: the future.* Leeds, NHSE, 1996.

These measures open the way for a radical change in the way that services outside hospital are delivered. The Act envisages, however, that change should be introduced on a pilot basis – in sharp contrast to the national imposition of the new GP contract in 1990. In EL (97)27, the Executive set out a timetable for the piloting process, which required expressions of interest to be sent in by 1 May and the subsequent steps completed so as to allow pilots to begin on 1 April 1998.

These proposals represent a measure of deregulation which, in Nick Mays and Angela Coulter's words:

> *...will sweep away many of the existing legislative, budgetary and procedural barriers to innovation, paving the way for experiments with a variety of new organisational forms for the delivery of primary care including general medical, dental and community pharmaceutical services.* (BMJ 15 Feb 1997 p510)

As Mays and Coulter go on to point out:

> *It looks as if much of the burden of accrediting, monitoring, and regulating the new arrangements will fall on local health authorities. They may not be able to do this adequately, especially if a large number of pilots are allowed to proceed. Health authorities are currently preoccupied with the annual contracting round and the pressure to reduce waiting times for hospital services. Most of the top jobs in the new merged and slimmed down authorities went to people with experience of secondary rather than primary care. Even those people who liaise with general practitioner fundholders or locality commissioning groups have been concerned mainly with developing the purchasing role of primary care rather than its providing role* (p512)

This assessment reflects experience in London, where in the so-called London Initiative Zone, a large number of projects were supported with the general objective of bringing London's primary care services up to the standards prevailing elsewhere. The programme has been successful in many respects: as last year's Review reported, substantial sums have been spent on GP premises and other physical assets. But the programme was assembled quickly and so many projects were accepted because they were ready to go rather than because they were the best that could be devised.

Not surprisingly therefore, Nicholas Mays and colleagues in *Evaluating Primary Care Development: a review of evaluation in the London Initiative Zone primary care development programme* (King's Fund 1997) conclude that the way the Zone was implemented did not provide a model for the development of primary care in the light of the White Papers.

> *If evaluation is a concern, then the LIZ experience does not provide a model of how to organise a programme. On the other hand, it has resulted in considerable and rapid investment in primary and community care in London. The focus of the LIZ programme has not been to provide complex evaluations of individual projects. While individual HAs are now beginning to look at the impact of the programme within their own areas, there has been no real effort yet to assess the overall impact of the programme across London.* (p74)

If the financial boundary between primary and secondary care were to be lifted as the 1997 Primary Care Act provides, a means has to be found to define what general medical services consist of. As *Core Services: taking the initiative*, a statement from the General Medical Services Committee of the BMA, puts it:

> *Given appropriate time and resources, GPs have already demonstrated their ability to provide traditional secondary care services nearer to the patient, and the Government has recognised the success of this shift in the focus of care by seeking to encourage it further through* Primary care: the future … *However, the lack of a clear mechanism for controlling and resourcing additional work which flows into general practice is presently threatening the quality of the core of general practice as well as frightening off potential recruits to the discipline. GPs now seek to resolve this dilemma by developing effective mechanisms for resourcing extensions to their services.* (p3)

The paper argues that:

> *The concept of core services is a positive one. It offers doctors a clear structure for saying 'yes' to new work if they consider it appropriate and within their capability. It also enables them to say 'no' if they fear that the quality of general medical services they provide to their patients might suffer as a consequence of extending their services.* (p3)

It then goes on to define what it considers non-core services: see Box opposite.

While the structure and role of general practice has changed markedly since 1991, the trust regime has scarcely changed since its inception and remains highly restrictive. In particular, insistence on annual targets, and the use of surpluses to finance investment, gives trusts very little financial leeway. This in part explains the difficulties that purchasers have had in reorganising services. Significant shifts in business undermine trust finances since they have no reserves to fall back on and it is not easy for them to cut costs in line with loss of income. Purchasers then find themselves in effect paying for services twice and hence risk destabilising their own finances.

A prime example of this arose in West Glamorgan, where the Glan-y-Môr Trust was finding it difficult to retain clinical staff at Neath

BMA: 'Non-Core' Primary Care Services

1. Medical care of highly dependent patients living in the community, often in nursing or residential homes.
2. Work, which if undertaken in general practice, should be the subject of an explicit contract with a health authority or other purchaser.
3. Prescribing in circumstances where GPs do not normally have the specialist skills or knowledge to accept full clinical responsibility for initiating, monitoring, modifying or terminating treatment.
4. Mental health and learning disability care for which GPs would not normally have the specialist skills to accept full responsibility.
5. Activities related to drug trials and research.
6. Work which is so infrequent in general practice that the generality of GPs do not have sufficient opportunities to develop or maintain their skills adequately.
7. Work that some GPs may wish to undertake which requires specialised training.
8. Shared care arrangements with other providers.
9. Organisation of services provided by other health professionals in the general practice setting.
10. Work which is either separately remunerated or presently undertaken without any specific payment.
11. Non-NHS professional services undertaken in accordance with nationally negotiated agreements.
12. Individually negotiated non-NHS professional services.

Source: *Core Services: taking the initiative,* BMA 1966

Hospital, in this case for emergency medical care. The health authority decided to transfer the services to the Morriston Hospital, which had itself lost contract income for elderly care services to a third trust, Singleton. Morriston found it could not cut costs in line with the reduction in income and also found that the actual costs of the transfer to it were greater than the increase in income allowed for when the transfer was originally arranged. At the same time, the cost reduction at the Glan-y-Môr Trust was much less than the income lost.

The situation which resulted was the subject of an investigation by the Welsh Affairs Committee, *Morriston Hospital NHS Trust: a case study in the workings of the internal market* (HC166,1997). The events set down in the Committee's report represent a catalogue of poor performance by all parties but the report itself rightly suggests that the framework within which the parties worked was critically at fault. Morriston's financial systems did not appear to be adequate to deal with changes in services, but more fundamentally, the straightjackets in which it and the other trusts worked meant that any change would be destabilising for them and for the health authority. The report was also critical of the role of the Welsh Office, 'the market manager' in respect of the little use it made of the information collected about trust performance, and its failure to clarify some of the key rules within which trusts and health authorities should work.

A second example indicates that major restructuring can occur, but not in the way that the architects of the 1990 Act envisaged. In September 1996, it became clear that the Anglian Harbours Trust would collapse, as its main purchaser indicated that it intended to place contracts for all its services elsewhere after the trust lost a contract for mental health services. This in turn was put down to its inability to recruit and retain consultant psychiatrists and also a desire to reduce management costs. However, the collapse was not the result of failing to win a tender; rather, it was the result of an administrative decision by the district purchaser to end the life of the trust. The ostensible reason for this was the difficulty it was experiencing in recruiting mental health medical staff but the measures taken appear disproportionate to that failing.

A process was set in train to find new providers and to ensure a smooth transition both for users and for the staff of the trust. A key factor in this process was that in general frontline staff transferred to the organisations taking on responsibility for the delivery of services. In effect therefore the 'market process' involved the management only, as indeed it has done in other parts of the public sector when major changes have taken place.

The limitations of the trust financial regime had been recognised through the establishment in June 1995 of an advisory group which was required to:

> *... review the trust financial regime, against the operational experience gained in the first four years of the internal health market, to determine whether it supports the aim of efficient and responsive services through competition and contestability.* (Report p3)

That regime imposed financial responsibilities, costing and pricing rules, and a prescribed method of calculating capital charges. The advisory group reported in September 1996, making a number of suggestions for improvement. Some are technical but nevertheless important to those wishing to understand what trusts' financial performance means. At present, poor financial performance can result from changes outside a trust's control, eg capital revaluations or (though not discussed in this report) the costs of redundancies which trusts are no longer allowed to capitalise.

An analysis by the Health Financial Management Association, using the CIPFA database for 1995/96 issued on 20 December 1996, found that half the 210 trusts that had failed to meet their 6 per cent target rate of return had done so for technical reasons: some of the much smaller number making larger surpluses also pointed to 'technical factors'. One, for example, had made a much larger provision for early retirements in the previous year than it turned out to need.

Some of the advisory group's proposals open the way for a more flexible regime: in particular the group recommended that the 'cost equals price' rule should be relaxed by:

- *removing the ban on cross-subsidisation so that trusts would be free to price as they wished for particular services;*

- *removing the ban on earning surpluses in excess of 6 per cent;*
- *confirming that surpluses in excess of 6 per cent could be spent without EFL clawback unless monitoring by the NHS Executive indicated that persistently high surpluses (say in excess of 8 per cent) were a reflection of excessive market power.*

But this in turn would require further changes.

- *Increase price transparency by requiring trusts to publish comparative costs or prices on offer for a standard form of contract for each healthcare resource group (HRG) of procedures. It would be beneficial if the National Steering Group on Costing in collaboration with the National Case Mix Office were to undertake a study of the practicalities and timescales for implementing such an approach.*
- *Greater clarity regarding the exit regime for trusts by the development of a set of criteria for assessing trust viability with the objective of minimising the discretion Regional Offices are currently required to exercise.*
- *A more sophisticated approach to costing and the use of more advanced costing systems in the contracting process. It would be beneficial if the National Steering Group on Costing were asked to give this issue further consideration* (p55–56).

Another proposal for expanding trusts' freedom of action came from the NHS Trust Federation in *Provision of Social Care by NHS Trusts* which argued that:

> *. . . at present there is not a level playing field between the independent sector, Local Authorities and NHS trust providers. This means that services to some residents with complex and variable needs are not as 'seamless' as they could be and that choice is unnecessarily limited. If the Government wishes to facilitate a range of services which include the option of provision of services by NHS trusts the following issues need to be addressed:*
>
> - *The provision of social care in nursing homes by NHS trusts.*
> - *The inability of health authorities to grant aid the provision of social care by NHS trusts as compared to other providers (through section 64 of the National Health Service Act).*
> - *The devolution of powers vested in a local authority to other bodies.* (p8)

These issues are particularly important for trusts providing continuing care in the community, since here they are in competition with public, private and independent providers, who enjoy greater flexibility in what they provide and how they provide it.

These proposals together with those contained in the NHS (Primary Care) Act 1997 can be seen as a second-round attempt to inject more scope for change and innovation into the NHS, while leaving the purchasing and providing structure unchanged. A parallel route to deregulation lies in the labour market, in particular reconsideration of the role of the professions.

The roots of the professions go back of course far beyond the origins of the NHS. Professional roles are supported by a statutory framework but also by tradition. The roles of the Royal Colleges in particular and the medical profession in general reflect not only their pre-twentieth century origins but also their current social status. Slowly, their roles are being modified but they continue to be important determinants of the way that health care is provided and the options for change that are deemed to be feasible.

The second primary care White Paper makes a series of recommendations bearing on professionals' roles, which can be seen as a limited if signiificant attempt to break down barriers which are no longer justified. In particular, it proposes the extension of the existing nurse-prescribing pilot schemes, extension of the role of community pharmacists and greater use of ophthalmologists and optometrists as well as measures to test alternative skill mixes in dental services.

A study from the Standing Medical and Nursing & Midwifery Committees, *In the Patient's Interest*, set out a large number of recommendations bearing on collaboration between professions which 'can overcome barriers of organisation and attitude'.(p3). When the proposals were announced in October 1996, they were described by the then Minister for Health, Gerry Malone, as a 'springboard for innovation' based on 'more integrated working'.

Pleas for better working between different professions are as old as the NHS but it does now appear that, in industrial relations terms, health care is entering the 1970s when the process of breaking the stranglehold of the craft unions on manufacturing industry began. In the case of nurse prescribing, the process has been painfully slow. The case for allowing nurses to prescribe was accepted in the Cumberlege report but it was not until 1994 that a series of pilots were initiated, results of which are still not available. *Choice and Opportunity*, however, announced an increase in their number.

The measures designed to develop new professional roles which the White Paper proposed appear sensible but piecemeal. They do not reflect a thorough-going attempt to reconsider the role of the professions. The issues that would involve range very far indeed. That range was demonstrated by a report issued in April 1996 from JM Consulting on the Professions Supplementary to Medicine Act 1960, which regulates the initial training and subsequent professional practice of some 100,000 health professsionals. The report identified a series of weaknesses in the current arrangements: in particular lack of the flexibility required to respond to changes in technology, as well as economic and social factors. It made a number of proposals designed to increase such flexibility and to reduce the dominance of the professions themselves in determining how care is provided, as well as a series of other recommendations bearing on professional standards, which are considered further below.

Whether this challenging agenda will be addressed remains to be seen. In the Queen's speech, the new Government made it clear that it intended to undo some elements of the 'new', post-1991 NHS by stating the intention: 'to bring forward new arrangements for decentralisation and co-operation within the service and for ending the internal market.' In Opposition Labour had indicated that the purchaser/provider split was to stay, but left it unclear what its role should be. On coming to office, it announced that there would not be a further wave of new fundholders and that it was considering a wide range of options for the future. In EL(97)33, *Changing the Internal Market*, issued in May 1997, a series of decisions were set out relating to fundholding, management costs, invoicing and breast cancer services (to which Labour had committed extra resources during the election campaign), which were described as 'the first steps in a longer term programme to replace the internal market by new collaborative arrangements'.

The new Government, however, has been clearer about what it does not like – the two-tierism associated with GP fundholding and the competitive framework that the 1990 Act provided for – than what it does. As this Review goes to press therefore, the future direction of health policy is far from clear. This lack of clarity reflects in part a more general ambivalence about the merits of the 1990 reforms in particular and institutional change in general. While it is clear enough that centrally imposed requirements such as the annual 'efficiency' increase have been more significant than locally experienced competition, there is little support for a return to the pre-1990 structures. That would suggest that the new ones were perceived as beneficial but exactly how is hard to demonstrate.

Nick Mays and Catherine Pope's report *Speech and Language Therapy Services and Management in the Internal Market* (King's Fund 1997), a rare if not unique study of the impact of the 1990 reforms on a specific service, found that the administrative workload of those running the service had risen but they had greater responsibility for running the service. The service itself had developed largely independently of the structures which the 1990 Act had introduced.

In contrast, there is little doubt that the introduction of fundholding has made a difference to the way that the NHS operates. But the conclusions cited last year from the King's Fund review of the research evidence, and Nick Goodwin's article in particular, showed that even when there was a substantial amount of research material, the findings were consistent with different views of the overall merits of the changes. In some cases the evidence was contradictory; in others poor or non-existent – yet in respect of health authorities and trusts the evidence was even thinner.

Further, it is arguable that behaviour takes so long to change that even after half a decade, the 'real' impact is yet to come. But the longer it takes to materialise, the less easy it would be to identify since so many other factors come into play. The 'two-tierism' of which Labour has complained may itself be a temporary phenomenon, as budgets are adjusted and as some fundholders find themselves in precisely the same mid-year financial difficulties as health authorities. Furthermore, it seems clear that while fundholding has produced benefits for some, it has not done so at the expense of others, ie there is no evidence that patients in non-fundholding practices have been disadvantaged relative to the situation before fundholding was introduced. Even so, it could well be argued that as effective fundholders are generally to be found in the more affluent areas, the scheme undermines the equity principle on which the NHS rests.

There is an awkward tension here. The provisions of the 1997 Primary Care Act for policy pilots might be seen as one response to the inherent ambivalence attached to large-scale change – the larger the change, the harder it is to demonstrate benefit. As noted already, however, it will take substantial research resources to derive general conclusions even from specific local 'experiments' and even if these resources are available, similar difficulties of interpretation as apply at national level will arise. Judging 'what works' will rarely be easy.

The pilot approach does have the substantial merit of allowing a large number of people to find their own routes to innovation rather than working to a national formula. In this way it allows the Government to get partly off the hook of having itself to find an alternative to the 1990 Act. However, if successful, it puts the Government on a different hook: how to reconcile the explicit encouragement of diversity and the resulting 'inequities' that would bring about, with a continuing emphasis on equity as a national objective.

1.2 Community Care

In March 1997, the Government issued a White Paper, *Social Services: achievement and challenge*, which summed up the impact of the NHS and Community Care Act 1990 as follows:

> *The community care reforms of 1993 caused a transformation in social care for adults. There is greater individual choice, and a wider range of provision available for residential and domiciliary care. The majority of residential care is now provided in the independent sector and the proportion of independently provided domiciliary care is growing rapidly. Local authorities have been developing their role as purchasers of services. The importance of assessment – both of users and of carers – as a means of ensuring that services are appropriate to need has become firmly bedded into the system.*
>
> *In central government and locally there is a new emphasis on close cooperation and joint working between all the agencies involved in community care, and in particular between social services authorities and health and housing authorities. Significant effort has been put into this area and important advances have been made.* (p11)

The White Paper is right to assert that there has been substantial change in the way that residential care is provided. This switch was largely brought about by the conditions attached to the special transitional community care grant which required that 85 per cent of it be spent in the private or voluntary sector. By 1995, local authorities were supporting more people in the independent sector than in their own, ie authority, homes: see Table 8. About one third of those in the independent sector were receiving local authority support: the numbers supporting themselves in such accommodation had fallen.

In respect of domiciliary care change has been much less marked, but the balance is nevertheless moving in the same direction. Local authority services still predominate, but the rate of growth in the private sector albeit from a low base has been very rapid: see Table 9.

While the impact of the 1990 Act on the source of provision is clear enough, that on purchasing is less so. As with the NHS, the new arrangements for community care created an explicit mechanism for determining needs, the assessment process. With some exceptions noted below, that process is now largely in place: the issue now is how effective it is.

One of the key objectives of the reforms was to remove the bias in the old arrangements towards residential care by introducing a gate-keeping function in the form of the assessment process. However the Executive's own

Table 8 Local authority supported residents, by type of accommodation, England, 1990 to 1996

	All staffed homes (exc small)	*Local Authority staffed*	*Registered Homes*		*Other accommo-dation*	*Unstaffed (group) homes*
			Voluntary	*Private*		
1990	117,300	103,300	9,800	3,100	1,100	-
1996	155,000	62,000	22,200	68,800	2,000	4,200

Source: Department of Health: Residential Care Statistics

monitoring of continuing care plans, issued with EL (96)89 found that:

> *There is growing evidence that a significant number of people admitted to nursing homes and residential care homes on a long term care basis might be inappropriately placed. Key factors affecting such placement appeared to be: premature assessment, lack of specialist input into assessment, lack of opportunities for rehabilitation and recovery and pressure on hospital discharge. The same factors may account for a proportion of hospital re-admissions. National data collected for the first time in June suggests that around, on average, 7.1% of non-elective admissions for people aged 75+ are re-admissions within 28 days. Every avoidable long term placement in a nursing home not only represents the unnecessary loss of independence for the patient, it also 'blocks' the money paying for the bed for months, if not years. This reduces the ability of social services to fund the care for people for whom rehabilitation is not possible and exacerbates 'bed blocking' in hospital.* (p 9)

The report goes on to recognise that the assessment process might be at fault:

> *A key issue relates to assessment. Consideration of potential for rehabilitation and recovery needs to be considered before any final decision is taken about the need for a long term continuing care placement. Premature assessment of a patient's needs and the lack of specialist input into assessment can lead to longer term potential for recovery being missed with considerable consequences for the individual and for the care system in terms of avoidable long term care costs* (p 9).

Further criticisms of the assessment process were made in the Health Advisory Service's report *Redressing the Balance* (HMSO 1997) which reviewed the provision of services for elderly people. In respect of assessment it found that the various parts of the health and social care system viewed the process in different ways.

Table 9 Households receiving home care: England

Provided by:	*1992*	*1995*
Local Authority	517,700	420,300
Voluntary	2,300	16,300
Private	8,600	75,700
All	528,500	512,400

Source: Community Care Statistics 1995

...ideally, assessment of elderly people in the community is a task which should be undertaken on a multi-professional basis involving care managers, who are usually social services staff (but in some areas may be district nurses), as well as the staff of primary healthcare teams, carers, clients and others. There was evidence from the fieldwork that this process is not as effective as health authority and social services commissioners would wish. (p 65)

The report highlighted some specific areas of difficulty where the assessment process fails: see Box. The report goes on:

It is of signal importance to the continuing care of elderly people that commissioners and purchasers should ensure that a plan is made to reassess each person at an agreed interval once continuing or long-term care has been agreed to be the most appropriate option and the elderly person has been appropriately placed. This ensures that, if a patient's status is unstable or changing, the appropriateness of continuing care is re-evaluated and it also allows patients and carers to review their wishes, opinions and options. Reassessment also ensures that each care package is appropriate and is a means of determining the need for any additional, or lesser, therapeutic interventions.

Whether this process of reassessment is led by social services or NHS staff is a matter for local agreement, and may depend on the identity of the lead funding agency in each case. But it is essential that all commissioners should ensure that specialist geriatric expertise is available for each reassessment and that the process is as multi-disciplinary and holistic as the pre-admission assessment. (p123)

The aim of reducing numbers in residential care was itself part of a larger objective: to target resources as a whole more effectively. Such targeting might involve identifying needs hitherto not recognised in official policy or developing a pattern of service which is better suited to each individual supported. As noted last year, *Community Care Statistics* treat as evidence of better targeting the fact that while

Care of Elderly People: Health Advisory Service Critique

- too frequently, social services-based care managers are unaware that medical illness may be behind functional failure. Consequently, there is a tendency for them to call on the staff of primary healthcare teams less often than is appropriate;
- the staff of some primary healthcare teams are slow to accept that some disability in older people is reversible, or, at least, may be improved by multi-disciplinary packages of therapy determined by comprehensive assessment. Consequently, there was a tendency not to refer people on for more specialised intervention sufficiently frequently ('It's your age, I'm afraid'); and
- assessment may be patchy, particularly because some problem areas are not assessed at all (eg through medical diagnosis) while others are multiply-assessed by different people (although there is a possibility that this imbalance occurs less when district nurses are also care managers).

Source: Health Advisory Service, *Redressing the Balance*, HMSO 1997

the volume of service appears to be increasing, the numbers receiving it appear to be falling. This suggests that the intensity of care appears to be increasing, ie the number receiving more extensive packages is rising and the number receiving restricted ones falling. In fact because of the way the statistics are collected even these conclusions must be qualified. However, even if the data are not misleading, they do not bear either on unrecognised need or on the appropriateness of provision to the needs of each individual.

In one respect, however, a new category of need was formally recognised when the 1995 Carers (Recognition and Services) Act which granted carers the right to an assessment, came into effect in 1996. However, the early indications from King's Fund field sites and from a survey by the Carers National Association published in May 1997 show that there is a long way to go before the majority of carers are aware of their rights and those rights honoured by local authorities.

For social care, the assessment process focuses on the individual needing care – and their carer – and the assessment itself was made the task of local authorities. No equivalent of fundholding has developed, ie no form of alternative purchaser, with the important exception that individuals are to be enabled to become their own purchasers through the direct payments scheme.

The Community Care (Direct Payments) Act legalising such payments was passed in 1996 and came into effect, for younger disabled people, in April 1997. In November 1996, the Government issued a draft guidance for consultation which it indicates is based on the already substantial experience of independent living schemes. *Social Services: achievement and challenge* goes on to suggest a number of measures which would strengthen the position of the individual:

> *The Government also wishes to encourage experimentation with other ways of reinforcing the individual's right to influence their choice of residential or nursing home. The Direction on Choice gave people receiving publicly funded care in a residential or nursing home the right to indicate the home of their choice from the range of suitable and affordable alternatives. Some authorities are looking at voucher schemes as a way of extending and facilitating this right to choice. The Government intends to ensure that there are no legal obstacles to the use of vouchers in this way.*
>
> *Finally, the Government considers that some service users would welcome more choice in the sources of advice available to them in the selection of the support which their local authority has assessed them as needing and is willing to finance. There are already some examples of local authorities encouraging some service users, once their needs have been assessed, to rely on specialist voluntary bodies or service user groups for advice on how those needs can best be met. It may well be that disabled people who choose to receive cash payments instead of services under the new legislation will also wish to choose their own sources of advice about how they might best use the money. It is more likely that such choices will be sensibly made where the user's needs are likely to remain fairly stable and the call for regular reassessment of basic needs is thus infrequent. But the Government would like to encourage a wider variety of choice in sources of advice available to users and will ensure that*

> *the legal framework within which social services operate does not place obstacles in the way of this objective*. (p 14/15)

The White Paper recognises that greater reliance on private suppliers brings with it a range of new responsibilities for the public sector. During the year, a number of cases were heard in the courts where those responsible for private provision had grossly abused those they were nominally caring for. For example, in May 1997, a former director of two care homes and two senior members of staff were found guilty of ill-treating residents and also of wilful neglect over a period of 10 years during which the home had been nominally subject to external inspection.

Cases such as this one highlighted the need for effective monitoring of care standards within residential or nursing home care. But there were a number of other reasons why the regulatory regime required attention. Experience had shown that standards in the public sector could not be taken for granted and it had also demonstrated that the distinction between nursing and social care needs on which the 1984 system of regulation was based was no longer tenable and indeed had become an obstacle to the provision of appropriate care for many people. Finally, the domiciliary care market had grown rapidly without any form of regulation. These and other issues were considered in a report by Tom Burgner, *The Regulation and Inspection of Social Services*, published with LASSL(96)17.

The Burgner report recommended a single system of regulation and inspection, supported by national standards and nationally organised training but put forward a choice of organisational models, one based on existing local and health authorities, the other based either on the Social Services Inspectorate or a new national body. The White Paper proposed a system of regulation, combining elements of each of these in the form of new local regulatory bodies:

> *The Government now considers it right to amend the regulatory machinery so as to make certain that duplicated regulation and differences of standards in the same locality would be avoided and that the necessary assessment expertise and regulatory authority is brought together within one body for each locality. It therefore intends that all regulatory responsibilities now exercised by social services departments (including those for children's services) and the regulatory responsibility for nursing homes now exercised by health authorities should be brought together into new local statutory bodies vested in law with the necessary regulatory powers and formed by consortia of local and health authorities in the area, with small but suitably representative membership drawn from the participating authorities*. (p 32)

In contrast, Malcolm Johnson and Lesley Hoyes report in *Regulating Long Term Care: proposals for a single registered care home* that there is wide support for national standards and for any regulatory body being independent of providing and purchasing interests. They propose a National Office for Standards of Care with the roles set out in the Box opposite.

The case for a national approach to this locally delivered service was underlined by a case in Gloucester which eventually reached the

A National Office for Standards of Care

The remit of the Office would be to:

- set national standards for each range of the single care home spectrum;
- develop tools and methods for monitoring compliance with standards;
- carry out the statutory functions of registration and inspection;
- monitor consistency in the performance of functions and the application of standards;
- carry out/commission research into standards/outcomes of regulation/methods of inspection;
- encourage accredited Quality Assurance mechanisms and training;
- develop accredited training for registration and inspection officers.

Source: M Johnson and L Hoyes, *Regulating Long Term Care: proposals for a single registered care home School for Policy Studies, University of Bristol 1996*

House of Lords. The case had been brought on behalf of a man in his 80s who, after being assessed as needing care and after receiving it for some time, was then told that some services would be withdrawn as the Council could no longer afford them. The House of Lords decided that the Council was justified in its decision, ie that it was proper to take costs into account, despite the terms of the 1970 Disabled Persons Act, which appeared to imply an absolute duty to provide a service.

Lord Nicholls of Birkenhead argued that the appeal by the Council against a decision in a lower court, should be allowed,

> *In deciding whether the disability of a particular person dictates a need for assistance and, if so, at what level, a social worker or anyone else must use some criteria. This is inevitably so. He will judge the needs for assistance against some standard, some criteria, whether spoken or unspoken. One important factor he will take into account will be what constitutes an acceptable standard of living today.*
>
> *Standards of living, however, vary widely. So do different people's ideas on the requirements of an acceptable standard of living. Thus something more concrete, capable of being applied uniformly, is called for assessing the needs of a given disabled person under the statute. Some more precisely defined standard is required, a more readily identifiable yardstick, than individual notions of current standards of living.* [Transcript of judgement, p13]

But there is no such defined standard and hence no frame of reference for decisions of this kind other than that provided by the judgement of the relevant local authority, in the light of the resources available to it. As Lords Nicholls succinctly put it:

> *A person's need for a particular type or level of service cannot be decided in a vacuum from which all considerations of cost have been expelled.* (p12)

Nevertheless two of the five law lords involved took the opposite view, accepting that if Parliament had accepted an absolute obligation to provide care in certain circumstances, then that should be met.

Another insight into the same issue can be found in a report from the National Association of Citizens' Advice Bureaux *Rationing Community Care*. This concludes:

> *CAB evidence has detailed how in some instances local authorities have pared their services to the legal bone and beyond in an effort to contain expenditure. Examples include failures to carry out adequate assessments for people with care needs, to provide services to disabled people as required under the Chronically Sick and Disabled Persons Act, and to ensure that charges for services are reasonable. However, there is a fundamental contradiction between a rights-based system and a limited budget, and social services departments are increasingly finding themselves caught between a rock and a hard place as they seek to meet their statutory duties from inadequate resources. But as local authorities and central government continue to argue over the extent to which the problem is one of inadequate funding or of inefficient administration, it is the care users who are bearing the brunt.* (p 42)

The report cites examples of those who have failed to receive care who like Mr Barry and others we have cited in previous Reviews who have an evident need for care but are not receiving it. The reasons are obviously specific to each case but a common theme is the effect of charges on take-up of service. Earlier Reviews have noted that local authorities were increasingly using charges to finance social care services. The proportion of expenditure remains low – see Table 10 – while the sums raised are increasing, the proportion of expenditure met through charges is not.

A series of studies supported by the Rowntree Foundation have looked at the way that charging policies are administered. Fran Bennett in *Charging Ahead* found that the administration of charges in the authorities studied fell short of the agreed criteria used by the Benefits Agency. In particular, there was no systematic response to those cases where clients stopped using services. She concludes:

Table 10 Local authority income from charges for home care services

	1993/94	*1994/95*
Income (£m)	57.3	63.1
% spending	7.9	6.8

Source: Department of Health

> *This aspect of implementing authorities' charging policies seemed at best 'hit and miss' and at worst virtually non-existent. Senior officers, and some care managers, were surprisingly complacent about the effects of introducing or increasing charges on take-up and use of services, or on the living standards of clients paying the charge. Their typical response was that service users might drop out of services or reduce their hours, for a short period after the charge was introduced or increased, but they always came back within a few weeks or months. These assertions were rarely based on evidence, since good systems for monitoring the impact of introducing or raising charges simply did not exist. The only exception was the one authority which had developed an impact analysis relating to the introduction or increasing of charges for all local authority services.* (p81)

According to Mark Chetwynd and colleagues in *The Cost of Care*, a study of the impact of charging policy on disabled people:

> *The quality of information that people had received about the charging system was highly variable. Some authorities had tried hard to explain a complex system in accessible terms, others had made a simple system incomprehensible. A common problem, however, was that the notification of charges did not make it clear why the individual's charges were as stated. People were left to deduce this, often from information they had received at an earlier stage, which was not always in a written form. Moreover, attempts to check their assessments with home care assistants or other domiciliary workers had often been unsuccessful. The misconceptions or misunderstandings that can arise in such circumstances may have serious effects. They may adversely influence people's actions or decisions about requests for care services.* (p 83)

Another Rowntree study, *Highly Charged* by Fran Bennett, discusses the general issues which charging policies raise, among them the relationship between local authority charges, the services people feel they need and other claims on their resources:

> *Alongside frequent changes in local authorities' charging regimes over recent years, users of domiciliary care have also experienced changes in service provision. In addition to the moving definitions of health and social care, the boundaries around the public provision of domiciliary care are also being redefined. In many areas, local authorities are withdrawing from providing domestic help – much of which now has to be paid for privately – and concentrating instead on personal care. This has occurred despite the high priority which many disabled and older people themselves place on domestic help ... Thus, as well as facing the imposition of, or increases in, charges, many users also have to pay for additional private services, to maintain the same level of provision overall as in the past – a double burden which is often not recognised.*
>
> *In this situation, a 'mixed economy' of welfare provision could result in people facing a combination of charges for services arranged via the local authority and privately, which together could be unaffordable.* (p 31)

Studies such as these, however, based on modest samples cannot show how many people are forced by a combination of charges and low incomes to live in circumstances which make a mockery of anything but the meagrest expectations of what care in the community should imply. Surveys cited later in this section suggest that in most instances, the services offered, and the terms on which they are made available, are satisfactory. But because of the vast clientele that social service departments deal with, such results are perfectly compatible with the implication of the Rowntree studies, that a large number of people are not receiving an adequate standard of care.

As with residential care, there is an obvious equity case for a national approach to charging for domiciliary services. As the NACAB report *Rationing Community Care* puts it:

> *The CAB Service recommends that if charges are to remain, they should be set within a common national framework established by the Department of Health. This would reduce the degree of variability between authorities, whilst retaining the flexibility which is an essential element of local democracy.* (p 41)

In respect of residential care, rules have always been set nationally and so the Conservative Government's decision to raise the amount of personal 'protected' capital which came into effect in 1996 appeared to apply generally. However, a judicial review brought by Help the Aged and two individuals against Sefton Metropolitan Borough found this was, in the court's view, not so. Sefton, which has a large number of retired people within its boundaries, had set lower limits – £1,500 – than the national rules. The ruling distinguished between the two individuals involved, but the upshot was that local authorities are free to make their own policies by deciding when to help someone with the funding of residential care – ie there can be no guarantee that even if someone is assessed as needing residential care, they will get local authority support once their capital is below £16,000.

Another area of confusion in the national rules has been the treatment of pensions. In some cases, one spouse has been left with a very reduced income, when the other has had to go into residential or nursing care and their pension used to pay for it. In LAC(97)5 the position was clarified; authorities were instructed only to take half the pension in these circumstances.

A further theme of *Social Services: achievement and challenge* is the need for collaboration. Government policy in successive issues of the annual *NHS Priorities and Planning Guidance* has been to promote collaboration between agencies. The White Paper asserts that:

> *Over the last three years the Government has taken steps to assist inter-agency working, and to address problems that have arisen. There has been a wide range of central initiatives from the Health Departments, and other Government Departments working together to support the development of local corporate approaches, and to ensure consistency of overall policy. The Government will maintain this emphasis. A current example of such work within Government, involving also consultation with local government, is the Department of Social Security's review of the use of Housing Benefit in financing supported housing.* (p 15)

But, as a King's Fund paper *The organisation of community care* indicates, there is widespread belief that the current arrangements get in the way of collaboration. In particular they:

- encourage artificial distinctions to be made between 'health' and 'social care' needs;
- blur responsibility for the care of people with long-term illness or disability;
- lead to cost-shunting from the NHS to local government;
- contribute to service fragmentation, with vulnerable people 'falling through the cracks';
- result in weak accountability and public influence.

The Department of Health's own monitoring of the development of policies for continuing care, issued with EL(96)89, confirmed the lack of integration between NHS and local authority services:

> *. . . in a number of areas there appears to be a lack of integration between NHS assessments for continuing health care and local authority community care assessments. This leads to a duplication of effort, delays in decision making and stands in the way of proper multidisciplinary decision making. The result of this can be inappropriate placements and the ineffective tying up of resources. The problem is most obvious in the community but also has a major impact on decision making in hospital. There is a related issue about who was responsible for pulling together the results of assessment processes, for ensuring that appropriate inputs are obtained and for bringing together a single care plan for an individual.* (p 6)

Another Rowntree report by Lorna Arblaster and others, *Asking the impossible?*, confirms this analysis, arguing that the aim of collaboration is frustrated by other policies which the White Paper promotes:

> *Whilst a market economy of welfare may result in a diversity of agency providers, in reality the emphasis is on the agencies' own specialism, and agencies continue in business by gaining the next contract. Health and social care agencies, in the statutory, voluntary and private sectors, have very specific roles to play in delivering services to individuals, whilst at the same time ensuring 'value for money'. However, collaboration between increasing numbers of agencies within this competitive arrangement is difficult, as each agency works to improve service access within conditions of expenditure control.* (p 43)

The Government could not be accused of failing to recognise the need for better collaboration. In *Housing and Community Care: establishing a strategic framework* published in January 1997, the Departments of Health and Environment acknowledged what previous Reviews have recorded:

> *Community care monitoring, research reports and policy development have recognised the increasingly important role of housing in the implementation of community care policy and some of the innovative developments that have emerged as a result of collaboration between housing authorities, social services, health and social housing providers.* (p 1)

It contains a large number of recommendations for joint planning – 16 in all – as well as other forms of joint working. Bob Hudson examines links between health and housing in more detail below.

The need for change in the way services are provided had been underlined by a report published in January for the London Health Commission – *London's Mental Health* – which identified in more detail than previous studies the nature and scale of the pressures on London's mental health services. Sonia Johnson and Graham Thornicroft, assessing the evidence collected in the course of the study found:

- *Lack of standard formats and of categories of services and of client groups for recording service provision across different agencies.*

- *Lack of co-ordinated systems for monitoring services within a catchment area across all statutory and independent sector agencies, and for making this information readily accessible.*

- *Lack of information about what provision is actually available locally at any given time – information about places occupied does not indicate what options there are for making new placements.*

- *Lack of procedures for regularly up-dating data collection about catchment area services and thus establishing trends over time.*

- *Lack of detailed information about the level of support which facilities can provide and the client groups for which they are suitable.*

- *A frequent absence of information on place of origin of clients in residential services, so that, particularly for voluntary sector facilities with wide catchment areas, it is uncertain how far they are providing for the local population and how far they are increasing local needs by importing patients into the catchment area.*

- *There is no regular system of data collection across London as a whole.* (p361)

Many of the issues the study identifies in this daunting list are not confined to London. A NAHAT survey of 38 trusts and 15 health authorities, *Mental Health Care: from problems to solutions* (NAHAT research paper 23) carried out in August 1996 found an equally dismaying list of problems:

- Pressure on beds is severe with trusts operating at up to 140 per cent occupancy and the majority reporting occupancy rates of over 100 per cent.

- Referrals of people with mental illness appear to be rising and the severity of their problems also seems to be increasing.

- Services are facing growing pressure from particular groups of patients, especially people treated compulsorily under sections of the Mental Health Act; offenders referred by court diversion schemes (aimed at keeping mentally ill people out of the prison system); mentally disordered offenders who need to be accommodated in medium and low secure units; and people with associated drug and alcohol problems.

- Community services are insufficiently developed in many places and this is causing delays in discharge and other problems. As well as health and social support, there is a need for a range of appropriate accommodation.

- Managers are concerned that GP fundholders could unnecessarily destabilise services by diverting money away from care for seriously mentally ill people and towards new services, such as counselling, for patients with moderate mental health problems.

- Many services are experiencing staff shortages – either because of recruitment difficulties or funding problems – particularly among psychiatrists, psychologists, nurses and occupational therapists.

- Patient caseloads for community psychiatric nurses are unacceptably high in most places.
- Legislation may be needed to enable health and social services to work together more effectively.
- Mental health services need investment both in revenue and capital.
- There are doubts that the private finance initiative will provide sufficient funds to meet the need for capital investment in mental health.

It concluded that there was:

- *An urgent need to review current funding and to correct assumptions. This would enable existing services to keep pace with growing demand and develop a more comprehensive range of services.*
- *A need to tackle organisational obstacles which interfere with collaboration between health and social services.*
- *A need to address tensions between GPs and those providing mental health services so as to achieve a shared understanding of service needs and service capability.* (p 19)

Despite these conclusions the survey found many aspects of good practice:

> *Against this account of huge change and massive demands, enormous strides have been taken. Services offered today are more comprehensive, more flexible, more varied and more efficient than 10 years ago. The range of services on offer is wide and includes crisis intervention, home care and support, outreach work, respite services, housing for homeless people with severe mental illness and secure beds for those who present a threat to the public. Counselling services are offered by half of all GPs, compared to ten per cent just five years ago.*
>
> *Working patterns have also changed substantially, with health and social services staff working together in community mental health teams and other settings. Users and carers are involved more than ever in decision making, although there is clearly a long way to go. The components of good community care are manifold. They include appropriate, well targeted services; partnership with users and carers; effective collaboration with social services and primary care; and responsible policies towards staff.* (p 12)

These paragraphs rightly reflect the vast changes that have taken place on the ground. But they have lagged behind the policy rhetorice and the expectations on the part of users and carers that the 1990 Act engendered. In February 1997, the Government made a partial response to these structural critiques and published a Green Paper, *Developing Partnerships in Mental Health*, which set out a number of options for bringing together the respective responsibilities of health and local authorities: see Box on p. 28.

Despite the range of options, the Green Paper did not however properly acknowledge the role of general practice in commissioning mental health services – be that through fundholding or some other form of locality commissioning – and hence it underestimates the task of integrating the purchase and delivery of services. But in any case, as the failings identified by the King's Fund

Options for Mental Health Services

Option one: mental health and social care authorities

A new kind of statutory authority, accountable directly to the Secretary of State for Health would be established, responsible for planning, commissioning and purchasing health and social services for working age adults with severe mental illness. It would be neither a health nor a local authority but it would need to work in association with both, and other existing agencies.

Option two: single authority responsibility

Either health authorities or local authorities would be designated as the single agency responsible for planning, commissioning and purchasing mental health and social care. Health authorities are the most likely choice as they spend more on mental health care than local authorities and their designation would be compatible with the continuation of GP fundholding within present arrangements. Current accountability arrangements would remain.

Option three: a joint health and social care body

Health and local authorities would establish a joint body to plan, commission and organise the contractual framework for delivering mental health and social care services. It would either commission services directly, through delegated powers and funds from the authorities, or it could co-ordinate existing successful commissioning arrangements. The joint body would be accountable to the local authority for the funds allocated for social care, and to the health authority and GP fundholders for funds allocated for health care. It would act as a single point of contact for other agencies. Staff would manage a single shared budget for mental health and social care services.

This would be optional – for authorities to choose to implement if it were appropriate for their particular local circumstances.

Option four: agreed delegation

Health and local authorities would be able to delegate particular functions or responsibilities to each other. For example, a health authority may decide to delegate the purchasing of mental health services to a local authority, accompanied by the necessary funds. Or, more probably, a local authority may ask the health authority to undertake commissioning for specific social services. Current accountability arrangements would remain. Staff would manage a single shared budget for mental health and social care services.

This would be optional – for authorities to choose to implement if it were appropriate for their particular local circumstances.

Source: *Developing Partnerships in Mental Health* CM 3555, HMSO 1997

and the NAHAT studies confirm, changes in structure do not bear on the full range of weaknesses which typefy the current pattern of provision.

The analysis presented in the Green Paper could be applied with only minor modification to other care groups whose needs cross the social, health and housing boundaries. The report from the Health Advisory Service, cited in section 1.1 found that:

> *The initial stages of clinical care and management, such as the immediate treatment of traumatic brain injury or the genetic*

> *counselling of families with Huntington's Disease, are often excellently delivered. However, post-acute services are often indifferently planned and delivered. Many patients do not receive necessary and co-ordinated long term management following their discharge from acute treatment. It is in this area that collaboration between the various agencies and professional groups becomes essential, and yet it is usually problems in this area that lead to the greatest difficulty in service delivery. At the clinical level of working with individual patients, there are many examples of good, effective collaboration, but at the higher levels of professional contact there is generally poor co-operation.* (p 55)

The report does not propose structural solutions but instead argues for the care programme approach to be applied to the groups it considers. While in principle that seems appropriate, failures in implementing that approach in respect of other mental health services form part of the argument for structural change of the kind set out in the Green Paper.

Another Health Advisory Service review *Services for People Who Are Elderly* identifies a large number of 'boundary' issues, many lying within the NHS, other straddling the border between the NHS and social services. Among the wide range of obstacles to effective linkage between the various elements of the care system, it identifies weaknesses which stem from developments within primary care which the Government had promoted or welcomed:

> *While, contrary to popular belief, contacts between GPs and patients in their own homes are continuing to rise, the development of out-of-hours co-operatives has had an adverse effect on the continuity of care between GPs and practices and patients in their own homes.*
>
> *In this respect, the establishment of fundholding has provided the possibility of a perverse incentive, in that fundholding GPs are responsible for the costs of nursing and therapy elements of care, as well as for the costs of drugs and consultations while each patient is in the community. With the exception of total GP fundholding, this commitment ceases when their patients are admitted to hospital, and these elements of care are included within the services paid for by social services departments (or the individual) when in nursing or residential home care.* (p 79)

In February 1996 the Government had announced that it intended to encourage health and local authorities to work together, as well as with other agencies, through offering financial incentives. A Target Fund was launched, financed from out Mental Illness Specific Grant – and used to finance schemes demonstrating some degree of joint working. Grants of some £30 million were announced in September 1996 for schemes covering:

- *crisis support services, many of which will operate on an 'out of hours' basis;*
- *outreach schemes to identify and maintain contact with the most vulnerable people;*
- *supported housing to support and maintain people in their own homes;*
- *services targeted at mentally disordered offenders to ensure they receive appropriate care.*

A much smaller sum was awarded on the same

basis for implementing schemes within the *Building Partnerships for Success initiative*, amounting to some £2.75 million for 62 projects.

Measures such as these continue the tradition of joint finance of attempting to 'build bridges' across the health and social care divide. While few would question the objective, the question remains as to whether the piecemeal approach can ever achieve more than a scattering of schemes which, though useful, are insufficient to provide a seamless service.

Most of the findings cited so far have emphasised what is not working. Two reports, however, identify general satisfaction with the services being provided. A study by the Social Services Directorate, *Caring for People at Home – Part II*, found, in a survey covering 270 users, that most were satisfied with what they were receiving:

> *In very general terms, the survey results show an encouraging picture of user satisfaction with services (ie content, timing, volume and the manner in which tasks were carried out) and of good levels of communication and consultation by social services departments with users and their supporters. However, local authorities were not very successful in providing information about services to the general public or in telling users about complaints procedures.* (p 19)

In June 1997, *Reviewing Social Services*, the first annual report of the review teams run jointly by the Social Services Inspectorate and the Audit Commission, was published. The report, based on the first set of reviews, also found much to praise in the authorities covered in the report and of the 1,000 users and carers expressing their views to the review teams. 71 per cent considered the services provided to be excellent or good and only 5 per cent thought they were poor.

Unlike the NHS, social services have not been pressed to extract more activity from their budgets via efficiency indices. Instead, pressure has been exerted through a much more vigorous attempt to impose market disciplines through use of private sector suppliers. In February 1997, the Department published *Better Value for Money in Social Services*, which embodied data already collected from local authorities and, for the most part, already available. The aim of the publication was in the words of the letter from the Secretary of State which accompanied it, to raise some serious questions such as:

> *Whether activity has increased or quality improved sufficiently to account fully for the 73% real increase in spending, particularly in the early years of the decade.*
>
> *Whether the rise in real costs of looking after children in local authority maintained homes from £600 a week in 1984/5 to £1100 a week in 1994/5 is fully justified (both figures in 1994/5 prices).*
>
> *Why some Social Services Departments are continuing to place elderly people in public sector residential care at an average cost (in 1994/5) of £283 per week, when the evidence suggests that the private sector option, at an average cost of £246 per week, is better value. These figures are even more striking when account is taken of the information in paragraph 4.7 that the independent sector contains a higher proportion of over 85 year olds who are likely to be the most dependent.*

Why there is such great variation in value for money between different authorities . . . 28 authorities are placing residents at average weekly costs of over £350 per week, despite the fact that 33 authorities are able to perform the same services at an average cost of less than £250 per week. Even allowing for some differences in labour costs, this spread raises significant questions.

The commentary on the figures however is tentative, reflecting the fact that, despite the length of time over which the figures have been collected, interpretation remains difficult. For example, the apparently rapid rise in weekly unit cost for the physically disabled may reflect changes in what is being recorded rather than a genuine increase in the cost of the service. This in turn reflects the weakness of the information available at local level.

Reviewing Social Services found that:

...many authorities simply don't know precisely how many people receive what service, at what standard and at what cost. (p 15)

As it points out, the implication is that:

- *users are less likely to get the service they want or need;*
- *staff are not clear about how well they are doing their jobs;*
- *authorities find difficulty in changing service patterns to fit needs;*
- *social services cannot use the most efficient means of delivering services or learn from other local authority departments on how better to specify services.* (p15)

Expenditure by local authorities on social services rose by 73 per cent between 1984/5 and 1994/5 – 61 per cent after allowing for the higher than average rise in prices. In the light of the Review's findings, it is easy to see why questions can be raised about the effectiveness of that expenditure. However, ensuring that services are effective is not just a question of managerial expertise in costing and budgeting: it also turns on the wider knowledge base available to those who design and plan services.

But as noted in 1.5 below, it was only in 1996 that the first effective steps were taken to establish a centrally driven research programme into social care and then on what can only be called a derisory scale. Yet, the Health Service Advisory report on elderly care services emphasises how complex the world is within which social care is provided, a complexity which the central research programme, with its emphasis on the individual intervention, has not begun to address.

In conclusion: the task in relation to community care remains that of implementing properly what is largely an agreed set of policies. That process has proved to be slow and complex and is far from complete. The barriers to progress arising from the health/social care boundary may be overcome in particular localities where good personal relationships have developed but they remain a general barrier to the improvement of services. Yet there is no one structural change which would command widespread support and any such change would in itself disrupt established relationships. At the same time, it is clear that however desirable structural change is, it is not in itself enough to ensure that services match the diverse range of needs that users of community care services present. The mixed economy of care which the Conservatives introduced has contributed to extending the range of services available but at the cost of making links between services harder to get right.

1.3 Public Health Strategy

As last year's Review indicated, the scope of public health policy is dauntingly wide. At the one end of the scale, it might include measures, as *The Economist* has proposed (11 September. 1993), for diverting asteroids from colliding with the planet, to, at the other, the risks involved in using toothbrushes – a risk which the Department of Trade and Industry thought it worthwhile highlighting when it announced, in January 1997, the results of its Home Accident Surveillance System Report for 1995. That reaffirmed the uncomfortable truth that accidental death in the home is almost as significant as that from road accidents and that about 3 million A&E attendances stem from domestic accidents.

The impact of an asteroid would be somewhat greater than a rogue toothbrush, but the risk of that impact is low. The likelihood of global warming, however, seems great enough to be counted as a probability and its effects, if not so drastic, equally significant at a global level. The process of estimating what its impact on health will be has begun, but with results that so far are inconclusive. One such study, *Climate Change and Human Health*, the report of a Task Group on behalf of the WHO, the World Meteorological Organisation and the United Nations Environment Programmes concluded that:

> *This complex mix of influences upon population health profiles makes it difficult to project the proportional contribution of climate change to future trends in population health indicators. For example, malaria incidence rates are continually changing because of many non-climate influences, and their future trends, even in the absence of climate change, cannot be predicted with confidence. Estimating what a predicted increase in the global incidence of malaria due to climate change would represent as a proportion of the total future increase (or decrease) in incidence is therefore very difficult. However, the main point of this volume has not been to attempt specific and quantitative projections of the health impacts of climate change. Rather, it has sought to create an awareness that, in destabilizing the world's climate system and its dependent ecosystems, we are posing new and widespread risks to the health of human populations.* (p232)

Given the high level of uncertainty attached to specific estimates of the impact of climatic change, what action should be taken as part of health policy is unclear.

Links between the physical environment and health are also hard to pin down precisely. Nevertheless, the UK National Environmental Health Action Plan contains a large number of commitments to action, many stemming from the Environmental Health Action Plan for Europe which had been formulated at the Helsinki Conference in 1995. (The UK is due to host the next such conference in 1999.)

The Plan:

- gives both an overview of the provision of environmental health and a detailed analysis of the many factors contributing to it;

Table 10 Environmental targets

Outdoor Air Quality	Achieve the air quality objectives to be set out in the National Air Quality Strategy (the Government is currently consulting on a draft version of the strategy). Fulfil our European obligations to: • reduce sulphur dioxide emissions by 80% by 2010 on a 1980 baseline • maintain overall NOx emissions at or below 1987 levels • reduce emissions of VOCs (ground-level ozone precursors) by 30% by 1999, on a 1988 baseline.
Indoor Air Quality	Ensure that advice on the health effects of key indoor pollutants, and means of avoiding or minimising exposure, is made available to everyone by 1999 through GPs, EHOs and other health professionals. Achieve a downward trend in mean levels of key indoor air pollutants such as nitrogen dioxide, formaldehyde and volatile organic compounds in homes by 2003.
Radon	Identify at least a further 30,000 homes that are above the radon Action Level by 2000. Encourage an additional 10,000 owners of homes above the radon Action Level to take remedial action by the year 2000.
Noise pollution	Increase the proportion of domestic noise complaints to local authorities which are satisfactorily resolved by 25% by 2000, on a 1996 baseline.
Drinking water	Continue to reduce levels of lead in drinking water, so that zonal levels by 2005 are generally no more than half the current standard.

- shows how the current provisions will deliver a steady improvement in environmental health or how they should be modified to do so;
- sets out a range of well over 150 specific actions across the spectrum of environmental health for remedying identified problems or for securing further improvements; and thereby,
- establishes the means to achieve the objectives of the Environmental Health Action Plan for Europe and the Health for All targets.

Reflecting these concerns, the Departments of Health and the Environment published a consultation document in September 1996, *The Environment and Health*, which proposed a new key area for the *Health of the Nation* initiative. The document points out:

> *It is often difficult to measure the influence of a poor environment on health in terms of the common 'burdens of disease', mortality, morbidity and cost. This is because:*
>
> - *environment factors are frequently difficult to distinguish as a cause of death and ill-health from among other potential contributory agents;*
> - *susceptibility and exposure to specific environmental health risks vary widely across the population;*
> - *the scale and nature of environmental effects on health vary widely with differing circumstances;*

- *not enough is yet known about the precise links between some environmental pollutants and ill-health.* (p25)

Nevertheless it went on to propose targets in five areas: see Table 10.

When last year's Review was written, the Government had just begun to grasp the nettle presented by the report from the Spongiform Encephalopathy Advisory Committee (SEAC) linking the new form of CJD to consumption of beef by authorising a large scale slaughter programme. In the face of the export ban imposed by the European Commission, it had little choice but to implement such a drastic measure. Within a year of the SEAC announcement, 1.3 million cattle had been lost and taxpayers faced with a bill of at least £3.3 billion – the estimates have kept rising since the decision to slaughter was made and no doubt the final figure will be much higher.

In February 1997, the first meeting of a Review Committee on Research into Transmissible Spongiform Encephalopathies took place. Its terms of reference are:

- to ensure that a research strategy, which fully addresses UK Government's policy needs in relation to human and animal TSEs, is in place and agreed by all funders;
- to ensure that mechanisms are in place to implement the agreed research strategy and that progress to implementation is taking place as quickly as possible;
- to ensure that all relevant sources of expertise are being called upon and the information is being released to them as freely and quickly as possible;
- to identify any barriers to progress and make recommendations for overcoming them;
- to make regular reports to the Prime Minister.

While it is clear that the direct economic consequences for the beef industry and for the taxpayer are very large indeed, the implications for health remain uncertain. The number of cases of the new form of CJD has not risen rapidly – only four cases were confirmed in 1997 after the original 10 plus one in France – but while this is encouraging, an analysis by the CJD surveillance unit and the London School of Hygiene and Tropical Medicine (*Nature*, 16 January 1997) concluded that it was still too early to be sure about the eventual number of cases:

> *It is likely to be several years before we can begin to make preliminary estimates of how large an epidemic might eventually be. Even though there have only been 14 confirmed cases to date in the UK, we cannot rule out the possibility of a large epidemic involving many thousands of cases, if the average incubation period is long, say 20 years or more.*
>
> *The numbers of cases with onset in each of the next few years may enable preliminary estimates to be made of the eventual size of the epidemic, but much uncertainty will still remain.* (p198)

Had we known then what is now known about BSE – still not conclusively linked to the new strain of CJD and still not explained in its own right (*Economist*, 18th January 1997) – would policy have been any different? The Southwood Committee were aware, when they reviewed the situation soon after BSE was first recognised, that there were risks that the then scientific understanding would prove wrong but the risks were deemed small, as they were in all subsequent official announcements. The judgement on what level of risk was small enough to ignore was then, and remained until 1996, a professional matter.

In his 1995 report *On the State of the Public Health* published in September 1996 (*Health Trends* Vol 28 no. 3), the Chief Medical Officer for Health, Sir Kenneth Calman, tried to start a wider debate on risk which would break into this closed circle:

> *The problem for decision-makers is not when the evidence is clear, but when it is weak or incomplete ... In such instances there is a need for openness and sharing of information, and the establishment of trust between those who make policy and the public at large.* (p83)

Sir Kenneth went on to suggest two classifications of risks, one in terms of the rate or level of risk, the other in terms of the circumstances surrounding the acceptance or otherwise of a given risk: see Box overleaf.

The Advisory Committee on Dangerous Pathogens, which was established in 1981 in response to an outbreak of smallpox, published *Microbiological Risk Assessment: an interim report*, in June 1996 which also suggests that risk should be consciously addressed:

> *Risk assessment is an area of increasing public interest especially where it impinges on our health and prosperity.*

Echoing the global theme of the climate reports, it goes on:

> *Recent outbreaks of plague in India, Ebola virus in Zaire and the HIV epidemic world-wide, have heightened the debate about how microbiological risks are identified and quantified, as well as how the principles of risk-based approaches should influence policy-making.* (preface)

It made a number of recommendations – see Box on p37 – bearing on the collection and assessment of the information required to make microbiological risk assessment feasible. As the report points out:

> *Unlike other potential hazards, such as chemicals, micro-organisms can multiply, mutate and transfer from one person to another.* (p4)

The ability to mutate and transfer accounts for the increase in strains of TB resistant to anti-biotics, a capacity which threatens the basis of much existing medical practice. In hospitals for example, (MRSA = Methicillin-resistant Staphylococcus Aukeus) has already claimed some lives and although it is currently under control, there is little sign that it can be eradicated. The Public Health Laboratory Service recorded incidents of MRSA at 177 hospitals in 1996, affecting some 19,000 patients. A 1997 report from the Service *Hospital-acquired Infection: surveillance policies and practice* found much larger numbers picking up infections in hospitals and an infection rate of 2.7 per cent in the 19 hospitals studied. Staff were often unaware of or failed to implement existing written guidance.

But while further scientific work is clearly needed, another kind of work is also required. As

Types of risk

- Avoidable – unavoidable: An important and clear distinction that can radically shift the perception of risk. Use of this dichotomy allows individuals to exercise choice, and the public to be involved in the decision-making procedure.
- Justifiable – unjustifiable: These words implicitly carry values with them, and risks may be taken in some instances but not in others. For example, the use of a drug with known side-effects, to treat a particular condition may be justifiable to achieve some benefit in some instances but not in others.
- Acceptable – unacceptable: Once again these are value-laden words, but need to be used in a particular context. In general, an unacceptable risk would not be tolerated except for special reasons in special circumstances – for example, in the use of an unproven method of treatment as a therapy of last resort.
- Serious – not serious: Again these are words which refer to particular situations, but in this instance refer to risks which are life-threatening or likely to cause disability or morbidity, and those which are not.

The second categorisation is in terms of the likelihood of the risk occurring

- Negligible: an adverse event occurring at a frequency below one per million. This would be of little concern for ordinary living if the issue was an environmental one, or the consequence of a health care intervention. It should be noted, however, that this does not mean that the event is not important – it almost certainly will be to the individual – nor that it is not possible to reduce the risk even further. Other words which can be used in this context are 'remote' or 'insignificant'. If the word 'safe' is to be used, it must be seen to mean negligible, but should not imply no, or zero, risk.
- Minimal: a risk of an adverse event occurring in the range of between one in a million and one in 100,000, and that the conduct of normal life is not generally affected as long as reasonable precautions are taken. The possibility of a risk is thus clearly noted and could be described as 'acceptable' or 'very small'. But what is acceptable to one individual may not be to another.
- Very low: a risk of between one in 100,000 and one in 10,000, and thus begins to describe an event, or consequence of a health care procedure, occurring more frequently.
- Low: a risk of between one in 10,000 and one in 1,000. Once again this would fit into many clinical procedures and environmental hazards. Other words which might be used include 'reasonable', 'tolerable' and 'small'. Many risks fall into this very broad category.
- Moderate: a risk of between one in 1,000 and one in 100. It would cover a wide range of procedures, treatments and environmental events.
- High: fairly regular events that would occur at a rate greater than one in 100. They might also be described as 'frequent', significant' or 'serious'. It may be appropriate further to subdivide this category.
- Unknown: when the level of risk is unknown or unquantifiable. This is not uncommon in the early stages of an environmental concern or the beginning of a newly recognised disease process (such as the beginning of the HIV epidemic).

Source: *Health Trends* Vol. 28 No. 3 p 83–4

John Wargo has argued (*Our Children's Toxic Legacy*, Yale 1996), there are philosophical issues too. Calman's first list of risk categories recognises that the nature of the judgement involved is critical. But there are significant differences not allowed for in the typology just cited between risks we accept for ourselves, and those which are imposed on us by individuals, companies or governments which we are not aware of. Wargo suggests that:

Advisory Committee on Dangerous Pathogens

The Committee made the following recommendations relating to data collection and risk assessment. It also proposed a study of the public's perception of risk and that government should use microbiological risk assessment (MRA) to underpin all relevant public health decisions.

Collection of epidemiological information

The confident assessment of risks to public health depends upon the use of high quality epidemiological data, especially those derived from the application of modern molecular methods. Systems for collecting, collating, analysing and disseminating such data should be actively conserved and developed in response to particular needs. New priority areas should be identified and regularly reviewed by Government in co-operation with relevant public and professional bodies. In particular, the Working Group considers that the Public Health Laboratory Service has an essential and unique role in the surveillance, recognition and prediction of microbiological hazards.

Targeted epidemiological studies

Targeted epidemiological studies represent the best quality information for informing certain types of MRA. Therefore, where appropriate, MRAs with major public health implications should always be underpinned by targeted epidemiological studies as far as is reasonably practicable.

Population immunity profiles – national reference banks

Knowledge of population immunity profiles is fundamental to MRA and public health. The feasibility of collating and collecting data to establish a reference resource for key diseases should be explored by a short term study. The development of non-invasive assays, especially those based on saliva, has made such profiles more realistically attainable. Such a study should cover, in particular, the current state of the diagnostic art, as well as the practicality and utility of establishing and maintaining national reference banks.

Ranking quality of information

A project should be established to define reliable and effective systems for indicating the quality, comparability and confidence of a MRA.

Emerging technology and conceptual advances

Agencies responsible for decisions on public health and microbiological safety should ensure they are aware of relevant advances in science and technology and assess the impact on MRA of such advances.

Survey of databases

A systematic survey should be instituted to identify relevant databases which may contribute to MRA. The results of this survey should be widely publicised.

Development of modelling – expert systems

Developments in mathematical modelling and systems such as StAR offer considerable potential benefits to the process of MRA. Such developments should be actively encouraged via the establishment of studies to assess their applicability to MRA and public health.

Study of earlier examples of MRA

A range of existing MRAs should be re-examined, in particular to assess the quality of information, the approaches taken, and the effectiveness of both the assessments and the actions arising from them.

Source: *Microbiological Risk Assessment; a interim report*, HMSO 1996.

Freedom from risk imposed by others, intentionally or accidentally, should be thought of as another type of individual right deserving legal protection. In this view, spheres of non-injurious freedom should be maximized and equitably distributed. The central problem posed in this book is that the definition of the boundaries among these spheres – which establish the limits of rights and the allocation of obligations – is organically tied to a highly uncertain, ever-changing, and fractured knowledge base. The most crucial knowledge is understanding when the exercise of one individual's right harms the rights or interests of another. The certainty and significance of the damage will always be contested, as will be the causal link between the reportedly offensive behaviour and the hypothesized damage.
(p 296)

This principle is particularly relevant to children not only because there is no sense in which they can be said to have accepted the risks they face but also because they are particularly vulnerable to certain kinds of hazard by virtue of their physiology:

If the most vulnerable deserve health protection, then how should precautionary policy be defined, and what conditions deserve its application? The strictest definition would require that the most exposed and most susceptible individuals be protected with an additional margin of safety to protect against the errors common to risk estimation. In determining maximum allowable contamination levels, risk averaging and the consideration of collective benefits would not be allowed.

This suggestion, however, is conceptually similar to 'safety net' policies that ensure equal access to minimum levels of income, health care, and education. Precautionary policy would prevent significant risks from falling on the most vulnerable and would take the form of an acceptable risk ceiling ...

Underlying this proposal is a belief that everyone has a fundamental right to be protected from significant and reasonably certain risks imposed by the behaviour of others. Definitions of what constitutes a significant risk, and when evidence is reasonably certain, should be articulated as clearly as possible for each environmental health threat confronting society. Precautionary policy is thus conditional, in that it should apply to cases where risks are deemed significant and when certainty is sufficient.
(pp 297/8)

Reports such as those cited above underline how the environment in its broadest sense can be threatening but in unknown degrees and hence how difficult it is to determine that 'sufficient certainty'. In areas such as screening, the risks are better known and here the issues are those central ones of health policy: access, equity, efficiency in service delivery and cost-effectiveness; in other words, who should be screened and for what conditions and is the process itself carried out well?

These issues arise even with well-established programmes. The cervical cancer programme continues to yield examples of failures to detect cancers through poor quality control. In May 1997 a special investigation revealed that 91,000 tests carried out at Kent & Canterbury Hospital had to be reviewed by an independent laboratory. Subsequently, the chief executive and chair resigned after the hospital had accepted that a woman had died because of its failure to detect her cancer.

In the case of breast screening the main issue is that of coverage. The programme currently focuses on women aged 50-64. *The Breast Screening Programme* results for 1994/95 published in 1996 showed that:

- 64% of women aged 50-64 resident in England had been screened at least once in the previous three years;
- In 86 of the 111 Districts the coverage was 60% or higher; in only 12 Districts was the coverage less than 50%;
- 77% of women aged 50-64 invited for screening were screened;
- One million women of all ages were screened within the programme;
- 5,387 cases of cancer were diagnosed among women screened.

The argument over breast screening was joined last year over the age at which women should be called. A study in the Inverness area (P J Hendry and C Entwhistle, Effect of issuing an invitation for breast cancer screening to women aged 65 to 69, *Journal of Medical Screening*, 1996 pp88-89) found that 76 per cent of women invited accepted and that a cancer detection rate of 9.3 per cent was achieved. This finding, as the authors point out, is in direct contradiction to the assumption in the Forrest report, on which current policy is based, that the response rate would be poor.

In contrast to breast cancer screening, screening for glaucoma is opportunistic, as there is no attempt to define and cover the population at risk. Instead, sight tests are used as the 'opportunity'. We noted in *Health Care UK 1994/95* that the introduction of charges for sight tests appeared to have reduced referrals to hospital but data from the General Household Survey suggest that overall numbers attending for sight tests have risen. However, as Richard Wormald and colleagues report (*BMJ* 314, 25 January 1997):

> *The incidence of glaucoma increases with age (from 0.08/1000 per year in white people in their early 40s, rising to 1.46/1000 per year in the over 80s). However, the data from the general household survey do not show the same trend for the likelihood of sight testing. This increased from 28% of those aged 25-34 having sight tests to 40% of those aged 45-54, but thereafter decreased so that 37% of those over 65 reported having had a sight test in the previous year. The peak in the fifth decade is likely to be due to presbyopia – the need for reading glasses, which usually starts in the fifth decade but stabilises by the seventh. Those aged over 65 are less likely to need more powerful reading correction and so have less incentive to seek sight testing. The survey's findings therefore indicate that the population subgroup at greatest risk of glaucoma are not the most likely to attend for sight tests.*
>
> *The survey also reveals differences between socio-economic groups. The highest percentages of sight testing are found in professionals, with*

> *39% of professional men and 40% of professional women attending compared with 22% of unskilled men and 29% of unskilled women. Stratification shows that this difference is not accounted for by age.*
>
> *The fact that those aged over 65 are at higher risk of glaucoma but are not the most likely to seek sight testing must be a matter of concern for a government which has proposed to offer free sight tests to those at increased risk of blinding diseases.* (p 245)

The authors do not argue on the basis of this evidence that there should be a nationwide glaucoma screening programme but suggest that a range of other measures might be taken:

> *So what can be done? We are not advocating a nationwide glaucoma screening programme as this entails questions of implementation, cost and diagnostic accuracy that have not yet been satisfactorily answered. However, the present system is clearly failing to detect large amounts of preventable blindness, and other options need to be explored – including free eye tests for elderly people, an educational campaign to increase public awareness of the need for regular glaucoma assessment, and locally based initiatives in areas with high proportions of Afro-Caribbean people. Finally, any strategy that increases glaucoma case detection in the community has to be backed up by adequate resources. Only then will an already stretched hospital eye service be able to cope with the resulting workload.* (p245)

A report from the Royal National Institute for the Blind, *Losing Sight of Blindness*, points to a number of similar issues. Its central argument is that the sight test is not properly organised to act as an effective health screening device.

> *The recent Government White Paper states the need for the 'systematic setting of standards' to achieve quality of care. Currently in optometry there are no official standards, with the requirements through regulations only providing a very broad framework. The service user has no benchmark from which to gauge the quality of eye test received.*
>
> *The quality of the test is a key factor, not only in the detection of eye disease but also for other conditions such as diabetes and hypertensive changes which can often be identified by the eye test. To detect many of these conditions a full inspection of the retina is needed. This is a key procedure which usually requires dilation of the pupil. This is infrequently performed.* (p 18)

This is just one of a number of areas where there may be a case for a structured screening programme. In July 1996 a National Screening Committee was established to consider all such areas. Its terms of reference are set out in the Box opposite.

In February 1997, the Committee announced that the costs of screening for prostate cancer in terms of impotence, incontinence, postoperative morbidity and psychological disturbance outweighed the benefits. This conclusion was based on two systematic reviews commissioned as part of the health technology assessment programme.

The case against extension of screening rests in part on the direct costs involved in the process itself but also on its wider impacts on

National Screening Committee: terms of reference

1. On the basis of sound evidence (including clinical and cost effectiveness, population needs, ethics, and outcomes information) to advise Department of Health ministers, the Government's Chief Medical Officer, the wider Department of Health and the NHS Executive Board on the timeliness and appropriateness of implementation, development, review, modification and where necessary, the cessation of national screening programmes.
2. To advise Ministers, the Chief Medical Officer, the NHS Research & Development Programme (through its Standing Group on Health Technologies) and the wider Department of Health on the need for research reviews, for research in relation to screening, and for analytical work to help focus and make best use of research.
3. Through the programme specific Advisory Groups and other groups concerned with national and local population screening, monitor and be advised of the progress, problems and research needs of ongoing NHS screening programmes and where appropriate advise on standards and monitoring arrangements.

personal behaviour. As Sarah Stewart Brown and Andrew Farmer (*BMJ*, 22nd February 1997) point out, screening can be counter-productive because of its impact on personal behaviour:

> *People found in workplace screening programmes to be hypertensive have increased sickness absence, increased anxiety, and reduced self perceived health status, regardless of whether their hypertension warranted treatment. Several studies on the effectiveness of cholesterol testing have shown a paradoxical effect: a reduction in deaths from heart disease but a small increase in total mortality. It has been suggested that men who know that they are at increased risk of dying of heart disease may be more inclined to take other risks. Some of these adverse psychological effects probably also have an impact on the family and friends of the individual who has been screened.*
>
> *Some of this literature on adverse effects is contradictory and many potential deleterious effects have yet to be researched. One of these is the 'certificate of health effect'. This suggests that people who have received a negative result on screening may be more resistant to advice on healthy lifestyles. For example, people who screen negative for cancer may feel safe continuing smoking, and those with low serum cholesterol eating their unhealthy diets. Screening programmes may also imply that good health can be maintained by regular visits to the doctor for check ups and that individual behaviour is less important.* (p 533)

National preventive programmes are currently largely aimed at children. The vaccination and immunisation figures for 1995/96 shows that by two years:

- uptake of three doses of diptheria, tetanus and polio immunisation was 96 per cent;
- uptake of three doses of pertussis and haemophilus influenzae immunisation was 94 per cent
- uptake of measles, mumps and rubella immunisation was 92 per cent.

The extent of progress during the 1990s emerges clearly from Tables 11 and 12.

Commenting on the figures the Chief Medical

Table 11 Completed primary courses: percentage of children immunised by their first birthday, 1988 to 1995/96

Year of 1st birthday	*Diphtheria*	*Tetanus*	*Polio*	*Pertussis (Whooping Cough)*	*Haemophilus Influenzae b*
1988/89	63	62	62	56	–
1995/96	93	93	93	92	93

Source: Department of Health

Table 12 Completed primary courses: percentage of children immunised by their second birthday

Year of 2nd birthday	*Diphtheria*	*Tetanus*	*Polio*	*Pertussis*	*Measles*	*Rubella*
1988/89	87	87	87	75	80	–
1995/96	96	96	96	94	92	92

Source: Department of Health

Officer was able to point to a reduction in measles notifications from 400,000 in 1986 before immunisation began, to 7,800 in 1995, of which 60 were confirmed. But while this highly focused programme appears to have been straightforwardly successful, the same cannot be said of the wider public health strategy of which it forms part.

The Welsh Office stole a march on its colleagues in Whitehall by publishing in 1989 its *Strategic Intent and Direction*. In August 1996, the National Audit Office published a review of its impact, *Improving Health in Wales*. The policy was launched within one health system and implemented in another, the 'new NHS' which, through its identification of the purchasing function was in some respects a more appropriate vehicle through which to work. The policy extended beyond public health but its prime emphasis was on health gain – by whatever means.

The audit revealed that, although the policy had been in force for several years and had, in most respects been well implemented:

> *its impact on the direct delivery of health services to patients has been relatively limited ...*

> *While changes in services might be expected to be marginal in the early years of the initiative, progress has been inhibited because not all health authorities were clear as to the present status of the initiative; there were some weaknesses in the way that targets were set and the arrangements for monitoring progress towards them; and health authorities had*

difficulty in realising savings from relatively ineffective services before embarking on service improvements. (p5)

The National Audit Office goes on to suggest a range of measures for the Welsh Office to take that might make the programme more effective:

- *clarify and communicate the status and priority of the Strategic Intent and Direction;*
- *review the targets, in the light of information now available, to focus on a small number of national priorities;*
- *devise measurable key targets for those aspects of health which are still considered to be important, but for which no measurable targets currently exist;*
- *work with health authorities to agree local targets and priorities which, while remaining broadly consistent with national objectives, ensure that resources are directed at those areas which are important locally and offer the greatest scope for impact;*
- *consult health authorities and other interested parties to ensure that guidance on implementing the initiative is clear and meets their needs;*
- *publicise best practice in consulting interested parties about local strategies, and encourage health authorities to find ways of securing greater input from general practitioners;*
- *hold health authorities to account for carrying out the action specified in their plans aimed at achieving national and local targets.* (pp6-7)

Within England, the National Audit Office published in August 1996 *Health of the Nation: a progress report*. It begins by quoting the Priorities and Planning Guidance 1997/97, in which the *Health of the Nation* is described as the central plank of government health policy and the main context for the planning of services into the next millennium. It then goes on to confirm what earlier Reviews have shown, that while progress is being made in some areas, in others such as obesity, female drinking and teenage smoking, the indicators are going the wrong way while in others such as male drinking, no information is available or the trend unclear: see Table 13.

The results of the 1995 Health Survey – the fifth such – published in February 1997 reaffirmed the findings reported last year of an increase in obesity as well as high levels of smoking among certain age groups. But it also found that the proportion of adults with high blood pressure fell from 24.2 to 22.4 per cent and the proportion of those with high blood pressure who were being treated for that condition rose. Furthermore 91 per cent of children from 2 to 15 were reported as having good or very good health. One lesson can be drawn from both these reports: that if the two initiatives do in fact have a central place in health policy, their implementation is defective. The National Audit Office concludes its report with the following recommendations:

The Department of Health should continue to address:

Table 13 Progress towards *Health of the Nation* targets

Code	*Target*	*Progress towards target*
A1	CHD under 65 years	✔
A2	CHD 65-74 years	✔
A3	Stroke under 65 years	✔
A4	Stroke 65-74 years	✔
B1	Breast cancer 50-69 years	✔
B4	Lung cancer, men under 75 years	✔
C2	Suicide	✔
D1	Gonorrhoea	✔
E1	Accidents under 15 years	✔
E2	Accidents 15-24 years	✔
E3	Accidents 65 years and over	✔
A5/B6	Cigarette smoking – males	?✔
A5/B6	Cigarette smoking – females	?✔
A8	Energy from saturated fat	?✔
A9	Energy from total fat	?✔
B8	Cigarette consumption	?✔
D3	Conceptions under 16 years	?✔
A7	Obesity	x
A10	Drinking – females	x
B9	Smoking 11-15 years	x
A6	Blood pressure	?
B2	Cervical cancer	?
B3	Skin cancer	?
B7	Giving up smoking in pregnancy	?
B5	Lung cancer in females under 75	*
A10	Drinking – males	*
C1	Mental illness	–
C3	Mental illness – suicide	–
D2	Drug misusers sharing needles	–

Key to last column:

✔ = Making substantial progress towards target
x = Moving in opposite direction to target
?✔ = Making some progress towards target
? = Not yet possible to assess progress in either direction
* = No significant change from baseline or no clear trend
– = No monitoring data consistent with baseline yet available nationally so no assessment practicable

Source: National Audit Office analysis

- *those areas where targets have already been met and areas where good progress is being made, with a view to considering whether it is desirable for targets to be revised within the existing framework, in order to maximise the effectiveness of the initiative and its value for money;*

- *those areas where progress is slow, or trends are running counter to targets to see what further action should be taken;*

- *the need to improve the quality, availability and timeliness of data generally and in the mental health area in particular.*

Beneath the blandness lie some fundamental difficulties. Governments do not have the means to determine personal behaviour and while they may try, to do so and fail is to squander resources. The Public Accounts Committee hearing on *The Health of the Nation: a progress report* attempted to pursue the effectiveness issue but very soon ran into the sand. Sir Graham Hart, Permanent Secretary at the Department of Health, was reluctant to say how much was spent on health promotion altogether offering a figure of £210 million plus 'a lot more things such as immunisation, vaccination and so on and so forth'. This by-and-large approach did not impress the Committee, as the extract from the Committee hearings in the Box opposite shows.

Many of the possible levers for change bear directly on the private sector. For example, the Nutrition Task Force in its 1996 report *Eat Well II* made a large number of proposals to each of which the Conservative Government responded, typically in broad terms as the example below indicate:

Spending on prevention

Mr Hall (Committee Member)

131. How much does the National Health Service spend as a percentage of its budget on health promotion?

(Sir Graham Hart) No, I do not think I can tell you that because it depends very much on how you define health promotion. As I said earlier, it depends on whether you include things like the payments to general practitioners and so on. I am sorry if that sounds rather unhelpful.

132. Is it going to get better?

(Sir Graham Hart) I will try to make it a bit better. If we add together the three elements I mentioned earlier, £45 million on the health education, the element in GP remuneration which is about health promotion specifically, which is £74 million, and the spending by health authorities and trusts on their health promotion units which is about £90 million, we are up to something like £210 million a year. You could put a lot more things into this pot if you wanted to such as immunisation, vaccination and so on and so forth, but the figures I have given you so far will be somewhere rather less than one per cent.

133. The obvious point to make here is that clearly prevention is better than cure, is it not?

(Sir Graham Hart) Yes.

134. But the Health Service does not direct its resources in that way for obvious reasons.

(Sir Graham Hart) It is not right to say and you would not be very pleased I think if I as accounting officer were party to any amount of spending on promotion. It has to be health promotion which has a payback, has to represent value for money. We have to be disciplined about this.

135. Have you worked out the actual payback the amount of money which is spent on health promotion gets you in good health and savings to the National Health Service?

(Sir Graham Hart) This is into very, very difficult territory. You have to look at these programmes one by one and try to put the best value on them that you can. We are better at that now than we used to be. For example, when the breast screening programme was introduced some pretty careful evaluation was done first of what it would cost and what we expected the benefits to be and it was thought on the whole to be a beneficial and cost effective programme.

Source: Committee of Public Accounts, *The Health of the Nation: a progress report,* HMSO 1997

Task Force Recommendation
Further action should concentrate on making the public aware that most of the fat in poultry is in the skin.

Government response
This is a matter for the industry itself.

The readiness of the Conservative Government to leave action to be taken by industry might seem to reflect its reluctance to impose extra 'burdens' on industry. However, in contrast to the relaxed response illustrated by this example, the Government accepted the recommendations of the Pennington report into the E. coli outbreak in Scotland in 1997, despite the risk that they would weigh heavily on smaller retailers in particular: see Box overleaf.

While the Government clearly did not trust food retailers to take the necessary measures, it became clear in other areas that the food industry could be relied upon to take some action of its own accord in part because of consumer pressure. Thus in June 1997, the Co-op announced they would cease to stock

The Pennington Group Interim Report and Priority Recommendations: Summary of Recommendations

1. Research

Early research should be funded (a) into the prevalence/incidence of E.coli 0157 in Scottish cattle and other animals and the biology of its carriage; (b) to help forecast its likely future incidence/prevalence; and (c) to improve the current DNA-based methods for its identification.

2. Surveillance

The Management Executive of SODoH and SCIEH should consider urgently the practicalities, costs and benefits of improvements to the arrangements for surveillance and data collection/analysis for pathogenic organisms and foodborne disease.

3. Enforcement and Measures to Recognise and Minimise Public Health Risk

A range of measures should be taken to enforce food safety measures and ensure the recognition and minimisation of the risks to public health from foodborne disease. These should include:

- changes to food safety legislation to reflect the importance of public health considerations and, in particular, to permit the introduction of selective licensing for food premises;
- the physical separation, within premises, of raw and cooked meat products using separate counters, equipment and staff;
- reviewing guidelines and Codes of Practice to help improve communications and to promote the recognition and assessment of risk and, again, public health considerations; and
- accelerating the implementation of HACCP for high risk premises.

4. The Handling and Control of Outbreaks of Foodborne Disease

Local authorities and health boards should ensure that there are in place joint local outbreak management plans setting out mechanisms and procedures for dealing with food poisoning outbreaks; and that they are backed up by training and exercises as appropriate.

Local outbreak control teams should be free to take decisions and act as necessary to investigate and control outbreaks.

The Scottish Office should review the guidelines relating to the investigation and control of food poisoning outbreaks and its internal arrangements for dealing with outbreaks when they occur.

alcopops while other retailers took less drastic measures to reduce the risks of them being consumed by under-age drinkers.

One route by which governments might be forced to take public health matters more seriously is a legal one. The outbreak of E. coli in Scotland was the worst ever recorded. As Table 14 shows, the incidence of such outbreaks is rising and although some of the rise may be due to better reporting, the PHLS which collects the figures suggests not all of it can be accounted for in this way.

Table 14 Confirmed cases of E.coli

Year	Cases	Year	Cases
1982	1	1990	250
1983	6	1991	361
1984	9	1992	470
1985	50	1993	385
1986	76	1994	411
1987	89	1995	792
1988	49	1996	660
1989	119		

Source: www.open.gov.uk/cdsc/ecolifc7.htm)

In December 1996 it was announced (*Guardian*, 20 December) that legal aid had been granted to bring a test case against the Ministry of Agriculture, Fisheries and Food and the Department of Health. In 1985 a government committee had recommended labelling to advise on cooking meat and also more research: but neither had been acted on. It also emerged in March 1997 that a report on hygiene standards in the meat industry had been suppressed by the Ministry's meat hygiene service.

In the USA, some states have succeeded in extracting large sums from the tobacco industry in respect of the health costs they have incurred and both there and in this country, individuals are preparing actions against the industry. The first passive smoking case in Scotland was decided in March 1997. The plaintiff lost on the ground that it was the employer's obligation to provide ventilation and air circulation but not to extract impurities.

The events recorded here have led to a general distrust of official advice in general and the role of the Ministry of Agriculture in particular. In response the Government announced in January 1997 that an independent food safety adviser would be appointed reporting directly to ministers and supported by a Food Safety Council consisting of independent scientists. Labour, while still in Opposition, made a similar proposal and soon after coming to office confirmed its intention to set up an independent regulator.

The new Government signalled its intention to take public health issues seriously by the appointment of a Minister, Tessa Jowell, with specific responsibilities in that area. It also announced on 11 June 1997 the appointment of Sir Donald Acheson to carry out a further review of the evidence relating to inequality and the link between health and wealth and was quick to announce restrictions on tobacco advertising. How quickly it will move on the more fundamental issues which a serious attack on health inequalities requires, remains to be seen. That would involve, at minimum, changes to the tax and benefit system as well as housing and other aspects of the physical environment which currently policies do not address. Within the NHS it would mean, as Michaela Benzeval argued in *Health Care UK 1995/96*, treating equity seriously through, initially, more effective monitoring of access to services as they now are and then, subsequently, effective action to remove the relevant barriers or alter the way that services are provided.

The announcement of the *Health of the Nation* in 1991 was widely welcomed at the time and the fact that it covered only a small part of the field discounted on the ground that at least policy was moving in the right direction. Events since have served to emphasise both the need for a perspective that comprises all the possible influences on health and the difficulties involved in achieving one. These difficulties stem in part from lack of knowledge and the complexity of the systems, be it at global or local level, which impact on health. They also stem from a

Health and wealth

During the Public Accounts Committee hearing on the *Health of the Nation Progress Report,* the discussion of cost-effectiveness led to one on the impact of economic and social conditions on health. An edited version, which speaks for itself, appears below.

Mr Hall (member of the committee)

138. I find the number of targets within this particular report very helpful and quite interesting. Have you done any evaluation? If you want to make health promotion efficient and effective we need to know the correlation between health and poverty, do we not, or the correlation between ill health and poverty? *(Sir Graham Hart)* That is a subject of some difficulty.

139. I thought there was almost agreement on this now.

(Sir Graham Hart) There has been a certain amount of academic work done on relationships between a variety of social factors and health but is too simple probably. These are matters of real –

140. I do not think the BMA would agree with you on that.

(Sir Graham Hart) It is too simple to say that poverty causes ill health.

141. But it is not too simple to say that there is a correlation between poverty and ill health.

(Sir Graham Hart) There is some kind of statistical association.

142. It is not 'some kind', it is proven and it is an absolute fact.

(Sir Graham Hart) A statistical association; yes.

143. The BMA do not see it in the terms you do. What about ill health and living conditions, if you want to be a little more precise, quality of accommodation?

(Sir Graham Hart) I do not know what the scientific evidence on that subject is. I would not find it surprising if there were some sort of connection between health and housing.

Source: Public Accounts Committee, as above.

reluctance on the part of Government to tackle vested interests as well as to make health inequalities an explicit policy objective. In July, Tessa Jowell announced that a green paper would be published in autumn 1997 setting out a 'new, wide-reaching public health strategy' which would tackle some of the underlying causes of ill-health such as social and economic deprivation.

1.4 Serving the Consumer

In September 1996, the Government published a White Paper, *The Citizen's Charter – Five years on*, which recorded progress across the public sector as a whole. As Table 15 shows, there has been an improvement in relation to most targets but in some cases, eg the number of patients not admitted within a month of the first cancelled operation, the position has worsened.

The White Paper also announced there would be new standards for A&E initial assessment and for response times for ambulances called to life-

Table 15 Patient's Charter 1991-1996

Patients	*Then*	*Now*	*Result* *Y=Better* *X=Worse*
England			
Number of patients waiting more than 18 months for hospital admission	21,077 in June 1992	nil in 1996	Y
Number of patients who had been waiting more than a year for hospital admission	169,761 in March 1991	4,600 in March 1996	Y
Percentage of patients assessed immediately in Accident and Emergency departments	75% in June 1993	94% in March 1996	Y
Percentage of outpatients seen within 30 minutes of appointment time	80% in Dec 1993	90% in March 1996	Y
Number of patients not admitted within a month of the first cancelled operation	1,343 in Dec 1994	1,675 in March 1996	X
Proportion of people seen within 13 weeks 83% 83% 26 weeks 96% 97% of referral by their GP or dentist	No change in Sept 1994	in March 1996	Y
Number of ambulance services that met the targets for responding to calls	68.4% in March 1995	70.3% in March 1996	Y
Wales			
Number of patients waiting more than 18 months for hospital admission	710 in March 1995	820 in March 1996	X
Percentage of patients assessed immediately in Accident and Emergency departments	90% in March 1994	95% in March 1996	Y
Percentage of outpatients seen within 30 minutes of appointment time	85% in March 1994	90% in March 1996	Y
Number of patients not admitted within a month of the first cancelled operation	63 in March 1995	76 in March 1996	X
Scotland			
Number of patients treated as inpatients or day cases	1,124,836 in 1991	1,232,141 in 1995	Y

cont.

Table 15 *(cont.)*

Percentage of Scottish Ambulance Service calls answered within target time:			
– High population density (14 minutes)	87%	91%	Y
– Medium population density	93%	96%	Y
– Sparse population density (21 minutes)	88%	91%	Y
in 1991 in 1995			
Northern Ireland			
Number of patients waiting more than 18 months for hospital admission	1,771 at 31 Mar 94	633 at 31 Mar 96	Y
Percentage of patients assessed within five minutes in Accident and Emergency departments	60% at 31 Mar 93	79% at 31 Mar 96	Y
Percentage of outpatients seen within 30 minutes of appointment time	80% at 31 Mar 93	81% at 31 Mar 96	Y
Number of patients not admitted within a month of the first cancelled operation	42 in quarter ended 31 Mar 95	52 in quarter ended 31 Mar 96	X

Source: *The Citizen's Charter – Five years on*, HMSO 1996

threatening incidents. The former reflects the criticisms recorded in last year's Review of the significance of the existing standards which have been widely criticised as meaningless since they could easily be met by slight changes in procedures which had little or no impact on patients. The latter reflects recommendations made in the review of ambulance performance standards (see page 7) which recommended the general use of a system of priority despatch which a number of services had piloted.

This system is designed to improve the chances of saving those with an immediately life-threatening condition such as cardiac arrest, while still ensuring that those with severe but not life-threatening conditions do not have to wait for long periods. However, Ministers did not accept the report's suggestion that a third category of call should be distinguished which would have allowed the ambulance service to divert calls judged not to require an urgent response to other sources of care. As a result, ambulances must now work to more demanding and more expensive standards without being offered the opportunity to find ways of reducing costs for less urgent cases.

But in any case, the change in ambulance standards does not go far enough since for those who reach hospital alive, the time from then onwards is critical but there is no standard for this stage of the care process. More significant, as Tom Judge argues in his article in this volume, the current pattern of provision does not offer the best prospect of saving the lives of those who suffer cardiac arrest.

The White Paper re-affirmed the

Government's commitment to further reductions in waiting times for elective admissions, but the pressure of emergency admissions during the winter of 1995/96 led to a small rise in the numbers waiting for more than a year and the same effect reoccurred following the winter of 1996/97. The financial pressures experienced by many hospital trusts – see section 2.1 – and those from the rise in emergency admissions have combined to make it impossible to reach the elective targets.

Table 16 Numbers waiting for elective care: England; end March

	0-11 months	*12-17 months*	*18+ months*
1995	1,006,526	31,358	277
1996	1,039,252	4,383	0
1997	1,133,050	31,160	155

Since the Charter was instituted, official figures suggest that there has been a massive increase in the number of elective cases treated in hospital. Since overall, there seems to be no reason to suppose that there has been a significant rise in morbidity during this period, it would seem reasonable to infer that on average, the severity of those being treated has fallen. If so, that would increase the risk, with targets in their present form, that the less urgent will be given preference over the more urgent and there is some anecdotal evidence that this occurs in practice. Jennifer Dixon and Bill New (*BMJ* vol 314 11 January 1997 pp86-87) report the development of priority measures in New Zealand which attempt to rank those waiting according to clinical and social factors. This approach, combined with maximum waiting times – promises to make more sense of waiting lists than the current arbitrary limits. A points system has already been pioneered in Salisbury but so far there appears to be no interest on the part of the NHS Executive in making moves in this direction.

In January 1997, the application of the Charter was restated (EL97(1)) in relation to mental health service together with some new or improved standards with respect to:

- Privacy and dignity in hospital
- Information
- Access to services
- Choice
- Care and treatment
- Care Programme Approach
- Assessment
- Discharge from hospital
- Care under the Mental Health Act 1983.

In the same month, after considerable media pressure, the first of these rights, which in principle applies to all patients, was also reaffirmed. In EL (97)3 health authorities were asked to agree 'challenging targets' with trusts so as to ensure that charter standards in respect of segregated washing and toilet facilities were achieved.

Last year the Review noted that the new complaints procedure was introduced, following the Wilson report, in April 1996. The NHS Trust Federation carried out a survey of trusts' experience of the first six months, reported in *Working Hard to Please.* Two main conclusions emerged: first, the initial process, called local resolution, was working well.

> *90 per cent of trusts said this process was working without difficulty. Comments from many indicated a pride was taken in the quality of Local Resolution. It was often given as the*

reason for not having any requests for Independent Review. (p1)

Trusts had more mixed views about the second stage, independent review. The report found that:

The process is also seen as bureaucratic. In some regions, regulation and 'advice' descend in encyclopaedic quantities. Prescription seems to be taken as a way to control quality. This is regrettable and mistaken.

There is also too great a presumption on the free time of Convenors. As one trust put it, 'Independent Review is additional and detailed work which places a great burden on Convenors. It is unreasonable to expect Convenors to contribute so many weekends and evenings in support of this system'. The time commitment expected from Convenors is not sustainable and threatens the Procedure. (p3)

From the CHC viewpoint, Toby Harris, director of ACHEW, has argued (*Health Care Risk Report*, November 1996) that the new procedure falls short of the Wilson proposals in significant ways: in particular that it has not achieved the goal of a single simplified system that Wilson envisaged. That might in part explain the rise in complaints made to the NHS Ombudsman. According to his report for 1996/97, he received 2,219 complaints, 24 per cent up on the previous year. 93 per cent of those received were upheld.

The need to take more effective response to complaints is underlined by the rise in payments for clinical negligence. Accurate figures and up-to-date figures are hard to come by but, as the figures cited in section 2.3 indicate, there is little doubt that their level has been rising rapidly and will continue to do so in the absence of reform in the ways that claims are dealt with and, more fundamentally of changes in the underlying behaviour giving rise to the claims.

Actions for negligence often begin because those seen to be responsible for what has gone wrong have not acknowledged error. If complaints were handled more effectively therefore, not only might patients be more content, but costs to the NHS might be lower. Equally, the arrangements made for meeting the costs of claims can also affect the number of claims arising.

One result of trust creation and the shift of medical contracts of employment from region to trust was a shift in liability from the individual clinician to the organisation. In 1995, the details of the new scheme for trusts were announced in EL (95)40 and in November 1996, new arrangements were brought in for dealing with claims for negligence on the part of trusts, set out in HSG (96)48. GPs continue to have to make their own arrangements to cover liability.

Trusts in the scheme have graded premia according to the degree to which they have in place explicit and appropriate policies towards risk. In principle therefore they have stronger incentives to avoid risks than they used to have. The scheme is run by the NHS Litigation Authority. The aims of the scheme are set out in the Box opposite.

The rise in claims for negligence belie the fact they are often difficult to pursue except for the very rich and the poor who can draw on legal aid. In *Access to Civil Justice*, Lord Woolf focused particularly on medical negligence and made a large number of proposals designed to both reduce claims and make claims easier to pursue.

Clinical Negligence Scheme for Trusts' Objectives

Maximising resources available for patient care

(i) to minimise the overall costs of clinical negligence to the NHS and thus maximise the resources available for patient care, by defending unjustified actions robustly, settling justified actions efficiently, and creating incentives to reduce the number of negligent incidents;

Proper payments

(ii) to assess the amounts (if any) to be paid by either Scheme in relation to any particular claim, and to ensure that sums paid out are properly so paid;

Impact on patient care and NHS costs

(iii) to minimise the risk that patient care in a particular community is jeopardised by a large settlement against its principal provider unit;

(iv) to spread the costs of clinical negligence settlements more evenly over time and (in respect of past liabilities) over health authority populations;

Incentives to improved quality

(v) to improve the quality of patient care by providing an incentive for provider units to improve cost effective clinical risk management, and by disseminating relevant information on clinical risks;

(vi) to maximise the incentive for provider units to improve claims management;

(vii) to minimise the incentive to provider units to resort to 'defensive medicine' as an alternative response to the threat of clinical litigation;

Access to appropriate remedies for genuine litigants

(viii) to ensure that, where actual clinical negligence has nevertheless occurred, patients have appropriate access to remedies including, where proper, financial compensations.

Source: *The NHS Litigation Authority Framework Document* NHS Executive, Sept 1996, p2/3

These are discussed in 2.3 below. In addition, the NHS Executive is piloting alternative dispute resolution methods in two areas.

However, although Lord Woolf makes recommendations targeted on the NHS as well as the legal process, he did not tackle the central difficulty head on. In Andrew Phillips' words:

> *... the fundamental difficulty of reform within medical negligence remains that accountability is shackled by the need for it to accompany proof of causation and harm in an adversarial setting in which there are incentives for parties to obstruct and hinder one another. Substantively, the current approach – ie involving something that no other doctor of ordinary or reasonable skill would do – could be replaced by another, which might, for example, be termed 'substandard care'. This would place more emphasis upon an absolute standard and diminish the strong influence of common practice in medical matters if this were desired. Substandard treatment would be that which fell below good clinical practice. It would accordingly be a higher standard than that in Bolam. Where this standard was transgressed, the present rules on proof of causation would apply, thereby guarding against a substantial increase in liability but redressing the balance in favour of the injured*

> *patient.(Medical Negligence Law: seeking a balance*, p194)

Phillips goes on to argue that improvements within the negligence concept are likely to be limited and other avenues must be explored. His suggestions are too lengthy to set down here, but his key suggestion is the separation of compensation from accountability.

> *The standard of care should improve as a result, and patients should be provided with explanations where these have not been forthcoming from the doctor originally. More fundamentally, though, in the absence of an adversarial litigation system there would be less perceived incentive for distrust and hostility between doctor and patient in the event of an adverse outcome; explanations would be more likely under the proposed scheme. This might even result subsequently in a lower complaints rate. Wider issues, such as organisational deficiencies, could be included within the remit of the new system, and even factors such as rehabilitation. As an audit mechanism, lessons in prevention and risk management would accrue as benefits from the proposed system. Appropriate and proportional accountability would be available for all levels of the medical system.* (p 212)

One of the underlying principles of the *Patient's Charter* has been that it should enable choice between different providers on the basis of 'quality of service'. The Government continues to publish indicators on the basis of performance to *Patient's Charter* standards. These are now available on the Internet as well as in 'user-friendly regional leaflets', and it has at last begun the process of moving on to indicators of clinical performance. Initially these are to be published within the NHS and then to the general public. In EL (96)87, *The Patient's Charter Progress and New Commitments*, it was announced that the following areas would be reported on:

- Perioperative mortality;
- Surgical wound infections;
- Length of hospital stay of stroke patients, and discharge home;
- District rate of hernia recurrence;
- In-hospital mortality for acute myocardial infarction;
- Adverse drug reactions while patients are in hospital;
- Reoperation after prostate surgery;
- Length of stay in hospital, mortality and discharge home after admission for fractured neck of femur;
- Frequency of diagnostic curettage in women under the age of 40 years;
- Perioperative organ damage (sentinel event marker);
- Perioperative pulmonary embolism (sentinel event marker);
- Perioperative central nervous system complications (sentinel event marker).

As noted in *Health Care UK 1994/95* the Scots have been quicker off the mark and although they continue to print a statistical health warning on each page of indicators, their scope has expanded since the first edition published in 1992. The introduction to the 1996 report further underlines the care with which the data should be interpreted and makes clear that their purpose is not to guide patient choice.

> *As before, therefore, the main reason for publishing these outcome indicators is to focus the attention of Health Boards and trusts, and above all of clinicians themselves, on disparities in outcome whose existence would otherwise have remained unsuspected. Some of these disparities will prove on investigation to be due to differences in coding or diagnostic criteria, or to differences at the time of treatment in the severity of chronicity of similar disorders in different parts of the country. Others, however, may turn out to be due to the persistence of outmoded practices, or other remediable deficiencies in service provision or therapeutic regimes, and correcting these should lead to an improvement in overall standards of care.* (p 3)

The Scottish Office has also announced its intention in a consultation document, *Primary Care: agenda for action*, to publish indicators relating to family health services.

In contrast to the intended (initial) audience for clinical indicators, the initiative relating to informed choice in childbirth is targeted at the patient. Leaflets were launched in January 1996. By July, 58 trusts and maternity units had purchased them and a year later the figure had reached 70.

A Pilot Study of 'Informed Choice' Leaflets on Positions in Labour and Routine Ultrasound (Centre for Research and Dissemination Report 7, December 1996) found a number of factors had reduced their impact in practice, particularly professional tensions:

> *It was difficult to pilot the ultrasound leaflet at all. Support for a pilot given before the leaflet had been read by key stakeholders, particularly ultrasonographers, was withdrawn once they had become familiar with the extent and nature of the evidence contained in the leaflet. It is clear from their responses that many issues are involved; the threat to non-evidence based practice posed by the systematising and dissemination of evidence; concern that women themselves will be upset to find out how little scientific medicine knows, and the thin relationship between knowledge and practice; opposition to moving the power base for decision-making from professionals to users; the argument that the social and psychological functions of a technology such as routine ultrasound offer more than 'simply' problem diagnosis and treatment, and that these covert functions need to be respected.* (p 59)

The pilot also looked at birth positions and the actual impact of the leaflet on choice: results here were meagre for a variety of reasons.

> *No midwife thought that the positions in labour leaflet affected care or provision offered in their unit, but some thought that it might in future. (p 29)*

In March 1997, the Audit Commission published *First Class Delivery* a study of maternity services. The report found that:

> *163.* Changing Childbirth *has succeeded in raising awareness of pregnant women's needs*

for information, and the importance of listening to their views and involving them in decisions about their care.

164. Some health authorities have made comprehensive, up-to-date and detailed information about local services available to women through GP surgeries and other outlets.

165. In trusts, clinicians and managers should work together to improve communication, especially in antenatal screening and testing which is known to present problems for staff as well as to women using the service. If staff need help and training in communication and communication skills, trusts should provide it. Clinical guidelines and protocols can improve continuity and consistency in information-giving, and a common maternity record will make it easier for clinicians to see what others are doing. As new evidence becomes available that challenges established practices, purchasers, providers and clinicians must take collective responsibility for educating women and the general public and for explaining the rationales behind the service that is being provided. (pp70–71)

Similar needs were identified in a study by Dympna Edwards of head and neck cancer care (*Face to Face*, King's Fund 1997). She found that:

Information was often described by people with cancer and their relatives as a one-way process in which the professionals gave and they received. The two-way process of listening to people to understand their concerns in order to better meet their information needs was what many people with cancer wanted but did not seem to receive. The willingness for more open communication and information was evident both with professionals and people with cancer but the means to achieve this need to be developed. (p 43)

As for choice:

Many more people wanted to be involved in their treatment decisions than actually were … Many people said that they were consulted but that an open discussion of treatment options with their relative merits didn't occur. Even when choice was presented many people felt that there was not enough information to help them make an informed choice. (p44)

In January 1997, the National Consumer Council published a review of the information available about NHS continuing care. Its main, and as it remarks, unsurprising finding, is that there is great variation in the quality and availability of local information and while some documentation was good, a lot more needed to be done. The report makes too many recommendations to list here but two are particularly important:

We recommend that the NHS Executive work with health and local authorities to develop an information dissemination strategy to assist the local implementation of continuing care policies. This local information strategy should, at a minimum, include the following sorts of information, in appropriate formats, easy to read and to understand.

> *Information about individual NHS trusts' continuing care discharge policies, to be prepared and disseminated by trusts, informed by health authority policies, and in co-operation with social services. This should include information about local eligibility criteria, the role of social services, patients' rights at the time of discharge, how to seek a review of discharge decisions, and how to use NHS and social service complaints procedures.* (p53)

The extensions to the *Patient's Charter* reported here may be welcome in themselves, but they lack obvious coherence or direction. The successive modifications to the Charter appear to be responses to pressures as they have arisen rather than the result of a considered assessment of what rights or expectations users ought to have. Mixed wards had, for example, been the subject of intensive media attention prior to the announcement in January 1997.

In November 1996, the Association of Community Health Councils for England and Wales attempted in *The Patients' Agenda*, to provide such an overview. Its basic argument is quite simple: the Charter as it exists, with its mix of rights and expectations, does not address key issues – such as equality of access, the scope for patient participation on the basis of information choice and the quality of care and treatment – nor does it provide for the enforcement of the rights it does offer. The Associations suggests that there should be an independent Health Rights Commission with statutory powers to enforce all Charter rights and standards and that the complaints system should be modified by creating:

> *A right, if you are unhappy with the initial response to your complaint, to put it to a genuinely independent panel.*
>
> *A right to make a complaint about any aspect of care or treatment without the constraint of an imposed time limit.*
>
> *A right to receive support, advice and advocacy from your local Community Health Council, in relation to any complaint you have about the NHS and its services.* (p10)

The Association's statement sets out a large number of proposed rights under the headings: access to care and treatment, health care regardless of ability to pay, advocacy, support and appropriate care, good quality care in matters of life and death, confidentiality and control over personal information, as well as redress. As it recognises, some of these would require more resources, eg free eye tests and free continuing NHS care, and higher levels of intensive care.

Another broad, though quite different approach, was set out in *Patient Partnership* in June 1996. This begins by noting that the inclusion as a medium-term priority in the 1996/97 Priorities and Planning Guidelines the aim of 'giving greater voice to users of NHS services and their carers' was based on at least five factors:

- appropriate and effective services are more likely to be developed if they are planned on the basis of needs identified in conjunction with users;
- growing social expectations of openness and accountability mean that the users of public services are increasingly seeking more say in

how the NHS is developed, what services are provided and to what standards;

- patients want more information about their health condition, treatment and care. *The Patient's Charter* responded to this trend by formally stating a right to such information, but it is of course integral to the whole notion of 'informed consent';
- there is some evidence that involving patients in their own care improves health care outcomes and increases patient satisfaction;
- as we become gradually more sophisticated in assessing clinical effectiveness and outcomes, it is important to find ways of communicating that information to patients in a form they can understand and to ensure that the information itself reflects the patient's perspective on the benefits of their treatment.

The Patient Partnership Strategy has four elements:

- to promote user involvement in their own care, as active partners with professionals;
- to enable patients to become informed about their treatment and care and to make informed decisions and choices about it if they wish;
- to contribute to the quality of health services by making them more responsive to the needs and preferences of users;
- to ensure that users have knowledge, skills and support to enable them to influence NHS service policy and planning.

To help implement the strategy, the Executive has established a Centre for Health Information Quality the purpose of which is to ensure that the information patients receive is based on the best evidence available. The breadth of the issues raised by this report together with the *The Patient's Agenda*, suggest that a fundamental change is slowly coming about between the NHS and its users.But, as the next section brings, this message has not reach all the policy areas to which it might apply.

1.5. Clinical Knowledge

In early 1997, the Department of Health published an extensive briefing pack: *Research and Development: towards an evidence-based health service*. This in many respects exemplary publication fails in one simple respect: it gives no information on the volume of resources being devoted to the activities it describes. The overall level of spending ie including the MRC, charitable trusts funding research such as Wellcome and the Cancer Research Campaign and the private sector, was estimated for the House of Lords Committee report *Medical Research and the NHS Reforms* to be £2.7 bn in 1992/93 of which over half was spent by the pharmaceutical industry.

Last year, however, the process of implementing the Culyer proposals for the financing of research in the NHS began, the aim of which was to enable the NHS commitment to research to be seperately identified. As a first step NHS providers were asked to identify the costs they currently incurred in supporting research. Altogether some £334 million in support costs was identified and some 39,000 projects. In contrast, the cost of the national programmes was about £10 million in total in

1995/96: some details of spending on particular programmes are set out in Table 17.

The new single budget for NHS research and development will be over £400 million financed from a national R&D levy; this will cover the cost of service support for non-commercial R&D sponsored by external funders as well as the NHS's own R&D spending and in principle allow a shift in the allocation of the funds ear-marked for research, eg away from its currently strong hospital base towards primary care.

During the year, further steps were taken towards implementing the new arrangements. In May 1996, EL (96)47, the outline of the new arrangements was published and in EL (97)7,

Table 17 National Programme Expenditure 1995/96

Programme	*£000*
Mental Health	1,415
Cardio-vascular Disease and Stroke	3,093
Physical and Complex Disabilities	1,513
Primary/Secondary Care Interface	1,934
Cancer	299
Mother and Child Health	40
Implementation Methods	40
Health Technology Assessment	2,027
TOTAL	10,361

Source: Department of Health

Bidding for R&D funding

NHS providers whose R&D costs are reasonably predictable in the medium term will be invited to bid for a four-year block of funding to cover the costs of all their R&D activities not met by external sources.

In order to quality to bid for Portfolio Funding, bidders will need to be able to demonstrate the capacity to manage a block of R&D funds properly subject only to periodic review by the NHS Executive. In other words, they must show the ability to formulate and implement a strategy for the use of the funds which will promote quality and efficient use of resources.

NHS providers will be able to bid either individually or in consortia. These consortia might be of similar providers (eg acute hospitals, primary health care teams) or might span different types of service delivery (eg acute hospital, community unit and primary care team). The purpose of forming an R&D consortium would be to present a stronger proposal for R&D Portfolio Funding.

Providers or consortia will be asked to demonstrate how they would make good use of the funds in line with the Strategic Framework for the NHS R&D Levy. The precise requirements will, of course, depend on the objectives of the Strategic Framework.

As with Portfolio Funding, providers will need to show how their proposed R&D activity will contribute to achieving the objectives of the Strategic Framework, and how it fits within the context of their strategic partnerships with universities, NHS purchasers and providers, and where appropriate others such as Local Authority Social Services Departments. Unlike Portfolio Funding, however, providers will need to specify when bidding rather more precisely what the funds are to be used for, and this will be reflected in the contracts they receive.

Source: NHS Executive, *The New Funding System for Research and Development in the NHS*, p 9.

NHS providers were given notice of how they should bid for support from 1998/99 onwards.

The funds will be allocated on a competitive basis, in two forms, portfolio and task-linked funding – see Box on p. 59. within a centrally defined Strategic Framework. The broad principles underlying this framework were set out in another NHS Executive document *Strategic Framework for the Use of the NHS R&D Levy*, (1997) and runs as follows:

> **Quality**
> *The R&D Levy should only be used to meet the costs of work of good quality, judged by the appropriate prevailing professional standards. It will not, for instance, support work which is unlikely, for whatever reason, to achieve its own objectives.*
>
> **Ethics**
> *The R&D Levy should only be used to support activity which is ethical and has obtained any necessary R&D ethics committee approval.*
>
> **Relevance, Impact and Importance**
> *The R&D Levy should be used to fund and support activity which is relevant to health gain in the short, medium or long term and which will contribute to the development and implementation within the NHS of evidence-based practice. The views of those working in the NHS must be taken into account in deciding how to use the R&D Levy.*
>
> **Primary Care**
> *The NHS Executive will seek opportunities to use the Levy to promote the development within primary care of good quality R&D activity which is consistent with the other principles set out in this Framework.*
>
> **Partnership**
> *The NHS Executive will work in partnership with others, and will seek evidence from potential recipients of funds that they too work effectively with appropriate partners, including universities, other NHS and academic bodies, service users, carers, local authorities and industry.*

The new arrangements also provide for the NHS to continue to carry out research funded from other sources, ie non-commercial R&D. According to a consultation document, *NHS Support for Non-commercial Externally Funded Research and Development*, published in May 1996:

> *The NHS Executive believes that the NHS derives considerable benefits from the R&D sponsored by external funders and from working in partnership with them.*
>
> *In doing so, of course, the NHS spends a considerable amount of public money supporting non-commercial R&D, money which might otherwise be used for patient care. There must be a point at which the NHS Executive would have to conclude that the NHS's expenditure on supporting externally funded R&D had grown too large in comparison with competing priorities. In these circumstances, the NHS might be unable to provide support to as much externally funded research as it would otherwise wish. If this situation were to arise, the NHS Executive would need to discuss with other funders a basis on which to prioritise its support for their work.*

At present, however, the NHS Executive does not believe there is evidence that too great a proportion of NHS resources is being spent in support of R&D, given the many benefits that the NHS derives. For that reason it does not propose to set up a new prioritisation mechanism at this stage. The NHS Executive does, however, propose to put in place better systems for monitoring the level of NHS spending in this area, and for judging the value gained from it. This will allow it to keep the position under review on the basis of robust information. (p 16)

But despite the apparent clarity of the process, a number of areas remain which are less than clear. According to Keith Peters and Richard Himsworth (*BMJ* 30 November 1996), there are a number of disputed areas:

Within trusts, how easy will it be to operate a hypothecated budget for research that requires underpinning across clinical services? How are the new funding arrangements to help areas such as general practice and public health research including epidemiology, where research is poorly funded yet fundamental to the operation of the NHS? The new funding system is intended to be redistributive. How will it be managed so as not to destabilise clinical units that are net losers? And, the greatest anxiety of all, in the longer term will the single research and development budget be exposed and vulnerable in a future crisis in NHS funding? (p1344)

The authors then go on to point to longer-term issues surrounding the effective prosecution and exploitation of research:

The new funding system is intended for recurrent expenditure; it makes no provision for capital. How will research facilities requiring capital be created? Equally important for the vitality of the NHS, how will service innovations come about? The former regional health authorities enabled the introduction of innovations such as transplantation or of Cinderella services such as geriatrics or genetics. Often these innnovations were combined with university developments – a most fruitful symbiosis. No mechanism has yet been identified to replace this vital function. Some trusts have continued to promote small scale developments, but there is little sign that coalitions of purchasing authorities are assuming this larger strategic role. For lack of suitable arrangements, the future quality of health care in the NHS may be undermined. (p1345)

In other words, the R&D initiative has focused primarily on the 'R' rather than the 'D'.

In another critique, Hilary Pickles (*Journal of the Royal College of Physicians of London* Vol.30 No.6 November/December 1996 p 509) points to problems in relation to:

- start-up pre-protocol costs, especially in centres that do not gain facilities funding;
- the cumulative effect on the budgets of purchasers who have to support academic centres where additional clinical care has evolved from research studies;
- ensuring that patients are appropriately allocated to studies that cannot be completed from the patient flows associated with routine care;

- ensuring that the approvals and funding streams come together at the right time, particularly for multi-centre studies.

She goes on to point out that if the new arrangements are to be effective, there will be losers as well as gainers.

> *Much current R&D may be of low quality, in particular studies which take place without the scrutiny of peer review. Few academics would argue that such work should continue to receive explicit NHS R&D levy support if other more worthy work had to go without. But even in the best centres such studies are common.* (p510)

The question this raises is whether the potential impact of shifts in research monies has been calculated, particularly on the 'research-intensive' trusts, many of which are in London. The same issue is raised by the role of the Higher Education Funding Council which carried out a second research assessment exercise in 1996 which rated all funding recipients to provide the basis for future funding decisions. Its strategy is explictly based on the principle of 'rewarding excellence', a policy which if pursued rigorously and consistently would have significant implications for NHS institutions. Peters and Himsworth point out that:

> *The government has accepted the national need for long term investment in research, and, most importantly, it has acknowledged that this investment should be largely insulated from the purchaser-provider contracting for clinical care. Nevertheless, if these investments are to yield the greatest benefit to the NHS they must both complement the activities of other agencies, such as universities and research funders, and articulate with all relevant parts of the health service.* (p1345)

But, as a King's Fund report, *The London Health Care System*, pointed out with reference to London, there is no point where all the strands linking research – as well as teaching and training – to care, come together and hence no obvious place where their various interests can be reconciled.

In December 1996, EL (96)110 *Improving the effectiveness of clinical services* was published. It provides a summary overview of current policy but emphasises two areas – population screening and innovation. As far as the first is concerned, it accepted the recommendation of the National Committee (see section 1.3) that no new screening programmes should be introduced or expanded until they have been reviewed and proven effective. As to the second, it confirmed that no further investment in services already listed in *Information on Clinical Effectiveness* should be made as part of routine care.

However, innovation may occur by other routes. In 1993, the Advisory Committee of Science and Technology recommended that a committee on safety and efficacy of procedures should be established to review and register novel surgical procedures, analogous to the Committee for Safety in Medicines. This recommendation was not accepted, but in 1996 the Department of Health announced funding for a voluntary system of registration to be established under the auspices of the Medical Royal Colleges.

The need for such a system is evident: Trevor Sheldon and Alex Faulkner (*BMJ* 313, 31 August 1996) point to:

While it is compulsory to evaluate drugs before their widespread use is permitted, other medical interventions are not subject to the same constraints. This has allowed a tidal wave of new health care technologies, which have diffused through health care systems before (or in spite of) proper evaluation to establish safety, effectiveness, or return on investment. This haphazard and uncontrolled adoption of procedures was brought to public attention most recently by the unseemly haste with which laparoscopic surgical techniques were adopted, the associated cases of severe complications, and the increased costs. The routine use of ultrasound during early pregnancy despite little evidence of benefit and the proliferation of unevaluated hip prostheses are other examples of the way in which health technologies or their modification can spread without sufficient caution. Highly publicised experiments with procedures such as xenotransplantation and fetal surgery are further raising professional and public concern. (p 508)

They go on to raise some basic issues:

This important initiative will be watched with interest internationally since no equivalent mechanism on a national scale seems to exist. It raises several fundamental questions, the answers to which will determine the register's potential usefulness and success. First, how does one distinguish a new procedure from a minor modification of an existing procedure of proved efficacy? Second, how safe or effective will a procedure have to be for it to be regarded as being suitable for routine use? What strength of evidence will be required? Who will decide, and how will the possible relation between skills, training, and outcome be taken into account? Third, how will the status of interventions be reviewed in the light of the results of more general and longer term use? The register might support recent calls for reliable nationally coordinated systems of audit for monitoring the outcomes of care on a routine basis. Fourth, what incentives are there for innovative doctors to adhere to the proposed system? Will there be penalties for using techniques that are not established as efficacious outside an approved evaluation? Would the guilty clinicians lose college membership or would purchasers who are not sufficiently vigilant lose resources? Will diffusion be sufficiently controlled by a voluntary system? (p508)

The response of clinicians to all the initiatives relating to effectiveness is of course critical: the evidence appears disappointing. The Audit Commission study of maternity care *First Class Delivery* observes that:

Obstetrics was the first specialty to have access to systematic reviews of evidence (via the Cochrane database), and the focus on evidence-based practice is well-developed. There is still a need for more and better evidence on some aspects of service provision. An improved focus on evidence needs to be grounded in a culture which accepts that evidence changes and practice should change to reflect it.

but it found that:

... there is also a need to pay more attention to bringing the evidence that does exist into

> *clinical practice. Systematic reviews are not well disseminated, with 72 per cent of trusts recently surveyed not having access to the database of clinical trials in maternity care, although progress is being made in this area. Eighty per cent of GPs surveyed by the Commission said they did not have access to the Cochrane database.* (p 72)

These findings are all the more disappointing as the Cochrane Centre's first project had focused on the evidence relating to childbirth. Other insights into the use being made of information relating to effectiveness came from a study by Kieran Walshe and Chris Ham for the NHS Confederation, *Acting on the Evidence: progress in the NHS.*

The authors summarise their findings as follows:

> *It seemed from our survey that progress in NHS trusts had been limited. Some trusts were making real efforts to introduce the ideas of clinical effectiveness, but many had yet to progress beyond the early stages of raising awareness and generating debate. Bearing in mind that our survey analysis was based on responses from 42 per cent of trusts, and that responders are likely to have had more to report than non-responders, it seems probable that most trusts still have some way to go before they can genuinely claim to have taken improving clinical effectiveness seriously, or to have made efforts to become evidence-based providers of health services.* (p 33)

They then go to a more general conclusion:

> *Finally, policy makers will soon need to acknowledge that just as evidence-based decision making is good for clinicians, it is good for policy makers too. New policy proposals will have to undergo the same kind of scrutiny that new health care interventions meet, and pilot-testing new policies should become the norm, not the exception. When evidence emerges that conflicts with policy aims, it cannot be ignored or denied; it must be taken seriously and used to change policy. With a greater role for evidence and rather less room for dogma, the policy making process and the policies it produces should be healthier, more robust, and more likely to do good than harm.* (p 34)

The Audit Commission report also concludes that the NHS Executive should support research into organisational as well as clinical aspects of maternity care, including postnatal care, where there continues to be uncertainty. This points to a more fundamental weakness in the new system of R&D support. As noted already, the share of the total budget devoted to national programmes is small and within that the share devoted to organisational issues is tiny. The bulk is devoted to clinical issues and is focused on specific interventions. The National Coordinating Centre for Health Technology Assessment describes its role as asking four fundamental questions:

- *does the intervention work?*
- *for whom?*
- *at what cost?*
- *how does it compare with alternatives?*

Yet, as previous sections of this part of the Review have indicated, many of the key issues in

Table 18 Has practice changed in accordance with Effective Health Care Bulletin recommendations?

Effective Health Care Bulletin and publication date		*Management of cataracts (Feb 1996)*	*Management of benign prostatic hyperplasia (Dec 1995)*	*Prevention and treatment of pressure sores (Oct 1995)*
Bulletin's recommendation		Increase proportion of day-case surgery	Substitute transurethral incision of prostate for transurethral resection of prostate operation	Use low pressure foam mattresses, not high-tech beds
Health authorities	Yes	48.3	4.8	8.5
	Don't know	35.0	74.2	78.0
	No	16.7	21.0	13.6
Trusts	Yes	48.1	12.1	36.0
	Don't know	17.3	53.4	16.0
	No	34.6	34.5	48.0

Source: *Health Service Journal* 3 April 1997 p24

health and social care delivery do not concern the efficacy of individual interventions at all but rather the extent to which a series of interventions form an effective whole. Research on systems of care has yet to begin on a significant scale.

As far as social care is concerned, a new research initiative was announced in November 1996 designed to 'improve the cost-effectiveness of social services through better use of research evidence'. (PR 96/345) In particular it aims to:

- translate the results of existing research into practice
- ensure that research findings are available to local authorities
- ensure that social work education and training incorporates research knowledge
- start new research where major gaps are identified.

The funds committed to this area of research – £1.5 million – are tiny.

Compared to spending on R&D as a whole, spending on clinical audit is modest, some £60 million or so a year – but it nevertheless exceeds the spending on the centrally funded research programme. Appearing before the Public Accounts Committee, Alan Langlands, Chief Executive of the NHS, was pushed hard to demonstrate the benefits. A member of the Committee, Alan Williams, attempted to extract an answer to whether or not the sums being committed were producing benefits which would justify them:

> *as a Committee of Public Accounts we have to put to you what we see as the costs against which you were judging the value of what you are offering. We only have one set of figures because you are not able to provide us with the other. If we just put together the £279 million you have already spent and then add for the*

> *next five years, five years of the £61 million you told the Chairman you will go on paying and five years of the £50 million which you have told us it is costing us in GPs' time – all in the report – by the end of the century it will have cost £834 million to pursue this policy without a costing for the GPs' time, the nurses' time and the other practitioners' time. The point I am trying to make is that we are not dealing with small money here, we are dealing with massive money and more attempts have to be made to quantify the gains.*
>
> (Mr Langlands) *We are dealing with massive money over time. If we were able to do what you asked, which is get behind the numbers set out in the tables in this report, and aggregate all the patient benefits that have been reduced to these very simple numbers, we would begin to find an answer to Mr Williams' question. Let me just repeat that there is no country in the world which has managed to do that yet.* (Committee of Public Accounts, *National Health Service Executive: clinical audit in England* HC 304, p 9)

Although not able to provide a quantified answer, Mr Langlands left the Committee in no doubt that he thought that the expenditure, massive money though it was, was justified. The Committee's own report expressed disappointment with various features of the implementation of clinical audit, the non-participation of some doctors and the use to which the results were put, but did not question the programme as a whole.

Others have shown themselves less sanguine. Anthony Hopkins (*Journal of the Royal College of Physicians of London* Vol 30 no 5 pp 415-425) concluded a lengthy assessment as follows:

> *A great deal of money has been spent on employing audit assistants with insufficient knowledge of the complexities of clinical measurement, and yet who try to impose this insufficiency of knowledge on the informal methods of directorate audit. No one can criticise the NHS Executive for failing to provide financial resources to help first medical and then clinical audit, but this money was thrown at the problem without a sufficient research base in clinical audit, without sufficient attention to the social structures in hospitals, and medical schools, and without sufficient recognition of the constructively critical faculties of health professionals.* (p 423-4)

The Government's position statement, *Clinical Audit in the NHS: using clinical audit in the NHS*, published in October 1996 reasserts its value by concluding as follows:

> *Clinical audit is and should remain a clinically-led initiative which seeks to improve the quality and outcome of patient care through clinicians examining and modifying their practices according to standards of what could be achieved, based on the best evidence available (or authoritative expert opinion where no objective research-based evidence exists). Although audit has been undertaken by some clinicians for many years, there is still much work to do if its full potential is to be realised.*
>
> *Clinical audit has exerted a powerful influence on those who have taken it up. There are many*

examples of successful audits ranging from audits of high technology medicine, to those of human dignity and privacy which can be used as starting points for local discussions. Renewed effort, building on early achievements, is now needed to secure greater involvement in clinical audit and to make it even more effective.

Clinical audit is central to the NHS approach on clinical effectiveness. Audit, along with clinical guidelines, the NHS R&D programme, work on health outcomes and variations can help to bridge the gap between routine clinical practice and evidence about the effectiveness and cost effectiveness of health care interventions. (pp13-14)

The Position Statement also contains a response to the Public Accounts Committee report. The Public Accounts Committee had been surprised to find that the knowledge gained through clinical audit was not made generally available to members of the public. Its 12th conclusion runs as follows:

We note that the Executive do not at present intend to make the data about quality of care gathered through clinical audit available to patients. We consider that the local reporting of quality indicators, suitably anonymised and interpreted, would be of great value in informing local action and public choice. We urge the NHS Executive to explore ways of achieving this. (Position Statement p23)

The Government did not respond to this directly in its Position Statement but instead referred to the fifth anniversary paper on the *Citizens's Charter* which promised the introduction, referred to above, of a range of clinical outcome indicators. The emphasis on the professional roles sits uneasily with the position taken in Patient Partnership. As Angela Coulter (The pros and cons of shared clinical decision-making, *Journal of Health Services Research Policy* 2: 2) has written:

Pressures are now building to persuade clinicians that decision-making should take account of evidence on clinical effectiveness, cost-effectiveness and patients' and public preferences. To do so adequately requires some form of decision support, which could include clinical guidelines, patient information materials and formal techniques for decision analysis. It also requires acknowledgement of uncertainties in medical care. It will depend on enhancing the skills of clinicians to facilitate knowledge transfer and sensitive determination of patients' values. (p118)

As noted in section 1.3, there are both central government, King's Fund and other initiatives designed to promote informed decision-making by users. These raise, as Coulter points out, a research agenda of their own:

The case for incorporating patients' values into clinical decision-making rests on claims that this will lead to improved satisfaction with the process of care and better health outcomes. Much of the evidence comes from North America. There is an urgent need for more research to establish whether or not this is the case in publicly funded health systems such as the NHS. We also need studies comparing alternative methods of informing patients using

> *a variety of types of decision support, including written materials and multi-media. The moral case for giving patients access to research-based information about treatment outcomes and allowing them a greater say in what is done to them has considerable appeal. Shared decision-making is now on the policy agenda. It will be crucial to ensure that implementation of this policy is informed by rigorous research evidence.* (p118)

As Walshe and Ham point out, there are also bridges to be built between policy towards clinical effectiveness and other national policy objectives:

> *Although clinical effectiveness is high on the policy agenda, the mechanisms by which the Department of Health and the NHS Executive measure and control performance among health authorities and trusts continue to value efficiency and economy but not effectiveness. For example, the much criticised Efficiency Index rewards needless clinical activity and punishes watchful waiting. The Patient's Charter standards for surgical waiting lists encourage surgeons to perform ineffective procedures on long waiters at the expense of more effective ones on other patients. The activity-based currency of contracting values all admissions and clinic visits equally, regardless of the appropriateness of the care provided. At the least, some of these perverse incentives to ineffective clinical practice need to be removed. Ideally, new measures which recognise and reward effective clinical practice should be put in their place.*

The main achievement of the past five years is, as Walshe and Ham suggest, that the argument about whether more attention to the effectiveness of health services has been won. While a great deal remains to be done within the original remit, as Gifford Batstone and Mary Edwards show below, the task now is to determine how it relates to the wider objectives being pursued in the NHS as a whole.

Part 2 Commentary

As in previous years, the second part of the Policy Review assesses developments within three broad headings, Efficiency and Finance, Equity, and Accountability.

2.1 Efficiency and Finance

The Autumn 1996 public expenditure settlement stretched the Conservative Government's commitment to ensuring that the NHS received annual real increases to the limit. The budget for health and community services was set to grow at 3 per cent and primary care by 3.2 per cent: see Table 18. The settlement assumed a general inflation rate of 2 per cent and the efficiency target was set at 2.7 per cent. Publicly financed capital spending was cut once again in the expectation that private finance would fill the gap. The longer-term prospect, however, appeared even tougher since the provision for the years after 1997/98 implied a real terms cut, after allowing for the higher relative inflation within the NHS in relative to the economy as a whole.

Last year's review reported a number of indications that NHS services, particularly hospitals, were under severe pressure both in financial and physical terms. In December 1996 the Department of Health made an emergency cash injection of £25m which was targeted at hospital bedblocking, intensive care beds and mental health care and a further £290 million was ringfenced for these areas in the 1997/98 financial year.

Prior to this, however, the Government had taken a number of steps to ensure, insofar as it could, that there would be sufficient capacity to cope with the usual increase in emergency admissions during the winter months. In August an emergency bed register was announced extending the system already covering part of the South-East and all health authorities and trusts were actively encouraged, through the NHS Executive regional offices, to have plans in place for the winter.

In May and July 1996 a series of measures were announced specifically for paediatric intensive care. According to EL(96)53:

> *In the short term, the imperative is to ensure that the extra beds are brought into use as planned before this winter, that purchasing arrangements are explicit and take account of predictable fluctuations in demand and that we take all possible steps to ensure that appropriately qualified nurses and clinical staff are available in sufficient numbers and in the right places to care for critically ill children.*
>
> *In the medium term, we need to plan for a pattern of provision which can cope with*

Table 18 NHS current spending, England 1996-97 to 1999-2000

Current Spending (cash)	*Revised Plan 1996-97*	*Plan 1997-98*	*Provisional Plans 1998-99*	*1999-00*
Hospital & Community Health Services	23,189	24,367	24,891	25,404
% real growth		3.0	0.1	0.1
Family Health Services	7,487	7,880	8,085	8,255
% real growth		3.2	0.6	0.1
Central Health and Miscellaneous Services	519	512	523	534
% real growth		-3.2	0.1	0.1
Department of Health Running Costs	290	283	283	283
% real growth		-4.5	-1.9	-2.0
NHS Current Total	31,485	33,042	33,782	34,476
% real growth		2.9	0.2	0.1

Source: Treasury statement, 28 November 1996

fluctuating demand and which operates according to a set of agreed principles. We also need to investigate nurse staffing and training issues to make sure that we have an appropriately skilled workforce available.

In the long term, we need more information about the outcomes for children who are cared for in different clinical settings related to the severity of their illness when they enter paediatric intensive care. (p1)

Despite these measures, it became apparent during the later part of 1996 that hospitals were finding it difficult to cope with both a reported increase in demand for emergency admissions and to keep waiting lists down to 12 months. Overall, according to the results of a survey carried out by NAHAT and the NHS Trust Federation during the course of winter 1996/97, the pressure of emergencies had been dealt with more or less satisfactorily. But elective work had had to be cancelled and as a result, the numbers of people waiting for more than a year in the final quarter of 1996 for elective treatment rose by some 6,300 and the total numbers waiting rose by around 23,400. One hundred and twenty-two were waiting longer than the 18-month *Patient's Charter* guarantee. The number of cancelled operations also rose to 16,372 in January to March 1997, fewer than in the equivalent period in 1996 (16,652) but subtantially more than in January to March 1995 (14,466).

This deterioration was accompanied by a general worsening of the financial position of many health authorities and trusts. At the end of the financial year 1996/97 it was estimated that the carry-over of deficits into the next financial year was some £300 million or even higher.

Quite how such figures should be interpreted, however, remains far from clear. Despite the Conservative Government's commitment to extra spending on the NHS, the extra allocated each year to the Service had fallen below the long-term trend of 3 per cent per annum in both 1995/96 and 1995/97. But while the overall financial situation was undoubtedly tighter than it had been in the years immediately after the 1992 Election when the settlements were more generous, other factors were also at work at local level.

The auditors of West Surrey Health Authority, for example, found that its massive deficit could be attributed to poor financial planning and control. According to an analysis by Jennifer Dixon and Rudolf Klein (*Health Service Journal* 15 June 1997), based on an analysis of auditors' management letters, it seemed that variations in the capacity of authorities to cope with problems at local level may be as important as variations in the nature of the problems themselves. The unexpectedly high cost of extra-contractual referrals has been a common source of over-spending, but the letters reveal that many authorities are over-optimistic about their ability to control them. However, another important source of instability was GP fundholders' failure to meet their spending targets and here there was little health authorities could do since they had no direct way of controlling that part of their budget.

To some degree therefore the reports of financial crisis during the second half of 1996/97 could be attributed to local failure to manage properly the resources that had been made available rather than a shortfall in resources as such. But equally, many trusts were faced with a combination of expenditure reductions and increasing demands for service which required significant increases in productivity to deal with. Although many hospitals have introduced new ways of dealing with patients, particularly emergencies, there is little evidence that they produce cash savings in line with the assumed increases in productivity.

There were other signs of continuing pressure. Incomes Data Services repeated last year's survey of professions considered to be in shortage, with the results shown in Table 19.

Similarly, the Specialist Workforce Advisory Group again identified a large number of specialties as areas of shortage or where there would be a need for further recruitment to meet expanding demand:

- accident and emergency medicine
- anaesthetics
- diagnostic radiology
- forensic psychiatry
- general surgery
- medical oncology
- obstetrics & gynaecology
- old age psychiatry
- opthalmology
- orthopedic surgery
- paediatrics
- palliative medicine
- psychiatry (mental illness)
- radiotherapy (clinical oncology)
- urology.

The Medical Practices Committee, however, found that, relative to last year, recruitment to general practice appeared to be easier in some respects if not in others:

> *The overall numbers of applicants for vacancies are down on the 1995 Survey.*

Table 19 Scarce professions

	Number of organisations finding difficulties recruiting and retaining	
	1996	*1995*
Specialist nurses (eg elderly care, children's, intensive care)	34	8
Mental health nurses	11	6
Qualified nurses generally	18	8
Health visitors	6	3
Midwives	3	–
Physiotherapists	27	22
Occupational therapists	17	14
Speech therapists	7	5
Professions allied to medicine generally	9	14
Medical staff generally	12	12
Junior doctors	4	7
Specialist consultants	3	6
Consultant psychiatrists	10	5
Clinical psychologists	9	–
Pharmacists	4	–
Ancillary staff	6	4
Health care assistants	2	–
Technical staff	3	3
IT specialists	3	–
Secretaries	2	–

Source: Incomes Data Services

However most positively the perception of doctors considering applicants are that they had good quality applicants and did not have to compromise in the vast majority of cases. The Committee would wish to see 100% rather than the average of 80% who did not have to compromise.

The evidence of previous years is confirmed again in 1996 in that the work patterns of male and females are very different, more females were recruited to general practice but the majority applied to work a reduced commitment. The impact on overall manpower must not be underestimated. (p5)

As these comments indicate, reports of staff shortages or difficulties in recruitment may reflect changes in supply, ie changes in willingness to work at the rates of pay and working conditions available rather than increases in demand for services. In principle, the introduction of local pay on which the previous Government had placed so much emphasis should have made it easier to balance demand for particular skills with the available supply. But whatever its potential merits, local pay has proved hard to introduce: indeed before the change of Government, developments this year took a step back towards the system it had been designed to replace.

In October 1996, Ken Jarrold, NHS Director of Human and Corporate Resources, and Colin Reeves, Director of Finance and Performance, wrote to health authorities and trusts urging them to plan for the 1997 pay round in preparation for the coming round of contracting. Attached to their letter was a report from an NHS working party of NHS pay, finance and contracting, chaired by the Regional Director of Finance for Northern and Yorkshire which conveniently summed up the development, or lack of it, of local pay:

> *There has been no additional in-year funding for pay increases since 1993, and the Government has repeatedly emphasised that this financial discipline will continue ... The Government believes that any increase in pay should be at least offset by improvements in efficiency or productivity.*
>
> *Trusts were encouraged to negotiate on local pay in 1995, but with staff expectations conditioned by the Nursing Pay Review Body's recommendation that local pay should bring increases to 1.5% – 3.0%. Most Trusts offered a 3% increase early in the pay round, but there were few agreements until national issues were resolved in September 1995. Over 90% of staff received a 3% increase in the 1995-96 pay round.*
>
> *The 1996-97 pay round began with a national increase of 2% for most NHS staff, and clear messages from the Secretary of State for Health that there would be no steer on the level of local pay offers. The pay increase for hospital doctors and dentists, determined nationally, was staged but presented a significant cost pressure to Trusts, particularly those employing large numbers of junior doctors.*
>
> *1996 is a year of transition: there is general awareness of the importance of local pay negotiations, and evidence of more sophistication in paybill modelling. By October local offers range from 2.0% (no increase above the new national rates) to 5% (including national rates), though with a majority of offers between 2.5% and 3.0%. Local pay offers vary in a number of ways, apart from the general percentage increase: allowances may be increased or left unchanged; some offers are staged, some offer more to low paid staff, or differentiate between staff groups, or between those on Trust terms and conditions and those on national terms and conditions.*
>
> *This is the first year in which employers have been in a position to give serious consideration to pay at the same time as they negotiate contracts. However it is clear that local pay and contracting and finance have generally been kept separate, with pay assumptions largely excluded from contract negotiations.* (pp2–3)

The working party report made four broad recommendations:

- Trusts should include their pay and price assumptions in their prices.
- Pay assumptions should be based on the local situation, taking account also of the wider economic context.
- Purchasers and providers should develop a dialogue about local pay.

- Purchasers and providers focus on the total cash increase, which together with efficiency gains, must cover service changes and pay and price pressures.

These recommendations would make sense in a world where local pay had been fully established. But although, as Jarrold's letter indicates, local variations were common, the nationally determined element of pay remained high. In the case of doctors, local pay had had very little effect on pay levels even if some trusts had used the flexibility open to create new staffing structures. With doctors effectively out of it, the key group was nurses, who were awarded 2 per cent by their national Pay Review Body, to take effect during 1996/97. Trusts were slow to reach settlements in excess of this figure, many no doubt mindful of their overall financial situation and so once again one year's pay round had not ended while the next was effectively beginning.

In January 1997 the Pay Review Bodies reported with their recommendations for 1997/98. In his evidence to them, the Chancellor had made it clear that the economic and financial environment for their recommendations was a tough one:

> *In its evidence, the Government informed us that its approach to public sector pay meant that in public expenditure terms, the cost of running government and the public services should not increase as the result of pay settlements and might fall to the extent that greater efficiencies were possible or additional savings were made in support of the overall public expenditure objectives. It meant also that any increases in pay should at least be offset by improvements in efficiency or productivity; that pay should reflect the needs of staff recruitment, retention and motivation in a way which reflected local circumstances, without assuming any automatic entitlement to annual increases or comparability with other groups; and that, although there was no guideline or going rate for the size of settlements, all pay settlements must be affordable and reflect the finance available and the other pressures on the budget from which the paybill would be met. The Government's evidence observed that there would be no access to the Reserve to fund settlements in the coming year.* (p 8)

The evidence from the professions was naturally enough designed to support the case for substantial increases using different criteria to those the Government wish to see applied. The BMA had commissioned a comparability study from Hay Management Consultants to support their claims. In fact it found that doctors' pay was broadly comparable to the comparators it used – even though it did not take into account earnings in the private sector – and also that the 'job weight' both of consultants and GPs varied a great deal. So while some might be underpaid, the reverse was also true.

> *We do not feel that the study showed GMPs and consultants were, on average, disadvantaged compared with the private sector. The range of job weights for GMPs and consultants is very large, and although the evidence suggested consultants' and GMPs' remuneration to be below that of the private sector comparators at the upper end of the job size range, the situation was reversed at the lower end of the job size range.* (p13)

While these findings served to undermine the BMA's case for massive pay increases for doctors, they were in any case beside the point – at least from the Government's position. The Conservative Government had repeatedly rejected the comparability argument, asserting in evidence to successive Pay Review Bodies that recruitment and retention were the key indicators. As noted already, the professional bodies had reported some indications of shortages in the medical labour market. The Review Body for Doctors and Dentists, however, was unhappy about the reliability of the evidence available to it as to the real state of that market and hence how to determine what level of increases the market for clinical staff required.

> *The evidence submitted to us this year has commented, often critically, on central manpower planning mechanisms. It is apparent to us that these have fallen well short of what is needed to bring about a satisfactory balance between the supply of and the demand for medical and dental manpower. The Departments assure us that the planning mechanisms now in place will allow them to be more responsive to changes in demand. We consider that to be most important as, to date, we have been given insufficient data on manpower planning generally. Current shortages in some hospital specialties increase the work pressures on those in the service, with implications for morale. Moreover we believe that past shortcomings in manpower planning have had a significant impact on the professions' perception of recruitment and retention. We have also been made aware that female doctors and dentists are playing an increasing role in the delivery of services to patients. We consider this development to be important in the context of manpower planning, as women's preferred working patterns, particularly in regard to hours of work, can be markedly different from those of men. In addition we consider it important that consultants' concerns about manpower shortages in particular specialties, as well as their concerns about their expanding non-clinical workload, should be addressed in the Departments' forecasting of future manpower needs.* (p 11)

But while these changes in the supply side of the medical labour market had been apparent for some time, response in terms of evidence and understanding had been poor:

> *We cannot simply accept uncritically the assurances in some of the evidence we have received that all is well. Given the persistent and widespread anecdotal evidence of shortages we might have felt compelled to take the view that shortages were worsening more seriously than we believe is the case. The need for statistics must be recognised not only by individual Trust Human Resource managers but also by those at all levels of the service who are responsible for providing adequate management resources.* (p20)

In respect of doctors, a parliamentary question (written answers, 5 November 1997) elicited the finding that the Government had no record of the numbers of doctors recruited from abroad. This information was 'not collected centrally'. As Peter Richards and other (*BMJ* vol 314, 31 May 1997 p 1567) put it:

A striking aspect of medical workforce planning is the failure to acknowledge [the] demand for changing patterns of work – or to track it in workforce statistics. How can a nation that invests about £200,000 to train each doctor fail to keep systematic records of where they are and what they are doing?

Furthermore in respect of nurses, the Department had scrapped one of the key sources of information, its survey of nurses joining and leaving the profession even though here too there are reasons for believing that the market has changed in recent years. Although the number of qualified nurses in hospitals has remained fairly steady in recent years, numbers employed by GPs and within the private sector have risen rapidly. As a result, according to a study commissioned by the Royal College of Nursing, (Ian Seccombe and G Smith *In the Balance: registered nurse supply and demand 1996*) the number of potential returners to the nursing labour force is now low.

They concluded that the potential pool of those genuinely available for nursing employment is little more than 20,000, most of whom have dependent children and hence the scope for increasing the number of nurses from among the existing workforce is limited. Looking ahead, the Royal College of Nursing argued in the evidence to the Pay Review Body that the overall labour market for nursing will change markedly.

With far too few nursing students and a steadily ageing nursing workforce, we are running out of time to deal with the problem. This evidence shows that the shortage of registered nurses will reach crisis point by the year 2000.

Registered nurses are a national resource and the Government must act nationally to deal with the approaching crisis.

To tackle nurse shortages, the RCN is calling for a comprehensive national overview of registered nurse recruitment and retention, underpinned by a national pay award for nurses. (Press Release 25 September 1996)

In fact, Executive Letter (96) 46, Education and Training Planning Guidance, issued in June 1996 accepted that there would have to be a substantial increase in training places, stating that:

The guidance annexed to this letter identifies not only national education and training priorities and the outcome of the national workforce modelling exercise but also professional and service issues relating to education and training. The guidance is addressed to all those engaged in commissioning non-medical education and training and builds upon EL(95)96. Last year's guidance emphasised the need for education commissioners to look carefully at supply and demand factors and they responded by increasing nursing and midwifery training commissions by 14%. The current workforce trends strongly suggest that a further similar increase of pre-registration nursing and midwifery training will be required nationally to meet future demand. There are similar staffing pressures in mental health and intensive care services and in physiotherapy, occupational therapy and clinical psychology. (para 3)

But that measure will take several years before it influences the effective supply. In the meantime, the Nurses Pay Review Body had concluded that:

> *The Health Departments are probably right in stating that there are not large, general shortages, but it is our impression that, given current workloads, even a low level of vacancies or vacancies in a few specialties can have a significant effect on the ability of Trusts to function effectively, and we believe that the situation has tightened over the last year.* (p19)

But in the light of the information available to it, it felt unhappy with that conclusion.

> *We were very disappointed that the Department of Health decided to discontinue its survey of nursing joiners and leavers, and that the replacement survey undertaken by the Office of Manpower Economics, despite intensive follow-up work, achieved a response rate of only 52 per cent. We also note that the Departments have taken no action in response to our request for statistics on the composition of earnings and we are most concerned that the annual non-medical manpower census may be discontinued, a development which would further reduce the Health Department's statistical evidence to us. We have commented on the inadequate manpower information systems in some Trusts and for the Departments to place their faith entirely in them seems to us to be an extremely risky strategy.* (p19)

While looking to the central department for better information, it also concluded that Trusts could help themselves with recruitment and retention policies.

> *It seems to us that Trusts could do more to deal with their recruitment and retention problems. Evidence from follow-up enquiries to the OME's surveys, confirmed by the case studies we commissioned into recruitment and retention, strongly suggests that in some Trusts the information systems supporting the Trusts' human resource function are inadequate. Paper-based systems for logging and tracking vacancies, and especially leavers, are often too slow or unreliable to provide a Trust-wide view in time for action to be taken. Integrated information technology systems that bring together payroll and personnel information so that vacancies and staffing changes can be tracked in 'real time' can significantly enhance management's ability to anticipate and respond to staffing problems.*
>
> *There is also evidence of a lack of a strategic approach in some Trusts to issues of recruitment and especially retention. In some cases this is apparent from the shortage of basic data on vacancies or on the reasons staff have left, but also from the failure to follow through Trust Board policies on flexible working and family-friendly employment practices to ensure that they are implemented.* (p19)

In *Finders Keepers* (HMSO 1997) the Audit Commission also argued that trusts could do a lot to help themselves maintain adequate staffing levels:

> *. . . to really understand their position, trust boards and top management teams need more detailed information, highlighting those professions and operational units that already have high turnover as well as others moving in that direction. The inclusion of other indicators, such as vacancy levels, recruitment delays and staff stability, provides a more complete picture.*
>
> *In the past, the ability of many trusts to monitor and analyse these factors would have been hampered by the inadequacy of their information systems. That is no longer the case: most trusts are now capable of producing reports that analyse turnover in different ways. The Commission's 1995 survey of acute trusts did, however, reveal that few trusts had carried out any recent analysis ... As more trusts experience problems of high turnover and recognise the need to monitor other indicators as well, the situation should change.* (p17)

In the event, the Review Bodies recommended increases of 3.4 per cent for doctors and dentists and 3.3 for nurses, awards which effectively removed any scope for local pay determination. The Government staged the award for doctors, agreeing to only 2 per cent from the beginning of the year. These awards were nevertheless larger than allowed for in the public expenditure settlement and thereby reduced the level of growth in terms of NHS prices to below the figure announced in autumn 1996.

Despite their recommendation of a large national increase, the Nursing Review Body went on to suggest that funds be made available to allow trusts to restructure their remuneration systems, accepting that many did not have the expertise to do so:

> *We therefore recommend that separately identified funds be made available within the Health Departments that Trusts might draw on, as and when they can demonstrate that they have a viable strategy for restructuring remuneration, to the benefit of the service offered to patients and the nursing staff who provide it.* (p iv)

Thus by the time the Conservatives lost office, they had failed to established a system of pay determination in which local factors predominated. In large measure that failure might be attributed to the sustained opposition of the staff side. The compromise agreement reached last year by which a national uprating figure to apply to trusts agreeing below average deals had to be determined and then applied retrospectively did not work so that the Review Bodies themselves determined what it should be. But if the Nursing Review Body and the Audit Commission are right, most trusts are not in a position to take on the full responsibilities of local pay anyway.

However, local flexibility once enjoyed even if to a limited degree will not be easily given up. Not surprisingly, NAHAT argued in a February 1997 statement that the Review Bodies should be abolished along with other limitations on their freedom to employ doctors. The new Government made it clear soon after taking office that they would be looking to the Review Bodies to recommend a national award but one which allowed some local flexibility. In May 1997, the NHS Confederation issued a consultation document arguing strongly for the retention of local flexibility: the union response, however, was cautious, suggesting that the Confederation was unlikely to get what it wanted very easily.

However, as noted in section 1.1, pay is not the only area where flexibility is desirable: another key area is the professional structure of the labour force. That was acknowledged in the Education and Training Guidance (EL(96)46):

> *The NHS Executive recognises the need for better integration of medical and non-medical disciplinary team working, together with the blurring of traditional roles and responsibilities, requires a more integrated approach to planning medical and non-medical education and training. In drawing up workforce plans, there needs to be a clear view of how services will need to be developed across both the primary and secondary care sectors. This will provide consortia and other relevant bodies, with the strategic framework in which to make their decisions. Similarly, ways of integrating medical and non-medical workforce planning and practice should feature highly on consortia and Regional Education Development Groups agendas.* (para 8)

In fact there is no clear view of how services will be developed across the primary and secondary care sectors, and it is precisely for that reason that workforce flexibility is important. A report from the Health Services Management Unit at the University of Manchester, *The Future NHS Workforce*, published in 1996 remarks that:

- *there is no mechanism for drawing together separate streams of development of reviewing them from a wider service perspective;*
- *there are signs of change in local initiatives, but these will be confined largely to support workers and incremental adaptations to current roles unless there is national agreement on the way forward;*
- *the healthcare workforce is organised in a wide range of occupations and separate specialisms within these occupations. The complexity of the structure complicates the planning process and can be a constraint on the re-alignment of services;*
- *the fragmentation of the workforce makes the development of supply plans more difficult so that, even in periods of high unemployment, the NHS has difficulty in recruiting some occupations;*
- *one of the biggest problems is the inflexibility which is the inevitable consequence of having to plan and manage such a wide range of occupations.* (p 75)

The report contains a large number of recommendations designed to deal with these issues. In particular, it concludes that increased staff productivity equivalent to 20 per cent of the current workforce can be achieved by a series of measures involving changes within the composition of the labour force and the way staff are used: see Box overleaf. Improvements on this scale would of course have a major impact on the scope for improving services within existing budgets.

The Private Finance Initiative continued to promise more than it actually delivered. None of the hospital rebuilding schemes referred to last year had reached the final agreement stage by the Election. Within London, where hospital

Future scenario for increased productivity

The University of Manchester study identifies the following areas as offering scope for achieving the productivity gains it believes are possible.

Substitution and Staff Re-profiling

- Development of generic roles;
- Use of trained support staff and increasing professional time in direct care;
- Substitution of junior medical workload;
- Staffing in primary care, including enhanced roles for non-medical personnel;
- Move towards service designs in the community based on client need and/or disease groupings.

Improving Care Processes and Rationalising Process Work

- Reduction in hospital bed levels;
- Rationalisation of process work;
- Devolution of diagnostic work to primary care;
- Devolution of diagnostic work within the hospital.

Overall these two trends will reduce the numbers of hospital-based diagnostic staff and give rise to rationalisation of departments between providers to ensure adequate critical mass.

- Development of evidence-based care pathways across all sectors of the service. Current initiatives to develop care pathways for hospital care will be extended to include primary and community care. The pathways will prescribe:
- more efficient care process through improved co-ordination and integration;
- less intensive use of the more expensive elements of care such as hospital stay;
- designing more appropriate roles for staff which better use their skills and training.

Source: *The Future NHS Workforce*, Health Services Management Unit, University of Manchester 1996

rationalisation and rebuilding are the key to the changes that had been agreed by the Government in the light of the Tomlinson inquiry report, no major scheme had progressed. In December 1996, the Guy's and St Thomas's Trust announced that it had decided to go for public funds and the scheme at the Royal Berkshire and Battle Hospitals Trust also foundered and turned to public finance for a much smaller scheme.

In November 1996, a commercial contract was signed between Norfolk and Norwich Health Care Trust and a PFI consortium but the final financial arrangements had not been agreed by the end of the financial year. A sticking point for those financing such schemes had been the risk that a trust would disappear leaving no one to pick up the liabilities. The Government had passed legislation in May 1996 to remove this risk. The NHS (Residual Liabilities) Act placed a duty on the Secretary of State to ensure that all liabilities are transferred to other specified bodies or to the Secretary of State. But it was not sufficient to provide complete reassurance to would-be investors. Accordingly, no major scheme had been completely settled when Parliament was dissolved. Immediately on coming to power the new Government announced a rapid review of the Private Finance Initiative as a whole, but confirmed that it would ensure that the necessary legislation was passed 'to clarify the existing powers of NHS trusts to enter into partnerships with the private sector'.

This was not the only obstacle, however. Some schemes had not proceeded for the more fundamental reason that they did not appear affordable to the NHS. In January 1997 the NHSE announced in a letter from Colin Reeves that some degree of financial support would be made available to allow schemes to continue, in the form of a trial scheme aimed to bridging the gap between the private sector's desire to see capital outlay recovered within 30 years or less as opposed to the full asset life, assumed to be 60 years. The amounts offered were small, however, and offered on a trial basis to projects which were already at an advanced stage of planning.

The letter suggests that the new arrangements might give an incentive towards the development of schemes with shorter lives which would lead back to the incremental investment strategies that have typefied hospital planning in the last 20 years. There may well be a case for such an approach, given the general uncertainty attached to the future pattern of hospital provision both in terms of the level of capacity to handle patients overall and also the distribution of that capacity between hospitals. However, in a study of the Private Finance Initiative in London, *A Capital Conumdrum* (King's Fund 1997), Richard Meara found that private investors were not attracted to schemes of this kind, prefering to be involved in schemes which involved total rebuilding.

In June, the Minister of State for Health, Alan Milburn, announced what he termed a three-point plan to 'remove the obstacles preventing the construction of new hospitals' and that a number of schemes would be given the go-ahead. He subsequently announced a list of 14 schemes that could proceed, although only two, the Norwich scheme and one at Dartford, were given the absolute go-ahead.

While this announcement had the effect of releasing the immediate log-jam, provided of course that agreement could be reached in the remaining 12 cases with the private sector, it offered no evidence that the PFI was a sensible option for hospital building, ie that it offered a way of providing the necessary assets which, taking everything into account, was cheaper than the purely public sector alternative. The Minister's early June announcement indicated, however, that the Government intended to look at ways of improving the way that the PFI worked inside the health sector.

Over recent years the NHS has come to rely on private finance in another sense – through the income earned from pay-beds. It is the largest provider of pay-beds and has increased its market share in recent years. In February it was reported that the NHS Trust Federation was attempting to come to a deal with a large private insurer to market NHS pay-beds nationally. In the same month, a partnership between PPP healthcare and two London trusts was announced by which the insurer would invest in equipment in return for cheaper prices in future.

Offloading services Successive Reviews have commented on the way that the NHS has attempted to cope with the pressures upon it by off-loading the finance of some functions to the personal sector in four areas in particular: sight tests, drugs, dentistry and long-term care. In all four areas there were interesting developments to report.

Table 19 Number of eye tests performed

Year	*Millions*
1987-88	13.5
1988-89	14.4
1989-90	10.8
1990-91	12.4
1991-92	12.8
1992-93	14.3
1993-94	13.2
1994-95	13.9
1995-96	14.6

Source: Department of Health

Sight tests Data for sight tests show a continuing if erratic increase – see Table 19 – but as noted in section 1.3 that in itself is not enough to give confidence that the barrier created by charging for tests is not important.

The report – already cited in 1.3 – from the Royal National Institute for the Blind, *Losing Sight of Blindness*, drew on the results of a survey by NOP Consumer Market Research of adults aged over 60 and found a sharp social class differential; where 83 per cent of respondents in social class A/B had been for an eye test the figure for D/E was only 65 per cent. The most obvious explanation for this difference, the report suggests, is that some of those on lower incomes are being deterred by the cost of the test. Another study, cited in the report and based on optometric practices within Oxfordshire, found increases in the number of people leaving longer intervals between tests over the period 1988 to 1996: see Table 20.

These data suggest that charges have had the effect of deterring take-up of tests and therefore have reduced their effectiveness as a screening device.

Table 20 Time interval between tests

Months between visits	*Percentage attending for eye test*		
	1988	**1990**	**1996**
0-3	2.7	9.8	5.8
4-6	3.8	3.6	2.6
7-12	15.7	14.7	11.1
13-24	27.8	28.6	29.2
25-60	28.7	33.6	42.4
61-120	7.6	4.9	6.4
120+	13.6	4.8	2.4

Source: *Losing Sight of Blindness*, Royal National Institute for the Blind 1997

Drugs The price of prescriptions was raised in the usual way. In November 1996, a consultation paper on extensions to the limited list of prescribable drugs was issued, covering some 60 products plus some 200 unlicensed products which have been assessed as having no therapeutic value.

The main instrument of cost control, as far as drugs are concerned, has been the Pharmaceutical Price Regulation Scheme (PPRS). The House of Commons Select Committee 1995 report on the Scheme had concluded that whether or not the Scheme was effective was unclear.

- *The secrecy which surrounds the PPRS makes it very difficult for Parliament, health care professionals or the public at large to know what the overall effect of the Scheme is; and in particular, whether the balance which the Scheme was created to achieve, between the interests of the industry and those of the NHS, is being fairly struck, or whether there is a pronounced tilting in one direction or the other.*

- *If the Scheme does result in an unfair tilting, there are grounds for supposing that this may be in the direction of the industry rather than the NHS.*

- *We also feel some scepticism as to the ability of the Department of Health fully to invigilate the financial performance of the companies subject to the Scheme.* (p xxi)

It went on to suggest that there should be a regular report on the way the scheme worked:

> *We therefore recommend that the Department of Health introduce greater transparency into the Scheme: in particular, by means of publishing an annual report on the PPRS which shall include the aggregate profit earned by each company as assessed under the Scheme, the total amount of profit which is assessed as being within profit targets, the total profit which is assessed as being above target profits but within the Margin of Tolerance, and total profit which is above the upper limit of the Margin of Tolerance, and the allowances for research and promotion founded upon these returns. It should also include the aggregate profit declared under the Scheme, the total value of all repayments made to the Department of Health as a result of excess profits and the total value of any price reductions. This report should be laid by the Secretary of State before Parliament.* (p xxii)

In May 1996 the first report on the Pharmaceutical Price Regulation Scheme was published by the Department of Health. It rejected the Committee's charge that the scheme had compromised other policy objectives:

> *The Department made it clear in the renegotiated 1993 scheme that the PPRS must not undermine other initiatives. The covering letter to the 1993 PPRS agreement states clearly that 'the Department cannot regard the scheme in isolation from other Government policies on the provision of medicines to NHS patients, and will not be able to agree to any action under the PPRs which would amount to undermining the effect of another policy, such as the extension of the Selected List Scheme'. Applications for price increases are therefore carefully scrutinised to see whether the fall in profits which supports the application has come*

about through the application of these other policies, in which case the application will be refused. In the particular case of the Selected List, where a product ceases to be available under the NHS as a result of that scheme, then both the product and any associated costs and capital are removed from the scope of the PPRS. Where a company reduces prices as a result of the Selected List Scheme, it is not allowed to take any compensatory action under the PPRS. (p33)

It concluded that:

... by focusing the level of control on profits rather than the prices of individual products, the PPRS has provided a stable framework which, while ensuring that prices to the NHS are reasonable, has enabled the industry to flourish. The PPRS provides a balance between the different, but overlapping, interests of the Government and the industry. (p38)

This conclusion, however, amounted to little more than a reassertion of the evidence previously submitted to the Select Committee. It did little to reveal how the scheme really worked: in particular, the nature of the trade-off between pharmaceutical prices and industry benefits remains obscure as ever. As Alan Earl Slater (*BMJ* 314:1 February 1997) has argued in a wider-ranging critique of the scheme the accountability issue remains:

The fourth problem is the lack of transparency. From the recent report on the scheme we now know for the first time that three teams at the Department of Health's pharmaceutical industry branch each deal with groups of drug companies. However, it is still not clear what data, information, skills, experiences, negotiation qualities, and specific objectives the parties have when they are striking their bargains or how the bargains actually unfold or even where they are struck. Thus the main concerns lie in the lack of transparency of the data, the process, and the outcomes of each bargain. (p316)

Dentistry At the end of last year, the Government remained in dispute with the dental profession and, according to the British Dental Association, in its *Manifesto for Dentistry*, a large range of problems remains to be dealt with: see Box.

On 12 June 1996, Gerry Malone made a statement to the House on the future of NHS

The state of dental services: British Dental Association

- Availability of NHS general dental services and some specialist services is poor in many areas
- Only half of the adult population is registered with a dentist
- Disease levels are still high in some minority ethnic and socio-economic groups and in many geographical areas
- Oral health is now deteriorating in young children in some localities after many years of improvement
- An ageing population is retaining its natural teeth and creating a new need for resources
- Cuts in higher education funding and low student grants are damaging dental education

Source: British Dental Association, *Manifesto for Dentistry*, p3

dentistry. He was able to announce that agreement had been reached with the dental profession on the way that dentists should be paid. His announcement contained a number of immediate proposals including a new method of calculating capitation payments for children's dentistry and tougher requirements relating to prior approval for treatment. He also announced the Government's intention to proceed with piloting a system for local contracting – as envisaged in the White Paper *Improving Dental Services* (Cm 2625, HMSO 1994) and on the lines envisaged for all forms of primary care in *Choice and Opportunity*. He also announced the establishment of a new class of dental auxiliary, measures to allow clinical technicians to practise, a 'redevelopment scheme' for dentists of a low level of competence and the establishment of a complaints system for private practice.

None of these measures bears directly on the question of access to NHS treatment. A report in the *Western Mail* (26 November 1996) said that although the Health Authority had received help from the Welsh Office for a community dentist, none had been forthcoming, so applicants were being sought in Scandinavia. The key issue is whether dentists in general will return to NHS practice in sufficient numbers. In the Minister's words in a speech to the House of Commons:

> *... Given the hypothesis that dentists were saying that they would not take on extra NHS work – or would withdraw from such work – because a dispute was in progress, I hope that a corollary of the end of that dispute will be many more dentists deciding to resume NHS care. I hope that the end of the dispute .... and, in particular, getting rid of the vexed issue of overpayments – which I know encouraged a number of dentists to give up NHS work – will enable us to put the matter behind us. The legislation to which I have referred is designed precisely to improve the teams, including orthodontists, who will provide care in the dentist's surgery.* (*Hansard* 12 June 1997 col 320)

Whether his hopes are justified remains to be seen but even if they are, the improvement may only be short-term. A Demos report, *Open Wide: futures for dentistry in 2010*, concluded:

> *An important conclusion of our analysis is that, contrary to much of the prevailing wisdom in the dental care industry, things cannot go on much as they are.* (p175)

In coming to this conclusion, the report draws not only on projections of possible technical change in the way that dental services are provided, but also on change in the way people perceive the role of dentistry in general and the NHS in particular. It concludes by suggesting that dentistry reflects in miniature the tensions affecting the NHS as a whole:

> *The future of dentistry is interesting and important therefore, not only for its own sake, but because making the right policy choices could yield lessons which help resolve much larger debates about how western post-industrial societies can manage the transformation of our post-war cultures and institutions of welfare.* (p179)

Long-term care Earlier Reviews have recorded the Government's response to the 'Leeds' case and its subsequent attempts to provide a clear framework for the responsibilities of health and social care authorities. In section 2.2 data are presented from a National Audit Office study which identified the range of availability for long-term care within the NHS before the new guidance was issued. In EL (96) 89, the Department of Health issued a progress report on the impact of its continuing care guidance. It found that:

> *The introduction of eligibility criteria has made some impact in confirming and clarifying the responsibilities for meeting continuing health care needs.*
>
> *Some progress has been made in reviewing needs and addressing significant gaps in services but the picture is patchy.*
>
> *It is too early at this stage to judge whether overall the introduction of eligibility criteria is leading to greater consistency in arrangements for continuing health care.* (para 6)

While the new guidelines are being introduced, evidence about the application of the old continues to emerge. A case considered by the Health Service Commissioner (HSC Selected Investigations completed October 1995 to March 1996) further illustrates that whatever the issues of principle may be, in practice the key may be poor organisation:

> *I was very concerned to find that, four years after the issue of national guidance which emphasised the importance of discharge procedures in A&E departments, no proper written procedures existed for this department: instead staff relied on custom and practice – not easily communicated – if at all – to newer staff. That lack is at the root of this complaint. Had there been a proper procedure, agreed with social services and local GPs – and properly recorded decisions – it would have been clear who was responsible for arranging the complainant's mother-in-law's placement and ensuring that she and her relatives understood the financial implications of choosing to go to the home rather than St Michael's hospital. No one at the Hospital took that responsibility.* (p61)

Last year's Review discussed the question of principle involved in determining whether social care should form part of NHS provision. In its report, the Select Committee clearly supported the position taken by the Royal College of Nursing that the nursing costs of long term care should be the responsibility of the NHS. In its reply to the report (Cm 3457), the Goverment declined to address the issue of principle, prefering the pragmatic judgement that:

> *It will keep this proposal under review but it does not believe that it currently represents the highest priority for NHS expenditure.* (p10)

The Government was, however, happy to accept the report's conclusion that there was no immediate crisis in funding and hence that there was a 'breathing space' which should be used to get a better understanding of the situation and the options available:

> *It is clear that there is no immediate funding crisis facing the nation in respect of long term care. There is a window of opportunity within*

which the national debate on this subject can proceed during the remaining years of this century and beyond. We believe that there is an urgent need to establish a much better knowledge base on the costs and benefits of health promotion, rehabilitation, and preventative social care, on the impact of future demographic, medical and social developments on long term care costs, and on the costs to the public purse of alternative funding options. Public awareness of the issues and choices involved must be improved, and we hope our report will be a contribution to that process. It is highly desirable that any major changes to current arrangements should be agreed on a basis of all-party consensus in order to provide the stable and certain background for individuals to take effective decisions about their future care. (p lvi)

A report from the Joseph Rowntree Foundation, *Inquiry into Meeting the Costs of Continuing Care*, attempted to find ground for such a consensus, recommending that a compulsory insurance scheme should be introduced. The Government, however, rejected that approach but proceeded with the policy announced a year earlier to protect personal savings. This was restated in *A new partnership for care in old age*, a policy statement from the Chancellor of the Exchequer in March 1997.

Although the statement indicated the intention to proceed with proposals similar to those made in the previous year, it contained evidence which suggested they were unlikely to be effective.

The statement indicates:

Different estimates of the average length of stay in residential care have been produced, but the important point for any individual to bear in mind, in considering how much he might have to pay, is that any estimate of the average conceals very wide variations in actual lengths of stay. (p28)

The statement gives no indication of the nature of the factors influencing these risks – family structure, lifestyle, home conditions etc. Accordingly individuals have very little knowledge on which to base any assessment of the risks they face. In these circumstances it is hard to see the merits of a private solution. Furthermore the policies which currently exist are very hard to assess. A report by Tania Burchardt and John Hills, *Private Welfare Insurance and Social Security* (Joseph Rowntree Foundation 1997), argues that:

We find long term care insurance to be by far the least suitable area for policy to rest on private insurance. The value for money of available policies seems virtually impossible to evaluate – even for those of us who have spent several months working on it. This not only causes problems for potential purchasers (affecting commitments worth thousands of pounds which could not be recouped), but also means that insurers are dealing with a product whose uncertain nature – and the way in which these uncertainties cannot be pooled away – makes it inherently unsuitable for private insurance.

Even as a way of reducing future public spending, regardless of the cost of the alternative to the average purchaser, reliance on, or fiscal encouragement of, private insurance in this area looks a dubious proposition, as so much of the 'downside risk' will inevitably remain with the state, while the considerable costs of private cover would undoubtedly tighten the general tax constraint on government.

At the same time, the distributional differences between income-related funding and risk-related premiums are immense – under private insurance those with low lifetime incomes, women, and those with poor initial health would pay the equivalent of tens of thousands of pounds more. (p 63)

The illustrative figures annexed to the Government paper bring out how expensive the insurance offered will be for some population groups, requiring in the case of those on modest pensions a significant proportion of what are already low incomes – unless they had substantial savings in liquid form. The scale of the public expenditure costs of offering this form of asset insurance is hard to estimate since take-up is impossible to forecast. The paper suggests £200 million as the 'maximum conceivable', implicitly recognising that take-up will be low.

Whatever the merits of these proposals, it has come to be recognised that the private insurance market requires regulation. In July 1996, the Office of Fair Trading issued *Health Insurance* in response to concerns that the products were complex, sold to vulnerable consumers and that there appeared to be substantial scope for misunderstanding and mis-selling.

In December 1996, the Treasury issued proposals to regulate the selling and marketing of long-term care insurance under the 1986 Financial Services Act in response to the consultation document. This reaffirmed the reasons for regulating these particular products:

- the potential purchasers, who are typically elderly and vulnerable, and in many cases will have only limited experience or understanding of complex financial products;
- the relatively large size of long-term care premiums in relation to the financial resources of the typical purchaser;
- the complexity of the product itself and of the decision to purchase a long-term care insurance product;

Soon after coming to office, the new Government announced fundamental changes to the regulation of all financial services bringing them under a single 'umbrella'. However, although it had promised a Royal Commission on long-term care while in Opposition, by the time of going to press, it had made no such announcement.

2.2 Equity

Fairness, or equity, has been an underlying principle of the NHS ever since its foundation. It follows that as resources are limited, what is available ought to be allocated in ways which are accepted as equitable or fair. So much is reasonably uncontroversial. But as soon as a particular word is used, political parties run for cover. 'Rationing', simply a name for this process of allocation, is studiously avoided by politicians. Priority-setting, on the other hand, seems acceptable, presumably because it does not give

Working Party on Priority Setting in the NHS

Conclusions

- Choices are inevitable
- Choices are needed at macro, meso and micro levels
- There is an inescapable tension between the interests of a population and the interests of individual patients
- A clear set of national values do exist (equity, efficiency and responsiveness), but it would be helpful if these were more widely debated, understood and promulgated
- Any set of values will entail trade-offs
- The practice of priority-setting varies tremendously across different health authorities and GP fundholders
- There is a danger that priority-setting may be pursued by health authorities as a peripheral activity

Recommendations: four types of action are needed

- To ensure that the Government, health professionals and the public all understand and accept that the need to set priorities cannot be avoided
- To encourage a wide debate and ownership of the core values of the NHS
- To ensure that those values are translated into action more consistently by health authorities, GP fundholders and trusts leading to more effective decision-making
- To provide training, support and development, to spread good practice and to improve the competence in the difficult art of making choices about health care

the impression that anyone is denied care. But beneficial treatments *will* continue to be denied to people and increasingly groups such as the Rationing Agenda Group (*The Rationing Agenda in the NHS*, King's Fund, 1996), have argued that there is a need to be more open and explicit about this.

The Government did come very close to acknowledging that all debates on this subject are, in fact, about the same fundamental issue. Towards the end of 1995 a working group was set up to develop a framework for priority-setting, co-sponsored by the NHSE, BMA, Royal Colleges and NAHAT. Such a group has never before convened at such a high level and with such a degree of official sanction. Their first, interim, report, *Priority Setting in the NHS: a discussion document*, was published in February – its conclusions and recommendations are set out in the Box. With regard to terminology, it stated:

> *we do not consider that there is anything to be gained by giving each of these terms different meanings ... We therefore use the term 'priority-setting' as a synonym for 'rationing'; both terms refer to the difficult and vexed issue of how to make choices between competing priorities when resources are scarce.* (p 6)

In other words, beneficial things must be denied to people. However, such a formulation is still too stark for the Government: no one from within the Department of Health signed the document. Nevertheless, it seems only a matter of time before the semantic debate is over. Whether this will lead to a significant government initiative on how rationing ought to be conducted is another matter.

In the meantime, events in the NHS continued

to bring these issues to the fore. Following last year's approach we have split the commentary on equity into two sections: territorial equity and choosing between people. This separation in some ways mirrors the fundamental distinction in discussions of fairness between horizontal and vertical equity. Horizontal equity requires that people who are the same in all relevant respects should be treated the same; vertical equity requires that people who are different should be treated differently to the extent that their differences are morally relevant.

In NHS terms, the former concept of equity means that those who are living in different parts of the country but who are otherwise identical should receive the same treatment (if they want it). The latter concept involves discriminating between competing claims on resources: choices have to be made between different client groups and individuals and these choices need to be made on the basis of relevant criteria. It is in the former category of decision that the fiercest controversy occurred during 1996.

Territorial equity

As last year, we analyse fairness between areas under four headings: purchasing power, availability, activity & quality.

Purchasing power The fundamental principle underlying the allocation of purchasing power in the NHS is 'need' – that equal need should receive equal resources. But while that principle has proved largely uncontroversial its implementation has not. Last year's Review reported the changes made to the formula for calculating how much each district should get for hospital and community health services following extensive analysis by the University of York.

While the Department of Health had accepted the main findings of this work, it had not done so in relation to community health services which comprise 24 per cent of HCHS spending – in opposition to the York team who, in the absence of better evidence, believed that the same weighting should be applied to 100 per cent of expenditure. This 24 per cent is made up of:

- 4.5 per cent on learning disability;
- 11.5 per cent on community services;
- 8 per cent on administration and other hospital services.

In June 1996 the House of Commons Health Select Committee report, *Allocation of Resources to Health Authorities*, included a calculation of what would have been the effect of using a 100 per cent weighting. The results are provided in Table 21. In general terms they are similar to the results cited last year of an alternative formula calculated by M Brennan and R Carr-Hill, ie the losers from not employing this alternative are industrial and deprived areas and the beneficiaries the reverse, but the individual authorities are different.

Clearly, if this alteration to the formula had been introduced for the financial year 1996/97, it would have caused a tight NHS budget settlement to have bitten even harder in Tory heartlands in the build-up to the General Election – not a convenient modification.

The Committee argued that

> *the current situation in which some 24 per cent of HCHS is unweighted for need is unsatisfactory. The sooner the gap in the research is filled the better.*

Table 21 Impact of formula re-weighting

Greatest losers (if change had been made)	*% change (where total budget is weighted by acute and psychiatric indices)*	*Greatest gainers*	*% change*
East Surrey	- 5.2	Barnsley	3.7
West Surrey	- 5.2	Newcastle and Nth Tyneside	3.9
North and mid Hants	- 4.6	Gateshead and Sth Tyneside	4.1
Cambridge and Huntingdon	- 4.3	St Helens and Knowsley	4.1
Oxfordshire	- 4.0	Sunderland	4.6
East and North Herts	- 3.9	Lambeth, Southwark and Lewisham	4.7
Buckinghamshire	- 3.8	Camden and Islington	4.9
Berkshire	- 3.8	East London and the City	5.6
West Herts	- 3.8	Liverpool	5.6
West Sussex	- 3.3	Manchester	6.9

Source: Health Committee, *Allocation of resources to health authorities* vol 1, HMSO 1996

In response to the Government's evidence to the Committee – which was that although zero weighting was not scientifically sound, until further research, it was the sensible 'default option' – the committee noted

> *this is debatable: we have sympathy with the argument that a genuine default option would have been to preserve continuity with the previous formula where the need to supersede it had not been demonstrably made out, and to continue for the time being to weight the 24 per cent on the 'square root of SMR'.* (p21)

Another alternative was to weight as in Table 21, as this would 'arguably prove closer to whatever objective evidence-based weighting is eventually arrived at than would zero-weighting'.

The Government, in their response to the Committee argued:

> *It is important to note that the 24 per cent is weighted for age and market forces. In the absence of any evidence or research to support a particular needs weighting for these services, it is a matter* ***of judgement*** [emphasis in original] *what should be used in the interim. In the current formula there are now two powerful well justified needs models for inpatient services and because they are so powerful in their effects, it is necessary to be able to justify any application beyond areas where this is not supported by statistical analysis.* (p5)

The 'market forces factor' was also claimed by the Committee to be deeply flawed. This was because of the clumsiness of the current division of the country into only four zones, the doubts that arise over the choice of comparator occupations, and small sample sizes for calculation of some of these occupations. They welcomed the Government's announcement of a fundamental review.

In the event the Government responded to the criticisms voiced by the Committee announcing two changes to the formula for the allocations to take effect during 1997/98:

- the introduction of an interim needs weighting for community health services;

- the introduction of a revised market forces factor.

The first of these was based on work by the Universities of Kent and Plymouth which had been commissioned to develop the interim weighting for community services. Simple application of the acute and psychiatric weighting was rejected, but establishing a specific community weighting proved difficult because of lack of data. The weighting was eventually based on utilisation (adjusted for supply) for the following services: district nurses, health visitors, community psychiatric nurses, community midwives, chiropodists, physiotherapists and occupational therapists. Data for family planning, community dental services, immunisation, screening and health promotion was not available and hence no weighting could be derived for these services.

For its part, the market forces factor was adjusted to take account, in a more sophisticated way than hitherto, of variations in staff, medical and dental (London weighting), non-pay, land, buildings, and equipment costs. The effect was to create a finer gradation between districts and to include more districts in this element of the formula. The details are set out in *HCHS Revenue Resource Allocation to Health Authorities: weighted capitation formulas*, NHSE, March 1997.

While most controversy has attached to calculation of the appropriate level of capitation payments for each district, what each district actually gets in each year depends also on a judgement as to how rapidly the target level determined by the current formula should be attained – in other words a pace-of-change policy which establishes how fast the gap between what a district receives and what it ought to receive is closed. If the target was reached in one go, significant difficulties would be felt in the losing districts which would be forced to cut back existing services.

Nevertheless, too much emphasis on safeguarding continuity and stability in the NHS might jeopardise the long-term objective of achieving an equitable distribution of resources based on need. Indeed the Health Committee reported that

> *the Secretary of State for Health subsequently told us that in his view the process of reaching targets would never be complete, because targets themselves would shift. His aim would be to move authorities closer to target while ensuring that unreasonable strains were not imposed on any particular authorities.* (p35)

In the event, the settlement for 1997/98 provided all health authorities with a minimum 1.35 per cent increase on their baseline, with under-target authorities receiving at least 1.89 per cent. Although a significant improvement on the previous allocation, even districts at the upper end of these settlements (who receive even more depending on their distance from target) are not treated generously when compared with the NHS average over the last twenty years of 3 per cent or so.

Other groups have criticised the basis on which weighted capitation is calculated. Help the Aged, in *Growing Old in the Countryside*, argued that rural areas are doing relatively badly and this is having a disproportionate effect on older people who tend to live in these areas. The implication is that the age weighting in the formula is not sufficient to counteract other factors militating against non-urban districts. The report claims that

In particular rural areas fare badly because:

- *the [weighted capitation formula] ... has no regard for the effects of isolation on the need for or costs for care;*
- *the adjustments for the higher costs in London – the market forces factor – also bend resources towards the most densely populated areas.* (p37)

The question is whether 'rurality' can meaningfully and practically be designed into capitation formulae, and whether it in fact constitutes a justifiable understanding of 'need' over and above those already utilised. More fundamental, perhaps, are the increased costs of access in rural areas – other things being equal, it is clear that the cost to the individual in getting to a health care provider will be greater in the less densely populated regions where greater distances have to be travelled.

This general consideration was echoed in a report published in 1996 by the Royal College of Physicians of London, *Future patterns of care by general and specialist physicians*. In it the authors accept that there will in general be a need to concentrate resources on hospital sites so as to achieve a 'critical mass' of medical expertise; however:

> *the care of patients in smaller more isolated communities of less than 150,000 require special consideration. Timely access to emergency medical services will require rapid transport to an accessible distant site or the local provision of health care at an accepted and agreed uneconomic cost.* (p19)

Quite how to build in a factor for this 'uneconomic' care has yet to be addressed in the development of ever more sophisticated needs formulae, at least as far as England is concerned. In last year's Review we reported how the distribution of GPs has not been calculated in the same way as HCHS funding, with the result that certain areas of the country receive more than their allocation of GP places than would be expected if RAWP-like measures of need were taken into account.

After the publication of the *Delivering the Future* White Paper, an editorial in the *Health Service Journal* (2 January 1997) suggested that in a service where responsibility is supposedly devolved to local level 'the Medical Practices Committee had become an anachronism' (p13). It also claimed that the distribution of GPs had grown grossly inequitable.

Mary Leigh, chair of the Medical Practices Committee, denied these claims (*Health Service Journal*, 23 January 1997, p 18), arguing that

- when measured against average list size, there are now 15 underdoctored areas compared with 400 in 1981;
- the MPC has also allowed more doctors in some areas on the basis of an assessment of need;
- it needs to be recognised that the MPC cannot direct GPs to go to certain areas;
- the UK compares very favourably with the rest of our international partners in the allocation of GPs.

The Committee is highly reticent about the way it works – it publishes no regular report on its activities – but it is almost certainly justified in claiming that without it, the distribution of GPs would have been much less equitable than it actually is: by the middle of 1997, the number of 'open' areas was down to six in England and Wales. However, Ms Leigh's reply ignores one of the White Paper's central points; that primary care need not be identical to general practice, and hence a 'proper' level of service does not depend on the distribution of GPs alone. Furthermore the Act offers levers to attract GPs which are not available to the Committee. For these reasons, there is little doubt the focus of the Committee's work is or will shortly be anachronistic. Furthermore, even in its own terms, work by Alan Maynard and Karen Bloor reported in *Health Care UK 1995/96* (p 73) indicates that the existing distribution remains inequitable. As the Primary Care Act is implemented, it seems inevitable it will bring with it changes in the way that resources for primary care are distributed.

Since 1990/91 regional capital planning totals have also been determined using a weighted capitation formula. Populations used in the formula are projected five years ahead (as a proxy for the lead time in completing large capital projects) and weighted for age and need, but on a much simpler basis than that for revenue budgets, and not including a market forces factor.
But the introduction of PFI has introduced another complicating factor. As Table 22 shows, public spending plans are relying increasingly on finance becoming available through the Initiative.

As noted in 2.1, the projected figures may not be realised but if PFI does increase the total supply of capital resources available to the NHS, its geographical effects are not at all clear. When announcing the short list of schemes to go ahead in July, the Minister referred to three criteria: health need, the state of negotiations and PFI-ability – none of which bear on equity. Recognising this point, in a report issued in September 1996, *Capital Allocation*, the NHSE suggested the Department of Health may need to retain a strong central grip:

> *to date, in terms of the value of potential investment, PFI appears to be steering investment towards the Thames regions and Northern and Yorkshire ... The distribution of major PFI schemes, combined with a shrinking quantum of discretionary capital available for investment, support the need to move to a national system of prioritisation of publicly funded capital schemes.* (p20)

The implication is that the Department will need to act as a strong counterweight to the activity of the private sector if it wishes to retain any semblance of equity in the supply of capital.

Table 22 Capital Finance 1995/96-1998/99 (£millions)

	1995/99	*1996/97*	*1997/98*	*1998/99*
Exchequer	1,687	1,543	1,495	1,430
Property sales	262	350	264	267
PFI	47	77	226	413
Total	1,996	1,970	1,985	2,110

Source: Capital Allocations, National Service Executive, 1996

Availability In *A Service with Ambitions* the Secretary of State stated that:

> *the Government has made it clear that there should be no clinically effective treatments which a health authority decides as a matter of principle should never be provided.* (p39)

This careful phrasing may have been devised to support the notion that rationing is not inevitable – that is, rationing defined *in this way* does not exist. However, even on these terms the Government's instruction is being ignored. Regardless of semantic quibbles, there is ample evidence that clinically effective treatments provided in some health authorities are not available in others.

'Availability' here is taken to mean that the NHS, or individual health authorities, purchases some level of a particular service – it is not specifically ruled out. In last year's Review the principal concern was whether certain health authorities were moving out of continuing care. The Government refused to establish national criteria for NHS provision leaving it to individual authorities to determine their own criteria, albeit in the context of national guidelines. The variation existing before the Government set out its guidance was evidenced in March 1996 in an NAO report of a survey conducted during 1994, *NHS residential health care for elderly people*. The report surveyed all 101 authorities to establish their contractual arrangements for 'continuous health care' for elderly people, such as nursing home care and community nursing. The summary results were as follows:

- 17 health authorities said they do not currently have a policy in this field;
- 11 health authorities have not funded any continuous health care beds for 1994–95; more specifically since 1993 in terms of funding for physically ill older people:
  - 40 had not funded any nursing home beds
  - 14 had not funded any hospital ward beds
  - 5 had not funded any community nursing in patients' own homes
  - 4 had not funded any community nursing in residential care homes;
- the NHS still provides the largest proportion of NHS-funded continuous beds, 4814, with the private sector providing 965 beds.

The Department's monitoring of the impact of their guidance on continuing care, cited in 2.1, suggests it is unlikely that situation has changed markedly in the intervening period. Hence the boundary between medical care (funded by the NHS) and social care (means-tested), is still a matter for highly variable local judgement.

Other services on the boundary of NHS care were again prominent in the debate during 1996. Infertility treatment, sex-change operations and vasectomies have all been ruled out by individual health authorities. The issues so far discussed, though, might all reasonably be considered to be about services which are not of central importance to the NHS.

However, during 1996 another variation on the availability theme emerged which concerned treatments which are squarely within the NHS bounds of responsibility: drugs for Motor Neurone Disease (Riluzole), AIDS ('triple therapy' of AZT and protease inhibitors), Alzheimer's (Donepezil), Multiple Sclerosis (Beta Interferon 1b) and ovarian and breast cancer (Paclitaxel and Docetaxel), as well as other technologies such as blood clotting agents for haemophiliacs (recombinant factor VIII). The issue turned into one of the dominant themes of media interest during 1996/97. No one questions whether addressing these kinds of ill-health is the job of the NHS; the issue is rather whether the effectiveness and cost-effectiveness of the particular treatments is sufficient to warrant the expenditure on providing them. As things stand, this decision is left to health authorities and individual clinicians; some are deciding that they are not willing to provide any.

Because it is clearly the responsibility of a health care system to seek out beneficial treatments for these diseases, and because in a large number of districts these drugs have been deemed cost-effective and are purchased, the public are faced with the bewildering spectacle of some individuals being denied medical care on the basis of where they live.

Once a drug is licensed – it has satisfied the UK Licensing Authority that it is safe, efficacious and of good quality – clinicians are then free to prescribe it. In principle the drug 'works', but only in a trial setting (for some patients in some circumstances); it may be less effective in routine settings. Furthermore, as Karen Bloor and colleagues showed in *Health Care UK 1995/96*, the question of cost does not enter the licensing decision, but is an important constraint on health authorities. Judgements about whether to purchase these drugs will therefore vary from health authority to health authority.

Clinicians have always made these decisions in different ways, but the way they did so was implicit, ie they have not rested on a public statement of prescribing intentions. Although health authorities cannot forbid the prescribing of a drug, they can refuse to allocate 'new' money to fund its use. In this way they can strongly discourage its prescription by consultants, without, again, any public statement of policy. If health authorities take different budgetary decisions, clinicians can find themselves treating patients who live in different health authority districts with different drug regimens. The result is variable availability for identifiable individuals. Such visible inequity provoked persistent media interest in the period leading up to the General Election.

Furthermore, the drugs were developed for types of ill-health which are largely incurable and degenerative – in other words those of most public concern. To add to the level of interest, a large number of these drugs were licensed in rapid succession. One which has been around a little longer, and therefore been the subject of more published analysis, is Beta Interferon 1b (Betaferon). It is a particularly good example of this type of new drugs, displaying their typical features: it is 'proven' to work in a trial setting; it is expensive (typically £10,000 per patient year); it treats a chronic, incurable, degenerative condition which afflicts many thousands of people every year; but it is not a cure – most of the drugs named above at best prolong life for a few months, or alleviate symptoms temporarily. Ferner has estimated Betaferon can:

> *reduce hospital admission by one day every three years on average in selected patients with MS but has no demonstrable effect on disability* (Beta Interferon 1b, *BMJ*, 9 November 1996, p1157)

Clearly, the availability of Betaferon poses particularly difficult decisions for purchasers, and for consultants who have to decide whether their budgets would be better spent on other treatments for MS sufferers, or on other patients with different neurological conditions. A King's Fund study published in February 1997, *Management of the Introduction of Betaferon*, examined how this new drug was adopted by a selection of health authorities in the North Thames Region. One conclusion of the study was that there can be pressure on purchasers to avoid explicit rationing. High public and media awareness of the licensing of these drugs means that refusing to purchase, when neighbouring health authorities do, can result in damaged relationships:

> *With Betaferon, although many health authorities queried its potential health gain, only one did not commit funding within North Thames. This was justified on the basis that the health authority had no allocated growth money. Negative media attention ensued. Eventually their provider paid for treatment with some bitterness resulting.* (p15)

It seems as though 'old fashioned' implicit rationing was the predominant means of keeping demand in line with supply: neurologists were not offering the drug, waiting lists were operating for first treatment. The report also reveals that 'GPs also indirectly rationed access, as around 20-25 per cent of potentially suitable patients who enquired about Betaferon were discouraged from seeking referral in one survey'. Such actions may have been taken 'purely' on clinical effectiveness grounds, but it is likely that the general atmosphere of pressure on resources played its part.

Many purchasers, interest groups and providers are now calling for greater central direction. In a letter to the *BMJ*, clinicians from a number of haemophilia centres drew attention to the similar situation with regard to recombinant factor VIII:

> *What is needed to help purchasers and trusts with haemophilia centres is for the Department [of Health] to engage in a constructive dialogue with our organisation and provide leadership on how [our] guidelines should be implemented. This will ensure patients are treated fairly. To leave the decision to the vagaries of local purchasers is to abrogate its responsibility for an important aspect of health care* (*BMJ*, 8 March, p749)

It will probably require more than simply advice on implementing guidelines, however. One possibility for drugs might be to allow the licensing authority to work as it does now, but separately assess whether the relative efficacy (compared to existing treatments) and cost-effectiveness of the drug are adequate within the NHD R&D programme. One consultant physician, RE Ferner, has suggested that 'Prescribing outside these trials would be prohibited or discouraged by a ban on general prescription within the NHS' (*BMJ*, 9 November 1996, p1157). Another suggestion, normally focused on issues of cost control rather than equitable rationing, is for the Safety and Efficacy Register of New Interventional Procedures (SERNIP) referred to in section 1.5 to include consideration of cost-effectiveness in its investigation of non-drug interventions. SERNIP is currently a voluntary system operating under the auspices of the Royal Medical Colleges. None of these mechanisms will lead to a straightforward solution, however, even if the new Government has the courage to grasp the nettle.

Variation in activity and quality Variations of availability are particularly stark and involve some districts offering no service of a particular type. However, the bulk of variation in health care provision occurs in levels of activity or in the quality of care. Two reports from the Health Advisory Service published during 1996 drew attention to this persistent issue. The first, *Achieving a Balance*, examined services for elderly people. It was access to specialist, secondary care through GP fundholders which caused concern to the review teams. In particular:

> *some GPs stated that they managed their acutely ill elderly patients in community and neighbourhood hospitals themselves rather than referring them to specialist secondary healthcare in which full investigative facilities were available. While this may be appropriate in many cases … no outcome measures were in place to ensure that the quality and extent of care had not been compromised.* (p55)

Another concern was the variation in assessment of appropriate discharge:

> *the review teams formed the impression that, in some non-geriatric specialist secondary care services, the driving concern was with throughput and discharging people who were seen as blocking beds for people with acute illness.* (p56)

A similar picture emerged from the second study, a thematic review of mental health services, *Heading for Better Care*, published in September 1996, which covered three particular disorders: acquired brain injury (ABI), early onset dementia, and Huntingdon's Disease (HD). The review team visited six districts in England and Wales in the process of the review; one of their principal findings was that:

> *… five of the six districts visited have specialist inpatient units which admit people with ABI, HD and early onset dementia … The sixth district was chosen as a reference site to represent the majority of districts that have no specialised services for these client groups. Para.29: Nonetheless, the visiting teams found no standard model of patient care and considerable variation in the categories of patient admitted, treatment programmes and criteria for discharge.* (p7)

Addressing these kinds of variations is a substantial task. A health care system the size of the NHS is bound to have variations which, when individual cases or circumstances are scrutinised, reveal themselves to be inequitable. Making sure that fairness operates in such a system requires the political centre to act: otherwise there will be no possibility for arbitrating on legitimate and illegitimate variation. But even if the sheer scale of information needs could be met, there may never be consensus on the scope for legitimate variation. Medical care, whether for head injuries or anything else, is too subjective a science. The consequences of this, in a system which is gradually opening up and becoming more transparent to the general public, are unclear. The challenge for the future may be to educate the public to expect an 'imperfect' service, rather than attempt to eliminate inequities entirely.

Choosing between people

There was no single individual care this year which matched the media interest generated by Jaymee Bowen last year, the young girl who was refused funding for a leading-edge treatment for cancer. Unlike the cases described above, Jaymee was not refused treatment because she happened to live in one area rather than another – there were no comparable Jaymees in other areas – but because the health authority had to make a decision about all the different people waiting in the 'queue' for that health authority's resources. On effectiveness or cost-effectiveness grounds – depending on your interpretation of the actions of the health authority – Jaymee was not funded. Others had a greater claim.

The issue of which criteria are appropriate, and how to balance them, did not go away in 1996, however. Rather than a named individual, the biggest controversy arose over a particular criterion: age. In a series of articles commissioned by the *BMJ* on various rationing issues, Professors Alan Williams and Grimley Evans debated whether 'age is an appropriate criterion for choosing which people who could benefit from health care should be offered it'. Alan Williams proposed the motion, arguing for a 'good innings' conception of fairness:

> *a reasonable limit has to be set upon the demands we can properly make on our fellow citizens in order to keep us going a bit longer ... My argument does not mean that benefits to young people take absolute priority over benefits to old people. It simply means that we give rather more weight to them than to us.* (*BMJ*, 15 March 1997, p10)

Alan Williams owns up to being one of these 'elderly' people – he is approaching 70 – and considers that he has already benefited from a life of good health and should therefore stand aside for those who have not yet had that lifetime of health. The opposing, academic, view is that this would create a defined class of people who would be publicly marked down as less eligible, which would be damaging for social relations; it also places a value on a life based simply on life expectancy rather than its uniqueness.

Not surprisingly, the media presented the arguments in rather more colourful terms: 'Prof. in "dump the old" health storm' was a not untypical response. More responsible reportage such as that in the *British Journal of Health Care Management* (vol 3 no. 4) also took an uncompromising view:

> *to ignore the injustices suffered by the generation who first financed the NHS is the mindset of a service with pretensions rather than realisable ambitions.* (p180)

A report from Age Concern predictably took a similar line. *The Ageism Issue* presented both an empirical and moral position. They cited evidence of 'ageism' in the admission policies of both coronary care units and dialysis units, and in the provision of treatment of lung cancer – see Box overleaf.

Opponents of Alan Williams were reluctant to acknowledge his careful statement that 'absolute' priority was not at issue; it was simply a matter of accepting age as *one* criterion amongst many. But perhaps the philosophical niceties of a position such as this are not as important as the fact that such a proposition is articulated at all. Admitting that not everything can be done for everyone – in particular, for an identifiable group which clearly

Age Concern's ageism claims

- 20 per cent of coronary care units operate age-related admissions policies and 40 per cent restrict the giving of 'clot-busting' drugs to older people
- 63 per cent of deaths from breast cancer occur in women aged 65 or over. Breast screening is more effective in detecting cancer in this group. Yet they are excluded from the programme for automatic invitations to screening
- More than 50 per cent of patients with inoperable non-small lung cancer are over 65, yet palliative chemotherapy, to relieve the symptoms, is reserved for younger age groups
- Two-thirds of kidney patients aged 70-79 are not accepted for life-saving dialysis or transplant, and this rises to seven-eighths of patients aged 80 or over

Source: Age Concern, *The Ageism Issue* 1997

needs a substantial proportion of NHS care – does not sound like the kind of statement which someone who supports a National Health Service *ought* to be making. The fierceness of the exchanges reported in the public debate are not really about moral philosophy, but about a growing and deeply uncomfortable realisation that the NHS has to face up to these issues at all. The issues are discussed further by Bill New and Nicholas Mays below.

Whether or not the NHS is about more than simply producing improvements in health status was brought into sharp focus with the case of a young girl reported in the *BMJ* in July 1996 who had no chance of survival. Clinicians were effectively faced with three choices: allow the girl to die quickly and 'naturally', send her home at a cost of £160,000 where her life expectancy was 16 months, or keep her in hospital in intensive care at substantially higher cost but with higher life expectancy. The middle option was taken.

A precise estimate of the benefit forgone to others by keeping the girl ventilated – albeit at home – was apparently not made. Such a 'calculation' would probably have come to the conclusion that more 'good' would be done by spending the money on others – for instance, by undertaking hip replacements for the large number of people waiting for that relatively inexpensive and effective treatment. Even if we accept that such a cost-benefit calculation is accurate, however, the decision to divert resources to particular individuals in particular circumstances such as this little girl are unlikely ever to be ruled out. Expenditure on hopeless cases can send out a signal to the wider community that every individual 'counts' and at the very least has a chance of treatment. The reassurance element in such actions is very difficult to quantify but illustrates the difficulty of any resolution of the debate about the true objectives of the NHS.

Are non-clinical-need factors relevant when choosing between people? This issue surfaced during early 1997 with respect to NHS abortions. Many authorities, according to the Abortion Law Reform Society, are introducing criteria for acceptance which vary from region to region and cause territorial inequity of the kind noted above. But, regardless or the regional variation, what is it appropriate to take into account? Enfield and Haringey Health Authority's criteria for eligibility are:

- women under 18
- those with medical or psychiatric conditions

- those with learning difficulties
- rape victims
- couples on sterilisation waiting lists or whose sterilisation has failed
- genuine failure of normally reliable contraceptive method
- women who are homeless, refugees or asylum-seekers
- there is a thirteen-week limit for those not meeting these priority criteria.

The list demonstrates how difficult it can be to entirely ignore non-clinical factors. There are many pregnancies for which the medical condition of the women is identical and under such circumstances it seems unavoidable that other factors will be taken into account. However, one could imagine another list of criteria developed by another authority with other, more conservative, values.

The vexed issue of how to ration equitably the resources of the NHS will not go away, and neither should it. There is no solution waiting to be found. But whereas there may never be a consensus about the 'right' allocation, there may be scope for greater consensus about particular aspects of rationing which are simply not acceptable in a modern state. One of these is differential treatment as a consequence of where people live. This is never the direct intention of decision-makers, just the result of having a large number of independent health authorities exercising judgement in varying ways. Government, acting from the centre, may have the potential to address the starkest manifestation of this activity – zero provision in some parts of the country coupled with significant activity elsewhere.

But availability of a service is only part of the story: most of the differential treatment received by otherwise identical individuals occurs for people's *likelihood* of receiving treatment of acceptable quality. In other words variations persist, and have done so for many years, in activity levels and quality of care. This is more pervasive and widespread than that for simple availability, and it is only its implicit nature which leaves it largely unknown to the general public – statistical variations do not make attractive news copy. It is also more difficult for Government to intervene in a centralist fashion: the variations may be the result of legitimate clinical disagreement, or differences in efficiency or levels of local need. More can be done even here, by promoting better dissemination of information on cost-effectiveness evidence, for example. But it seems certain that increased centralism will remain controversial and problematic, even when it is recognised that it is necessary.

2.3 Accountability

Allegations of 'sleaze' dominated the run-up to the General Election, as trust in those elected or appointed to discharge public duty continued to decline. Much of the public disquiet focused on the particular activities of named members of Parliament, but the activities of 'Quangos', which appear to most people to include health authorities, continued to add to this unease. Evidence of fraudulent use of NHS funds continued to emerge both in relation to prescriptions, which the Audit Commission reported on last year, and opticians' services.

The Audit Commission bulletin of

December 1996, *Protecting the Public Purse*, reported that:

> *Although detected fraud in the NHS remains low overall, the level of detected fraud in 1995/96 … almost doubled rising from £0.75 million to £1.4 million.*

Furthermore:

> *cases under investigation involve potentially large sums, suggesting that the figures reported may under-represent the true level of fraud. … Financial systems need to be improved and internal audit requires strengthening* [and] *managers should review the effectiveness of their internal financial controls.* (p1)

Probity in Primary Care, a survey by the Healthcare Financial Management Association published in June 1997, found that there was a general belief among health authorities that fraud was on the increase. 96 cases of fraud were identified by respondents, of which the majority related to payments for ophthalmic services and 43 per cent of respondents considered that not enough resources were being devoted to detecting fraud.

The losses identified in these two reports are the result of frauds carried out by individuals or firms which are not part of the NHS itself. In contrast, a report from the House of Commons Committee of Public Accounts published in March 1997, *The Former Yorkshire Regional Health Authority: the inquiry commissioned by the NHSE*, uncovered 'excessive' and 'unseemly' spending on hospitality by officials and a number of other examples of inappropriate behaviour very near the top of the NHS hierarchy.

As the extracts in the Box opposite indicate, although the investigation clearly identified those responsible, they were able to 'walk away', in some cases both retaining monies they had improperly acquired, eg for relocation expenses and also continuing to be employed elsewhere in the NHS. Not surprisingly the Committee concluded that steps should be taken to make this impossible.

In his oral evidence to the Committee, the NHS Chief Executive, Alan Langlands, argued that the series of measures taken to improve accountability at local level would be more effective than relying on the long lines of hierarchical controls that had characterised the old NHS. At the top of that heirarchy was a chief executive who could not take action against individuals working within the NHS, since they were employees of the individual parts of it – health authorities, trusts etc. The process of tightening up at local level was taken a step further in March 1997 with the publication of *Corporate Gorvernance in the NHS: controls assurance statements* (HSG (97)17). The aim of the Controls Assurance Project is to bring together the range of measures already taken to improve corporate governance. Controls assurance requires boards to declare themselves satisfied within their organisation to ensure that risks are assessed and properly managed. The new arrangements are to be phased in over a period of years. The 1997/98 Accounts are to include a statement by the board of directors on internal financial control: by 1999/2000, it is envisaged that a more comprehensive statement will become mandatory.

These measures are aimed primarily at financial systems. As we reported last year, a parallel process has been under way in respect of appointments, following the report of Lord

Accountability in Practice

The Committee of Public Accounts investigation into Yorkshire Regional Health Authority occurred some time after the events that gave rise to concern. As the first extract from the Committee's examination of Alan Langlands, the events which covered a wide range of areas – relocation expenses, severance payments, official cars, consultancy contracts, land disposal,excess hospitality and a range of other matters – were serious. But as the extracts which follow indicated, those responsible were able to 'walk away' and in some cases be re-employed in other parts of it.

Sir Michael Shersby

21. *I must say that when I read this report I came to the conclusion that it was really one of the worst cases that I have had the misfortune to consider since I joined this Committee in 1983. It seems all the worse to me because it follows on the other cases that this Committee has considered and to which you have quite properly drawn our attention. It seems that despite the recommendations that have been made by the Committee in the past these problems continue to recur.*

Sir Michael then went on to pursue the issue of relocation expenses and whether they could be recovered. The answer he received from Mr Langlands was not encouraging. He therefore asked

23 .... *whether there are new legal remedies available and if there are will they be taken? That is all I want to know.*

(Mr Langlands) Active consideration is being given in all cases. If there are remedies available, subject to the things I have said, they will be pursued.

That also was scarcely encouraging for those concerned about the misuse of public funds: nor was the next question and answer.

24. *May I draw your attention to this particular point? We are told that when someone has left the National Health Service the NHS Executive are advised that they have no power to take legal or disciplinary action against that individual.*

(Mr Langlands) That is correct.

Sir Michael went on to ask whether there was an expectation that things would get better.

35. *What guarantee does the taxpayer have that things are going to change? Are you saying that all that you can do in effect is to issue stricter guidelines calling for approval of schemes by whoever it may be right up to the Secretary of State? If at the end of the day the individuals concerned choose to ignore them, until such time as the district auditor or the National Audit Office crawls over the accounts there is not very much you can do.*

(Mr Langlands) Stricter guidelines and also a change of climate. The corporate governance initiatives which I ran through earlier with the Chairman instil that discipline at a local level. I would not imagine that a health authority or a trust board would allow their chief executive to behave in the cavalier way that people behaved in this instance. That has been the change from 1994 and that is the change we must continue to promote.

Another member of the Committee, Mr Alan Williams then expressed the doubt that the new arrangements would be effective.

47. *We have 430 NHS trusts, 100 health authorities in England alone and the chief executives have been designated as accountable officers. You go on to say, '. . . ensuring that they are answerable to Parliament through him', that is the holder of*

your office, 'for the efficient, effective and proper use of all resources in their charge'. Those are laudable objectives which everyone here would support. Do you seriously suggest the present arrangement makes that a practical possibility?

(Mr Langlands) I would just make one point. These lapses, these failures, occurred when we were operating a hierarchical system of management in the NHS. The alternative that I am setting out here is aimed at instilling the discipline and the attitudes you would expect in me at a local level. That has been an important step which we have been taking since April 1994. Yes, I am here alone in this case, and indeed I suspect many others in the future. Given the particular nature of the accounting officer post I would not want to abdicate that responsibility to anyone else.

49. *Yet at the end of the day it is an unfillable responsibility is it not? Five hundred and thirty accounting units in England alone, authorities and the trusts. May I explain to you that where accountability lies seems almost impossible to pinpoint. Let us just take today's case. We cannot take action against the accountable officer: he has gone.*

(Mr Langlands) He was not an accountable officer.

50. *He would still have been the person responsible for the decisions that have come here.*

(Mr Langlands) Had RHAs been continuing he would have been an accountable officer.

51. *We cannot take action against the person who is holding that position because he has gone. Is that McLean?*

(Mr Langlands) Yes.

52. *He has gone. Martin has gone.*

(Mr Langlands) Yes.

53. *The personnel director with all the things against her name has gone.*

(Mr Langlands) Yes.

In the light of all this, it is scarcely surprising that the final recommendation of the Committee report (para 116) ended as follows:

> *We also consider that the accountability process must have teeth. It is likely to remain less effective than it should be, if staff can avoid repaying money they have improperly received and can escape disciplinary action simply by moving to a different part of the National Health Service.*

Source: Committee of Public Accounts, The Former Yorkshire Regional Health Authority: The Inquiry commissioned by the Chief Executive, HC 432 HMSO 1997

Nolan's committee into standards in public life. In February 1997 the Government published *The Governance of Public Bodies: a progress report* in which they summed up progress on the implementation of Nolan's recommendations. The Government acknowledged that:

> *... there have in recent years been some public concerns expressed about [boards]: about their methods of appointment, approaches to taking board level decisions, and the degree of transparency about the decisions they take.* (p65)

Nolan made 55 recommendations in its first report (the second report was not concerned with NHS bodies) in the areas of public appointments and pay, accountability, propriety, openness and audit. The

Conservative Government broadly agreed with these recommendations and was careful to show how it had taken some action on each one. Nevertheless there seemed to be some differences concealed in the coded language of Whitehall civil servants. Whereas Nolan had made it quite clear that it saw its recommendations applicable throughout the public sector with suitable modifications, the Government was keen to emphasise the difficulties created by the enormous diversity of public bodies within the British state which, though requiring certain standardisation of principles:

> *does not necessarily imply that the same systems and procedures apply equally to all sectors. So there are certain areas in this White Paper – for example, board members' remuneration – where the government does not see the need for total uniformity.* (p67)

This concern for diversity may be a legitimate desire to ensure flexibility in provision and decision-making procedures, or it might simply be a means of obscuring clear monitoring of progress in an intensely complex field.

Nevertheless, in the critical area of public appointments the Government made a real effort to make it easier to establish progress according to several well-established criteria. It has long been supposed that members of the new health authorities and trust boards were predominantly white, middle-class males, with a strong political leaning toward the Conservative Party. The Department of Health produced their *Public Appointments Annual Report 1996* partly in response to these concerns. It is the first time

Table 22 Membership of NHS Boards

People from ethnic minorities at 1 April 1996	*per cent*
Health authorities	5.88
NHS trusts	4.99
SHAs	5.45
Executive non-departmental public bodies	9.89
Total	**5.31**

Women at 1 April 1996	*per cent*
Health authorities	40.69
NHS Trusts	39.6
SHAs	36.63
Executive non-departments public bodies	37.36
Total	**39.56**

that details of public appointments have been comprehensively collected and published in one document. The main findings are set out in Table 22.

These figures to some extent support both the Government and their opponents. The figure for women does not match the proportion they represent of the population as a whole: that for minority ethnic groups is roughly equivalent to it. Both exceed the target the Government had set of 4 and 40 per cent respectively.

The report also provides details of employment type, which prove to be overwhelmingly middle class. As long as a criterion for appointment is the 'necessary skills and expertise relevant to the running of the NHS' this is probably inevitable. Perhaps more significant is the section where appointees' 'significant political activity' is recorded. Such a declaration is required if the individual in question has as a matter of public record

> *office holding in, public speaking in support of,*

> *or candidature on behalf of any political party (or affiliated body) which fields candidates at local or general elections in any part of the UK or in the Elections to the European Parliament.* (p iv)

The report does not provide summary statistics for this category, but a random perusal of the individual records presented shows only a tiny minority of declared interests – the policy only applies to appointments made after July 1995. As a consequence, the suspicion that 'political' appointments were made to smooth the passage of the 1991 reforms cannot be confirmed by these data.

While in Opposition, Labour had declared its intention to ensure that Boards were more representative of local communities. Measures to ensure this were announced in July 1997: new and very explicit criteria – see Box – were set out for the new and re-appointments designed to take effect from 1 November when many existing non-executives terms of appointment were due to end.

Another aspect of the Nolan recommendations – openness – received further government action with the publication in early 1997 of the second edition of the *Code of Practice on Access to Government Information* which came into force on 1 February. The code was not markedly different from the first edition, which gave an undertaking that the underlying principle of disclosure should henceforth be that information (not necessarily documents) ought to be provided unless specifically exempt, rather than the presumption being that disclosure should itself be justified.

However, a survey by the journalists' magazine *UKPG* carried out in early 1997 asked 50

Qualities Required of Non-Executive Directors of NHS Trusts: new guidelines

Essential

You must:

- live in the area served by the Trust;
- have a strong personal commitment to the NHS;
- be able to demonstrate a commitment to the needs of the local community;
- be a good communicator with plenty of common sense;
- be committed to the public service values of accountability, probity, openness and equality of opportunity;
- be able to demonstrate an ability to contribute to the work of the Board;
- be available for about 3 days per month; and
- be able to demonstrate an interest in health care issues.

Desirable

You might:

- have experience as a carer or user of the NHS;
- have experience serving in the voluntary sector, particularly in an organisation working in health issues;
- have already served the local community in local government or some other capacity;
- have an understanding and/or experience of management in the public, private or voluntary sectors;
- be able to offer specialist skills or knowledge relevant to the work of the Trust.

government departments and Quangos for information to which the public is entitled. Their findings were that 11 replied 'quickly and willingly' 25 responded 'adequately', 11 gave wrong or inadequate information and 3 refused to reply.

Openness codes are not statutorily binding, although the parliamentary ombudsman is now able to investigate complaints relating to authorities' failure to follow the code. His report *Access to Official Information in the NHS* (HMSO 1997) found that uptake by members of the public and others of the provisions in the code had been modest:

> *[In sixteen months] I had received only 31 written representations. Of these ten were inquiries. Of the 21 complaints, I have investigated three.* (p3)

Clearly, either publicity about the provisions has been inadequate, or the system is working well, or the public and media are not interested. The fact that the formal disqualifications from disclosure are not markedly different from those implicit in any previous period in recent British history may have contributed to the less than rapturous response to the proposals. The Labour Government has promised a White Paper as a forerunner to a Freedom of Information Act which, in principle, should introduce more significant reforms.

Medical negligence

If developments in the governance of the NHS are moving slowly, the management of clinicians' activity may be undergoing more significant change. In *Regulating Medical Work* (OUP, 1996), Judith Allsop and Linda Mulcahy argue that the web of controls affecting clinical practice is expanding steadily, both from inside and outside the profession. The General Medical Council is improving its mechanisms for dealing with poor doctors, managers are becoming more closely involved in clinical audit, and the Health Service Commissioner has been given the power to investigate clinical matters, but so far no results are available from its use.

Use of existing legal mechanisms for holding clinicians to account is, however, on the increase. According to Patrick Hoyte (*Medical Law Review* 3, 1995, pp 53-73) in 1978 about 1 in 1000 of all doctors in the UK had a claim paid on his or her behalf; by 1988 this had risen to 13 per 1000. Furthermore, the frequency of claims brought against doctors doubled in the years 1985-1988. Because of the introduction of the NHS Indemnity Scheme for hospital medical staff in 1990, 1989 is the last year for which statistics are available over the entire medical spectrum. However, a *Hansard* written answer for 11 March 1997 gave the value of clinical negligence claims for England settled over a four-year period in NHS trusts up to 1994/95: see Table 23.

Even taking inflation into account this is a rapid rate of increase. It seems unlikely that the medical profession is becoming more negligent over time. A more plausible explanation is that

Table 23 Value of claims for clinical negligence

Year	*£ 000s*
1991–92	280
1992–93	626
1993–94	1414
1994–95	3307

Source: *Hansard,* written answers 11 March 1997

the pressure for this increase lies with the increasingly demanding 'consumer' of health care who is less happy to passively accept (apparently) negligent care. Whether or not the NHS reforms and the persistent emphasis on limited resources and considerations of cost are damaging doctor-patient relationships, and contributing to this growth in litigation, is hard to say.

Lord Woolf in his *Access to Justice: final report* (HMSO 1997) did not touch on these matters but considered that medical negligence deserved special attention nonetheless. He cited a number of reasons why the current system was not working adequately:

- the disproportion between costs and damages, particularly in lower value cases;
- the delay in resolving claims;
- unmeritorious cases are often pursued, and clear-cut cases defended, for too long;
- the success rate is lower than in other personal injury litigation;
- the suspicion between the parties is more intense, and the lack of co-operation frequently greater, than in many other areas of litigation.

The chief concern is with access for those on incomes not low enough to qualify for legal aid but not high enough to permit them to risk the substantial outlays that legal action involves – the poverty trap applied to justice. Woolf noted that a Supreme Court Taxing Office survey found that 92 per cent of successful parties in medical negligence cases were legally aided, for the simple reason that the cost of pursuing a claim for those without legal aid is prohibitively high. Woolf's criticisms can be presented in economic efficiency terms. In many cases which are brought to trial the final cost may be greater than the benefit derived because parties involved have an incentive to 'over-provide' legal services. Once legal aid is available, legal services are effectively free at the point of use: the litigant will reasonably wish to exhaust every possible legal avenue, even when not appropriate, and the legal counsel will be happy to oblige. On the other hand, those who do not qualify for legal aid may not pursue a claim because of the expectation that the costs will significantly exceed the benefits. Thus justice is simultaneously over and under-provided.

Woolf's reforms in part are an attempt to restrain the costs of pursuing claims to an 'economic' level and hence both curb the costs of supported cases and allow those not enjoying legal aid to risk taking legal action. This objective lies behind the first of his proposals summarised in the Box opposite. Other proposals were designed to ensure the appropriate degree of expertise in medical and legal matters to ensure a swift process, and to ensure that other avenues of redress were also fully utilised before complainants had recourse to the courts.

Not surprisingly, these proposals were not greeted with unanimous acclaim. The Association of Personal Injury Lawyers were quoted (*Health Service Journal* 14 November, p.2 supplement) as claiming that it was 'denial of access to justice' and that Woolf's intention was to cut costs rather than make justice more accessible. This is an unsurprising accusation from the body that stands to lose from the reforms: it is a common accusation of any public policy designed to promote efficiency that it is merely reducing quality and cutting costs.

Lord Woolf's proposals

- A fast-track procedure for non-complex claims under £10,000, which sets time limits for the overall process at each stage, and fixes the level of fees lawyers can claim
- Establishment of a separate medical negligence List in the High Court and other designated court centres outside London
- Training in medical negligence procedures for judges and instruction on legal matters for health professionals
- Solicitors obliged to provide information to clients about alternatives to litigation, such as mediation and the NHS ombudsman
- A multi-track procedure for cases worth more than £10,000 - or those of public importance, test cases, and cases requiring legal argument or significant oral or documentary evidence

Source: *Access to Civil Justice*, HMSO 1997

Nevertheless Woolf's proposals have found broad support from within both the legal and medical professions. Whether it will significantly affect the accountability of individual clinicians is another matter. As noted in section 1.3, NHS trusts are now responsible for meeting the costs of medical negligence claims. This switch from individual clinician to organisation may eventually lead to changes in behaviour and even a reduction in the number of incidents giving rise to claims, eg if clinical or general management introduces new procedures designed to reduce the incidence of risk-taking.

At the moment, however, it seems that the predominant means of controlling the profession will remain with the General Medical Council, which had its powers augmented during 1996. Whereas previously a doctor had to be guilty of serious professional misconduct, now the Council, through a new Committee of Professional Performance, will consider complaints about a doctor's pattern of performance – it will no longer be necessary to wait until there is a tragic event. Further refocusing of the Council's role so as to acknowledge the patient's perspective was evidenced in November 1996 when lay membership on the council was doubled to 25 per cent.

The chipping away at clinicians' self-regulation continues from other quarters. The practice which has come to be known as whistleblowing received some endorsement from the Nolan Committee, who defined it as (in Cm 3557 *The Governance of Public Bodies*):

> *the confidential raising of problems within an organisation or within an independent review structure associated with that organisation, not in the popular pejorative sense of leaking information to the media.* (p43)

Recommendation no. 2 in Nolan's second report was that:

> *Local public spending bodies should institute codes of practice on whistleblowing, appropriate to their circumstances, which would enable concerns to be raised confidentially inside, and if necessary outside, the organisation.*

However, others believe that these Codes should be enshrined in legislation. The case of Chris Chapman, who alleged fraud in his department at Leeds General Infirmary in 1987 and who was later dismissed, was only finally resolved in 1997 with the publication of a report by Lord Merlyn Rees. In it the trust was cleared of financial fraud (earlier inquiries had established there was scientific fraud) but found that there were numerous mistakes and omissions. Lord Rees argued that no amount of 'guaranteed protection' and 'in-house' codes of practice will assuage the apprehensions of some would-be complainants (*Health Service Journal*, 27 Feb 1997, p. 12). A charity formed to help whistleblowers, Public Concern at Work, campaigns for primary legislation to ensure that those bodies 'which are less committed to the principles of accountability or perhaps feel defensive about what is going on in their trust' (ibid.) do not ignore the codes.

The independence of the individual medical practitioner to conduct his or her affairs answering only to their conscience continues to ebb away, from both within and without the profession. It remains to be seen where this process is heading. However, it is easy to exaggerate: clinicians and their professional bodies start from a position of substantial strength. As Allsop and Mulcahy conclude:

> *What is clear is that, whatever the regulatory style, the profession is still in a position to determine what constitutes appropriate medical practice. Their knowledge is unique and, even if guidelines and protocols were to be generally implemented, there would remain a large element of judgement in medical decision-making about their application to a particular patient.* (p203)

The report by JM Consulting Ltd *The Regulation of the Health Professions* published in April 1996, makes similar points about the Professions Supplementary to Medicine Act 1960, concluding for example that the statutory bodies established under the Act are dominated by medical representatives and have too few lay and employer members. It goes on to recommend that a new bill should be formulated to provide 'a state-of-the-art regulatory system'.

Rationing

As noted in last year's Review, decisions by health authorities to deny treatment to individuals have become increasingly explicit and the subject of intense media attention. A parallel development has been for the individuals concerned, or their parents, to challenge such decisions in the courts. In general, however, such actions like the Gloucester case referred to in 1.2 above, have not been successful. The original test case, known as *Wednesbury*, found that in decisions relating to the distribution of limited public resources, the court would not intervene unless no reasonable person would in the court's judgement have taken the same decision in the same circumstances. It is practically unknown for the courts to invoke the principle and find for the plaintiff.

In fact, the few occasions in which a judicial authority tends to rule in favour of the plaintiff involve those cases referred to the Health Service Commissioner, whose decisions are not binding and are therefore based on more relaxed criteria. On more than one occasion, most prominently in the Leeds case, he has required a health authority to reconsider their decision to discharge an elderly person from (free) NHS care to a nursing home where they would be means-tested.

Nevertheless, one of the noticeable developments during the past year has been the number of cases of health care rationing which ended up, or threatened to end up, in the courts. In many ways this is not surprising. Rationing is increasingly recognised as a fact of life in the current health service, even if it is not believed to be inevitable. But denial of care is not something that people warm to readily; indeed, they often believe such a practice to be illegal as well as immoral. Lawyers evidently agree, judging by their willingness to assist aggrieved patients to press claims against health authorities.

It is health authorities, not individual clinicians, who are sued because even though it is the doctor who typically makes the final decision, the responsibility for providing health care in a given district is with the health authority under the 1977 NHS Act. There are no statistics collected on precisely how many cases take place each year, but the anecdotal evidence suggests an increase. In early 1997 alone health authorities were challenged in the courts over Beta Interferon (*Guardian* 11 April), a sex-change operation (*Guardian* 27 February) and the new recombinant factor VIII for haemophilia (*Independent* 22 February).

The details of the cases are less important than the fact that the courts are being used to hold health authorities to account over their allocation of NHS resources. What seems less clear is precisely what the plaintiffs believe the health authorities should be accounting for. As indicated above, the test case only offers the criteria of 'reasonableness' in the way a decision was made. According to Christopher Newdick (*Health Care Risk Report*, April 1996) a court has on one occasion ruled in favour of a body or individual other than the health authority, but it was not on the basis of an unreasonable decision [White *v* Chief Adjudication Officer (1994) 17 BMLR 68]. The circumstance was not a civil action in tort, but a local (government) authority applying to the court for a declaration of its rights and obligations. The court found that the degree of dependency of a patient requiring nursing care meant that he was the NHS's responsibility, contrary to the health authority's view. However, even here the court did not instruct the particular deployment of resources, just the acceptance of responsibility. It is not clear what would have happened if the NHS had continued to refuse to treat, citing resource constraints, and the plaintiff had sued the health authority instead.

Does this mean that the use of courts for accountability purposes is negligible? The answer must be yes, and until central government adopts more explicit rules about how the NHS should conduct its rationing and clarify the range of its responsibilities, it will continue to be so.

Indeed, where central guidance *was* issued, as with EL (95)97 the result was a successful High Court decision (11 July 1997) for the plaintiff, urging – though not ordering – the health authority concerned to reconsider its decision.

Last year, we reported on a number of developments aimed at finding ways of making contentious decisions on the allocation of health resources. Since then, there have been a number of experiments with citizens' juries covering a wide range of issues. Citizens' juries bring together lay people over a number of days to consider a matter of public policy and make a more direct contribution to the decision-making process than is normally possible within a representative system of government. A series of pilots supported by the King's Fund were completed in early 1997. The issues the juries considered, and a summary of their conclusions, are provided in the Box overleaf. It is too early to say whether juries have a long-term future but they have caused considerable interest in the policy world, which is perhaps a reflection on the continuing democratic deficit in the NHS governance. The measures taken with regard to NHS Boards are unlikely to be perceived as sufficient in that respect.

Citizens' juries in practice

Sunderland

The Question

A number of services are currently available from GPs. Would local people accept some of these services from any of the following:

1. a nurse practitioner
2. a pharmacist
3. another (salaried) doctor?

Conclusion: a qualified yes, with nurse practitioners to work only as part of a GP's team, and pharmacists only to be responsible for repeat, not first, prescriptions.

East Sussex, Brighton and Hove

The Question

Where should women with gynaecological cancer who live in Brighton, Hove and East Sussex be offered treatment?

1. continue services in their current format
2. centralise services in Brighton
3. refer women for treatment at specialist cancer centres outside the county

Conclusion: option two, qualified by a desire to investigate an alternative centre outside Brighton (where parking and accessibility are difficult) in the future.

Buckinghamshire

The Question

Should Buckinghamshire Health authority fund treatment from osteopaths and chiropractors for people with back pain? If yes, given that

(a) these services are not currently purchased by the health authority, and
(b) no extra resources are available for back pain services,

should some of the money we currently spend on physiotherapy be spent on osteopathy and chiropractice?

Conclusion: yes, on a pilot basis, and with the possibility of introducing chiropractors and osteopaths into physiotherapy departments as staff leave these departments, or through increased funding.

Part 3 Overview

The political debate over the NHS during the 1997 election campaign was curiously muted. Neither Labour nor the Liberal Democrats were able to offer a comprehensive alternative vision to that underlying current policies. Election pledges were made or unmade around such issues as sight tests, waiting times for cancer patients and cuts in management expenditures. The implication would appear to be that there was nothing wrong with the NHS which a few minor adjustments would not fix.

It was more natural that the Conservatives, after so long in power, should take this line. In their White Paper, *The National Health Service: A Service with Ambitions*, published in December 1996, the then Government argued that the Service 'is one of the success stories of modern Britain' and that it had not, in its fundamentals, changed at all:

> *The principles on which the NHS is built command support across the political spectrum and they are endorsed by the overwhelming majority of the British people. They require the NHS to be:*
>
> - *universal in its reach, available to anyone who wishes to use it;*
> - *high quality, applying the latest knowledge and the highest professional standards;*
> - *available on the basis of clinical need, without regard for the patient's ability to pay.*
>
> *The Government is wholeheartedly committed to develop the NHS on the basis of these fundamental principles.* (p4)

The White Paper goes on to add a further requirement:

> - *responsive, a service which is sensitive to the needs and wishes of patients and carers.*

The need to assert commitment to a publicly funded NHS arose precisely because that commitment was alleged to be weakening. Last year's Review reported both the modest increase in real resources that the NHS received for the current year and also the difficulties it appeared to be having in coping with the pressure of demand, particularly on hospital services. The White Paper argued that such pressure was not new:

> *Providing the best service possible within the limits of the available resources has always been the challenge for the NHS.*

Obviously, the level of available resources is a

major influence on the extent of the pressure perceived by those running the Service, and also those using it – see Jo Anne Mulligan and Ken Judge's analysis on page 123. The White Paper reaffirmed the Government's commitment to 'providing real increases, year by year, in tax-funded support for the NHS'. The public expenditure settlement announced soon after it did allow for such an increase for 1997/98 but the forward spending projections provided for much more modest increases.

Such projections had been made before, yet substantial real increases had resulted. More surprising, therefore, was the then Opposition's commitment not to raise income and expenditure taxes, which appeared to give it very little room for manoeuvre once in power. In the event, Labour's mid-year budget did allow for a larger increase in NHS spending during 1998/99 than that proposed by the previous Government, but no long-term assurance on spending levels was forthcoming.

The implication of the unwillingness of both sides to make an unqualified long-term commitment to spending on the NHS was that the pressure for improved performance would continue. In the words of the White Paper:

> *The search for better and more efficient ways to meet the needs of patients must be relentless.* (p5)

The White Paper itself did not spell out what this relentlessness meant but suggested that the 'ambitions' it embodies 'do not rely on further radical change'.

In fact, the consultation document, *Primary Care: the future*, the two White Papers elaborating the main proposals and the subsequent 1997 Primary Care Act did open the way for precisely that. Although the Act allowed for a managed process of innovation, the relaxations it embodies could lead to new ways of delivering care quite different from any now in operation.

Moreover the Green and White Papers bearing on mental health and social care also contained options or proposals which could lead to substantial changes of roles and responsibilities. Thus, after 18 years in office and 7 since the passing of the 1990 NHS and Community Care Act, the process of reform continued at an undiminished, indeed relentless pace.

That spate of activity is curiously at odds with the self-satisfaction of *A Service with Ambitions*:

> *No better model than the NHS has been found for adapting to change and development and making the best use of available resources to demand for health care.* (p33)

The Conservatives of course were not responsible for the original model, but they could claim with justification that they had developed a range of policies for trying to preserve it, which no other health system could, in their entirety, match:

- An explicit purchasing function designed to reduce 'producer domination' and, through fundholding, to bring clinical decision-making within an explicit financial framework;
- Competition or contestability in some services and a sustained pressure on all providers to improve performance through specific efficiency targets;
- An explicit commitment, through the *Health*

of the Nation, to promoting health rather than health care alone;

- An R&D programme designed to support service delivery rather than the interests of researchers;
- A clinical effectiveness programme designed to promote 'what works' and eliminate what does not;
- Explicit commitments to specified service standards through the *Patient's Charter*.

And finally, with the Primary Care Act 1997:

- Major deregulation in primary care allowing new forms of service delivery.

None of these existed before the Government came to office and most have been implemented in the second half of their administration in an unprecedented wave of reform. Furthermore, they are policies which command broad support. In each of these areas, however, major issues remain to be resolved:

- There is no clear policy for maintaining contestability; the present structure of provision and the financial rules under which it works are inappropriate for market type processes, as the Morriston case (see page 11) shows. The new Government has in any case rejected competition in favour of collaborative structures, but they still have to reconcile that approach with the need to maintain pressure for greater efficiency and the preservation of some degree of user choice of provider.
- Purchasing agencies are often unable to impose themselves on providers. They lack the intelligence, in the broad sense of the term, to do so. In the absence of a competitive structure this weakness is all the more important. Unless it is remedied, then it is hard to see why an explicit purchasing function should be retained.
- The *Health of the Nation* continues to attract little priority on the part of those whose responsibility it nominally is. Its true impact cannot be assessed – where trends are moving in the right direction, it is impossible to attribute that to the initiative itself. In a number of areas such as obesity, smoking and drug abuse, trends are moving in the wrong direction and while that does not undermine the logic of the policy, it suggests that the task is more difficult that originally envisaged. Finally, a number of key clinical areas lie outside its scope and, more fundamentally, the framework within which health inequalities can be addressed has yet to be put in place. In sum, it would be foolhardy to expect it to produce a measurable improvement in health or any reduction in demand for services.
- The R&D initiative remains too focused on clinical issues. Service development attracts very low priority and the share of research which is commissioned in the light of nationally determined priorities remains low. The level of resources devoted to research into community services and social care remains pitifully small, as it does for issues of clinical organisation generally. The serious work involved in refocusing what is currently being spent has scarcely begun. Moreover,

the publicly funded programme is dwarfed by private sector research designed to create new demands for the NHS to meet, rather than to reduce or eliminate pressures on existing services.

- The clinical effectiveness drive is making little apparent headway, in part because of professional resistance and inertia and in part because evidence in many areas remains weak – see Gifford Batstone and Mary Black's article on page 167. This in turn reflects the bias in research activity towards the specific intervention rather than the wider system within which they take place. As a result, critical questions on the future structure of provision cannot be answered by turning to evidence rather than opinion.
- *Patient's Charter* standards are confined largely to process, are subject to creative recording and are not enforceable by patients. Key areas remain to be addressed such as clinical priorities within waiting lists. The process of devising and publishing outcome measures has only just begun.

It could fairly be argued that, while correct, the points set out above reflect the complexity of the real world. There are no quick fixes but at least policy in most of these areas is focused correctly and pointed in the right direction. It may be slower to deliver major benefits than was hoped for, but eventually they will accrue.

There is considerable merit in that argument. But equally, there are several significant areas which the previous administration failed to address as follows:

Demand management: despite the *Health of the Nation*, the screening programmes etc, the emphasis in terms of targets has been on doing more rather than less. *Commissioning Better Health*, a report on the roles and responsibilities of health boards in Scotland, found that:

> *The contracting system currently gives no incentive to reduce use of secondary care*. (p9)

The purchaser efficiency index institutionalised this bias. Current policy appears to assume that the development of primary care purchasing and providing will somehow contain demand. In fact the primary care led NHS may be seen as a device for generating demand for community services while not reducing the demand for hospital services. In the case of mental health, for example, enlarging the GPs' role has sometimes meant that hitherto neglected needs have been met, rather than already recognised needs met in a more appropriate way.

In many respects the NHS has been highly adept at managing the demands placed upon it so as to reconcile them with the resources available. But its ability to do so is being undermined by media pressures and a more demanding public: what makes matters worse is that the very attempts to make the NHS more user-friendly – desirable in themselves – make the task of containing demand more difficult. Thus minor injuries clinics, desirable if they offer more accessible care, appear to promote as well as to divert demand away from hospitals. While, as Thomas Judge argues below, attempts to provide a better service for some patients mean that the present system of emergency care tends to 'manage up' demand across the spectrum of needs, rather than manage it down to the levels where it can be most appropriately dealt with.

The experiments with total purchasing represent the first attempt to alter the incentives facing local decision-makers. But they, like *Patient Partnership*, appear as isolated initiatives rather than part of a coherent and sustained strategy for influencing the ways that demand for care is generated.

System Management: the Conservatives finished their term of office with a sustained attempt to cut management costs and Labour pledged further cuts. This was a mindless exercise based on no apparent reflection as to how the NHS should function. Within the NHS as the Conservatives left it, the roles of the centre and the periphery are confused. Despite the continued rhetoric focused on primary care and the role of localities, in fact, the policy direction from the centre became stronger rather than weaker during the 1990s. But the centre was not designed for that increasing role and hence it is overloaded. So it is scarcely surprising that it backs off issues such as continuing care or the availability of new drugs, both of which it should determine, and fails to provide the strategic lead in relation to service delivery that Judge calls for in emergency care.

What is needed here is a re-think of the respective roles of centre and locality. The main question to be addressed is whether a new balance can be struck between local freedom and central control and accountability which allows both to perform better.

Information: key areas remain completely unilluminated. To give one example, despite the emphasis on cross-boundary work, there is virtually no information on transfer of patients between providers – the new statistical return relating to hospital discharge is a rare example and only a partial one. The case for a new approach to collecting information about how the NHS is performing is made in Tom Judge's paper on page 183. At present, there is simply no way of knowing how often users are let down by failure to link services properly or failure to direct them to the service most appropriate to their needs.

However, new data sources are not enough. The ability to analyse what exists and explain current trends (eg emergencies) is missing. It is hard to extend beyond the fingers of one hand reports issuing from the Executive which contain any serious analysis of the data they hold and which illuminate any major current issue.

The NHS needs much greater analytic capacity. The capacity to monitor and assess new development is as limited as the ability to assess the merits of different ways of providing care in hospitals and between hospital and community. The Service needs much greater service design capacity and that in turn would have to be based on a much more thorough understanding of health care provision.

Linkages: the main failure within the current pattern of provision is linkage between providers and the overall design of services, be they for small groups such as those with brain damage from head injuries or large ones such as the elderly: see pp 24–25. It is hard to see signs of progress and indeed the 1990 regime may well have made it harder to forge effective links between different providers because of the 'hard' boundaries it created between organisations and, through a general pressure to do more with fewer resources, increase cost-shunting.

The previous Government recognised the need for better linkages with its endless urgings for providers to work together, but did not find effective ways of overcoming the obstacles to effective joint working that successive reports have identified. The new Government will not achieve any more simply by urging collaboration. Some barriers might be removed by the institutional and financial reform which the Primary Care Act 1997 addressed and some by the development of service or disease group approach. But others are too deep-rooted. Much of the relevant agenda was identified in the IHSM/University of Manchester report, *The Future of the NHS Workforce* – see section 2.1 for some of its key conclusions – but radical though this was it did not tackle the role of professionalism in defining how clinical work shall be carried out and the 'vision' or model which underlines clinical practice. Modifying these represents an even more difficult agenda.

To conclude: the previous Government can be judged to have succeeded in addressing a number of the central issues of health policy. That they were not entirely successful may be attributed at least in part to the genuine difficulty of making progress in these areas. The best, if back-handed, compliment perhaps to pay the Conservatives is to point to the difficulty the new Government has had in devising a new set of policies to replace those already in place.

Tinkering however may not be enough. As we argue below (p138), the environment within which the NHS now operates is one which it will prove harder rather than easier to maintain it in its present form. To do so will require a new range of policies desired to ensure support for the basic principles on which it is based, not simply modification of the existing set of institutional arrangements which currently embody them.

Part 4 Calendar of Events

April 1996

1 **NHS Organisation**: 100 new authorities come into effect combining responsibility for primary and secondary care.

3 **Private Finance Initiative**: new hospitals announced for Swindon and Norwich.

15 **Bureaucracy**: campaign launched to cut paperwork in general practice, cutting some 17 million forms.

18 **Users**: group created to advise Central Research Development Committee on how to increase patient involvement in the NHS R & D programme.

22 **Public health:** campaign announced to tackle head lice.

23 **Public health**: Nutrition Task Force Report, Eat Well II published.

Patient's Charter: review announced of NHS performance tables.

May

1 **Public health**: report of Task Force to review Services for Drug Misusers published. £6 million announced for more treatment services and £2.5 million for voluntary organisations.

2 **Ethnic minorities**: directory of Ethnic Minority Initiatives launched.

3 **Public health:** survey of drug users and attitudes to drug use published.

7 **Long-term care**: consultation paper *A new Partnership for Care in Old Age* published setting out two partnership options.

8 **Renal care**: guidelines published for renal services.

9 **Patient's Charter:** reductions in long waits for elective treatment announced.

14 **Public health:** contract awarded to Health Education Authority for Adolescent Health Network.

23 **Community care**: 62 projects for community care development announced, costing nearly £2.75 million.

Private Finance Initiative: Royal Assent given to NHS (Residual Liabilities) Bill.

29 **Emergency care**: five-point plan to improve paediatric intensive care announced, including 37 more intensive care and high-dependency beds.

Public health: 1994 Health Survey published covering cardiovascular disease.

29 **Drug prices**: first report of Pharmaceutical Price Regulation Scheme published.

31 **Research & Development:** details announced for funding of NHS R&D implementing the Culyer report.

June

6 **NHS Management:** NHS Priorities and Planning Guidance 1997/98 issued.

17 **Education and Training:** Education and Planning Guidance issued setting out new arrangements for education and training.

10 **Primary care**: consultation document: *Primary care: the future* published, developing ideas identified in the 'listening exercise'.

12 **Dental services**: reforms announced for adult and children's services, maintenance of professional standards and new contractual forms.

26 **CJD**: research advisory group established to co-ordinate research and development strategy.

July

2 **Patient's Charter**: NHS Performance Tables published reporting 23 per cent increase in number of 5-star awards.

Public health: voluntary guidelines published on the content and presentation of educational materials relating to nutrition.

4 **Public health**: reports published on control and prevention of tuberculosis.

Community care: Community Care (Direct Payments) Bill receives Royal Assent.

5 **Emergency care**: action plan published for paediatric intensive care, covering both short-and long-term proposals.

8 **Public health**: fourth anniversary conference of *Health of the Nation:* environment announced as new key area.

R&D: National Co-ordinating Centre for Health Technology Assessment opened.

9 **Genetic testing**: new advisory committee on safety and ethical issues.

12 **Dementia**: action plan for people with dementia living in the community.

16 **Public health**: extensions to childhood immunisation programme announced, covering measles, mumps and rubella.

17 **Public health**: National Screening Committee announced to oversee national screening programmes.

19 **Public health**: ninth report of COMATAS published.

23 **Professions**: additional lay appointments to General Medical Council announced raising the number from 13 to 25.

24 **Professions:** report of review of Professions Supplementary to the Medicines Act 1960 published.

29 **Emergency care**: proposals to prioritise emergency 999 calls aimed at better

response to life-threatening events.

30 **Cancer care**: guidelines announced for breast cancer services.

August

1 **Bureaucracy**: reporting requirements on extra-contractual referrals reduced.

21 **Medical staff**: measures announced to ease appointment of part-time junior doctors.

22 **Patient's Charter:** further reduction in long waiting times announced.

27 **Emergency care**: emergency bed system launched, extending the system operating in the South-East to the whole country.

September

5 **Child health**: guide to community health services, *Child Health in the Community: guide to good practice* published.

17 **Mental health**: grants totalling £30 million announced from Mental Illness Specific Grant Target Fund.

NHS design: expert group announced to advise on ways of promoting standards of architecture and design.

19 **Patient's Charter**: proposals to improve standards for ambulance response times and admissions to A&E departments announced.

27 **Public health**: fourth report of Committee on Medical Aspects of Food and Nutrition Policy published.

October

8 **Self-care:** personal asthma card launched.

14 **Clinical negligence**: framework document for NHS Litigation Authority published, to run schemes for the funding and administration of clinical negligence claims.

15 **Primary care**: *Choice and Opportunity*, primary care White Paper published, covering general practice, community pharmacy and dentistry.

16 **Professions:** study on professional collaboration and flexible working by Standing Medical and Nursing & Midwifery Committee published.

21 **Pay:** report of working party on NHS pay, finance and contracting published.

28 **Long-term care**: Government response published to House of Commons Select Committee report.

Patient's Charter: new standards outlined for emergency ambulance response times and A&E departments.

30 **Community care:** initial evaluation of impact of continuing care guidance issued.

31 **Dental services:** 22 schemes funded from the NHS Dentistry Access Fund.

Health Advisory Service: new role announced involving merger with Royal College of Psychiatrists.

November

2 **Quality of care**: programme announced to improve quality of care.

4 **Bureaucracy:** restrictions on elective ECRs relaxed.

6 **Accountability**: first annual report on public appointments published.

11 **CJD:** priorities for R&D set out in report covering all departments.

13 **NHS**: White Paper *The National Health Service: a service with ambitions* published, setting out the 'case for the NHS'.

21 **Drugs**: consultation on limited list announced.

Patient's Charter: further falls in long waits for elective care announced but more people on waiting lists.

25 **Fraud**: efficiency scrutiny on prescription fraud announced.

Private Finance Initiative: completion of negotations on new Norwich Hospital announced.

December

2 **Quality:** programme announced for 'driving up' standards of patient care.

12 **Information**: programme announced for improvement in provision and use of information in the NHS.

16 **Professions**: programme of professional development announced.

17 **Primary care**: White Paper *Delivering the Future* published.

24 **Finance**: extra cash allocation announced for intensive care, mental health and continuing care.

January 1997

6 **Dental care:** pilot peer review scheme confirmed as substantive scheme.

7 **Patient information**: health resource centre announced as part of patient/partnership strategy to provide high quality information for patients.

16 **Patient's Charter**: charter booklet for mental health services published.

27 **Patient's Charter**: plans announced to promote 'privacy and dignity' in hospitals, ie separate male/female wards and facilities.

28 **Professions:** General Chiropractice Council established.

29 **Professions**: campaign launched to improve nursing recruitment.

February

6 **CJD**: first meeting of Review Committee on Transmissible Spongiform Encephalopathies.

27 **Public health**: 1995 Health Survey published, covering health of children and adults.

ANALYSIS

Public opinion and the NHS

Jo Ann Mulligan and Ken Judge

For more than a decade, health policy has been one of the most fiercely contested aspects of British political debate. One consequence has been an explosion in the number of polls and surveys which seek to elicit the public's views about many different aspects of the health care system. But the interpretation of public opinion data is fraught with difficulty, not least because of the way in which questions are posed or the context in which they are set.[1] Despite these complexities, a change in government provides a timely opportunity to monitor any shifts in public opinion about the NHS.

The aim of this article is to examine public perceptions about the NHS during a period of rapid policy change using data from a range of sources. In particular, it has three specific objectives: first, to examine trends in public opinion over the last decade in the UK and to compare these with recent European findings; second, using data collected exclusively for the King's Fund, to compare levels of dissatisfaction with the NHS and its key components in the periods before the 1992 and 1997 General Elections; and finally, to investigate in more detail what changes have occurred in the patterns of opinions among different regions and sections of the population and to consider some possible explanations for any shifts in public opinion between 1992 and 1997.

What becomes clear in explaining these findings is that, as Mossialos has suggested,[2] opinions about dissatisfaction with the health service appear to be heavily influenced by the level of health spending. Consequently, it is important to examine changes in public opinion in the context of trends in government spending on health and it is to these that we first turn.

Trends in NHS spending

Figure 1 shows that the generosity of funding for the NHS fluctuates from year to year and it would be surprising if public disquiet did not increase during hard times and diminish during good years. In 1991/2 the spending growth of 4.3 per cent in real terms for the NHS was the highest since before 1973.[3] By contrast, the latest estimates for 1996/7 show that NHS expenditure is likely to rise by only 0.7 per cent. Dixon and colleagues convincingly argue that no single approach can determine the right level of funding without controversy since these kinds of decisions require value judgements which are currently made by Government.[4] Nevertheless, while the use of public opinion polls is limited in their value as a guide to levels of NHS funding, Dixon and colleagues conclude that:

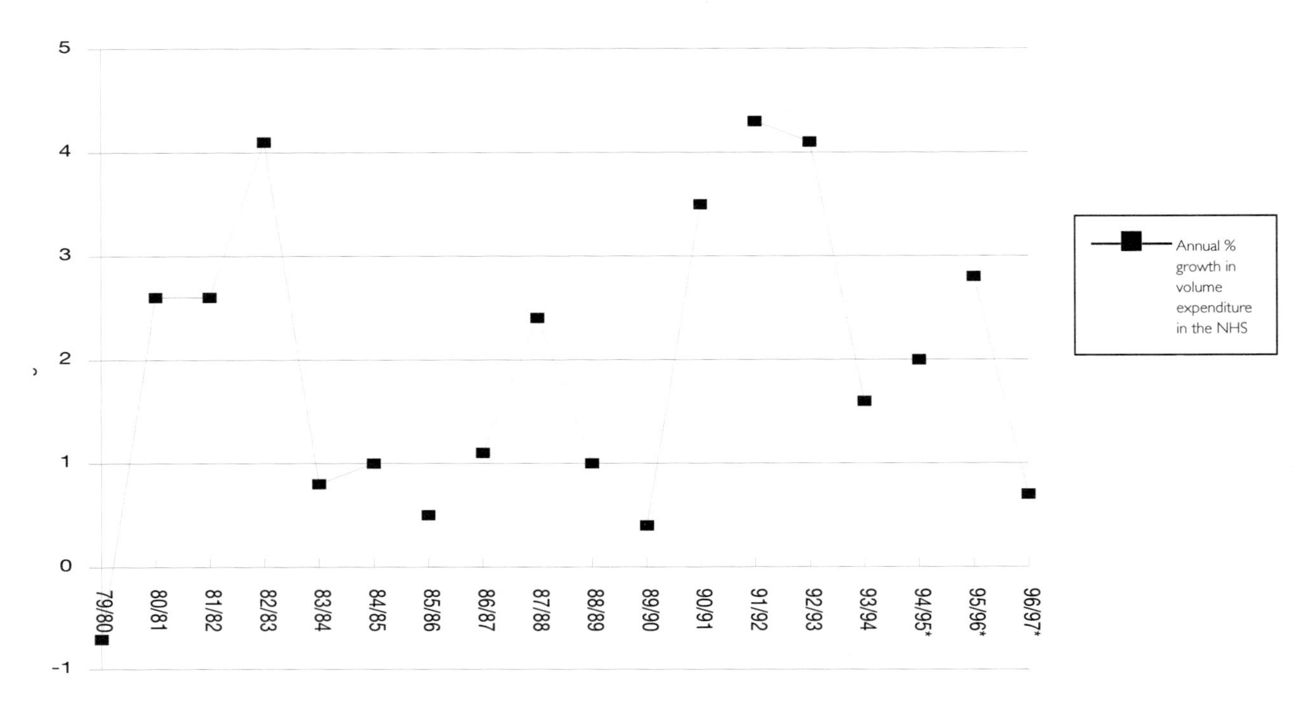

Source: Dixon and Harrison[3]

Figure 1 NHS funding, 1979–1997

> *... the ultimate test of NHS funding will be the expression of satisfaction in opinion surveys, and by continued use of NHS funded care by the majority of the population.*[4]

Such sentiments suggest that we should examine satisfaction and dissatisfaction with health services both in the context of funding levels and in the context of the quality of the services provided.

British Social Attitudes Survey

Social and Community Planning Research (SCPR) fielded its first survey in 1983. Since then it has been conducted every year with the exception of 1988 and 1992. The broad aim of the series is to supplement the mass of factual and behavioral data about British society. Each year a random sample of approximately 3,500 respondents is selected to answer interview and self-completion questionnaires. Questions cover a wide range of topics, usually including party political allegiance, aspects of national economic and social policy, as well as attitudes to more sensitive subjects such as the portrayal of sex and violence on television and birth control. The data presented here are taken from a report prepared by SCPR for the Department of Health on attitudes to health care from 1983 to 1995.[5]

Spending priorities and dissatisfaction

We begin by describing trends in public opinion towards the Health Service using data obtained from the *British Social Attitudes Survey* since 1983.

Table 1 Proportion of respondents naming health as a first or second priority

	1983 %	1984 %	1986 %	1987 %	1989 %	1990 %	1993 %	1994 %	1995 %
Health	63	76	75	79	83	81	70	72	77

Source: British Social Attitudes Survey[5]

The Conservative Government's Health Service reforms were introduced in the early 1990s in the wake of a striking rise in demand for more spending on the Health Service. In each year of the survey series, respondents have been presented with a list of ten areas of government spending and asked to name one as their first priority. Each year a large majority has named health as the first priority, followed by education, with the other spending areas a long way behind. Table 1 shows that between 1983 and 1989 the number of people who cited health as their first or second priority rose steadily before dropping somewhat between 1990 and 1993. However, 1994 and 1995 have both seen further increases in the proportion of people who attach high priority to health spending. How does this fit in with the public's perception of the overall running of the NHS? Since 1983 respondents have been asked:

> *All in all, how satisfied or dissatisfied would you say you are with the way in which the National Health Service runs nowadays?*

Figure 2 plots the proportion of people who cite health as a first or second priority and the proportion of people who are dissatisfied with the NHS. It is clear that the two lines follow more or less the same pattern: rising in the 1980s, falling in the early 1990s before rising again quite sharply. This similarity suggests that fears that the NHS is underfunded are associated with dissatisfaction. Commenting on the 1993 results Nick Bosanquet argued that:

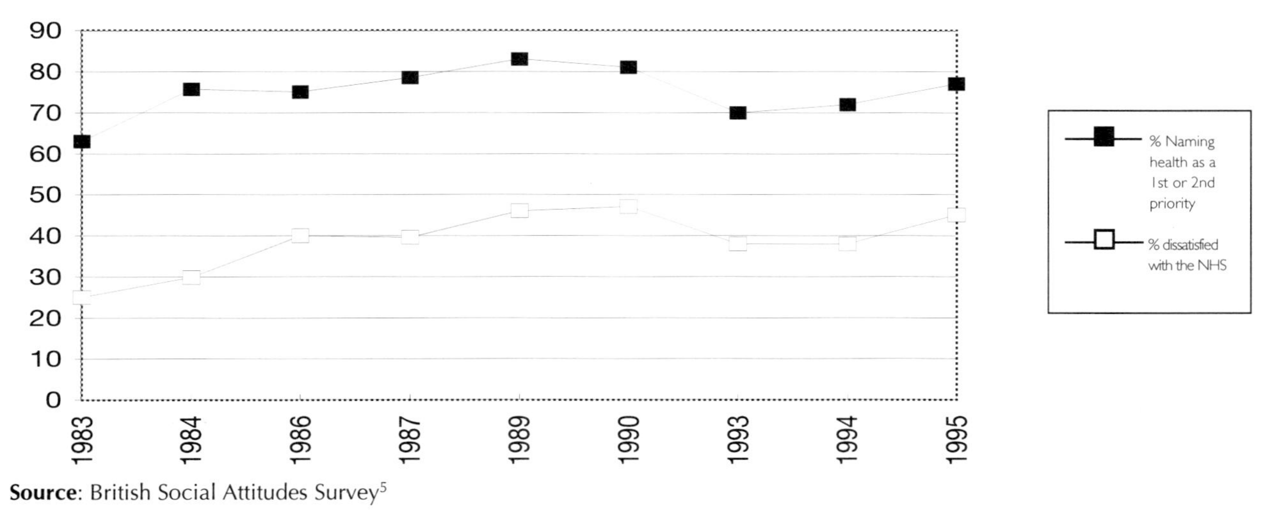

Source: British Social Attitudes Survey[5]

Figure 2 Public concern for the NHS, 1983–1995

> *The implementation of the NHS reforms was preceded by a rise in public dissatisfaction with the service accompanied by a rising demand that more should be spent on it. However, these latest results suggest that the (Conservative) government's reforms are beginning to reduce the level of political conflict surrounding the NHS.*[6]

The trend Bosanquet observed has clearly reversed again and the proportion expressing dissatisfaction with the NHS in 1995, at 45 per cent, is almost as high as at the worst point of the spending crisis in the late 1980s. So what went wrong for the Major Government?

Working for Patients initially appeared to reduce public concern about the running of the NHS, probably aided by high profile initiatives such as the waiting list initiative and the *Patient's Charter*. Furthermore, the unusually large injection of cash for three years in succession from 1990 that is illustrated in Figure 1 helped allay fears that the service was underfunded. The latest results, however, suggest that these public concerns are increasing again.

But there may be other reasons why dissatisfaction is rising once more. For example, as Bryson suggests '*... decreasing levels of satisfaction could well indicate rising, but (as yet) unfulfilled, expectations as to what quality of service the NHS can deliver*'.[5] This is indeed plausible given that the Conservative Government under John Major's stewardship placed great emphasis on the growth of consumerism. However, it could also be that specific aspects of the service, not addressed by the reforms, are responsible for the increase in general dissatisfaction. These are discussed below.

The hospital service

The results from the latest BSA survey revealed widespread support for the NHS in terms of spending priorities coupled with considerable dissatisfaction about its performance. It is worth exploring, therefore, which aspects of the NHS gave rise to dissatisfaction. Figure 3 shows the proportion of respondents who were dissatisfied with inpatient and outpatient services. Two points are worth mentioning here. First, while dissatisfaction with inpatient and outpatient services overall does not seem to be particularly high, both experienced increases in 1995. Second, the gap in levels of dissatisfaction between inpatient and outpatient services has narrowed dramatically from 14.6 percentage points in 1983 to 5.4 percentage points in 1995.

A slightly different picture emerges when we turn to specific features of NHS hospitals. Since 1987 the BSA have asked respondents about eight areas of the NHS hospital service covering waiting times, staffing levels, waiting areas and quality of care. All but three of the aspects of the hospital service attracted some criticism from at least half the respondents in every year the question was asked. However, those reporting recent experience of using hospital care in 1995 are still more satisfied than those who have not (63 per cent as opposed to 50 per cent for inpatient care, and 58 per cent versus 47 per cent for outpatient care).

Furthermore, while the proportion of respondents reporting that waiting times to see a consultant and waiting lists for non-emergency operations were still high in 1995 (over 75 per cent of respondents thought that each was in need of 'a lot of' or 'some' improvement) the overall trend as shown in Figure 4 is downwards.

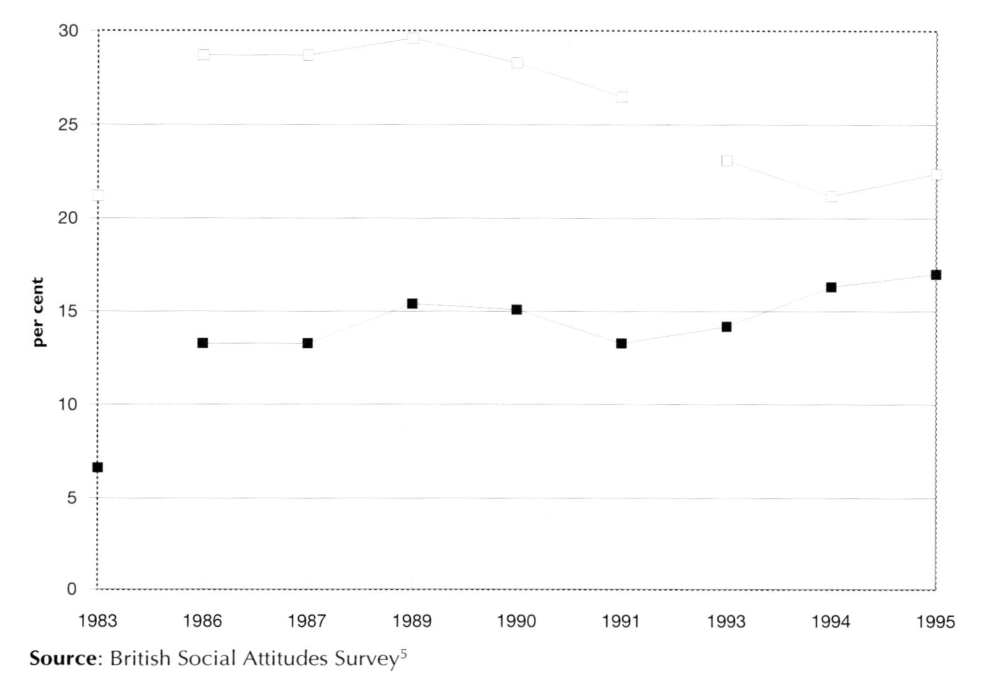

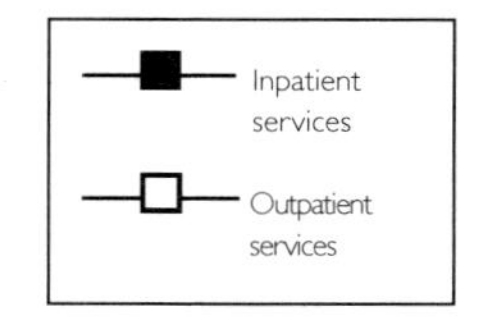

Source: British Social Attitudes Survey[5]

Figure 3 Dissatisfaction with the hospital service, 1983–1995

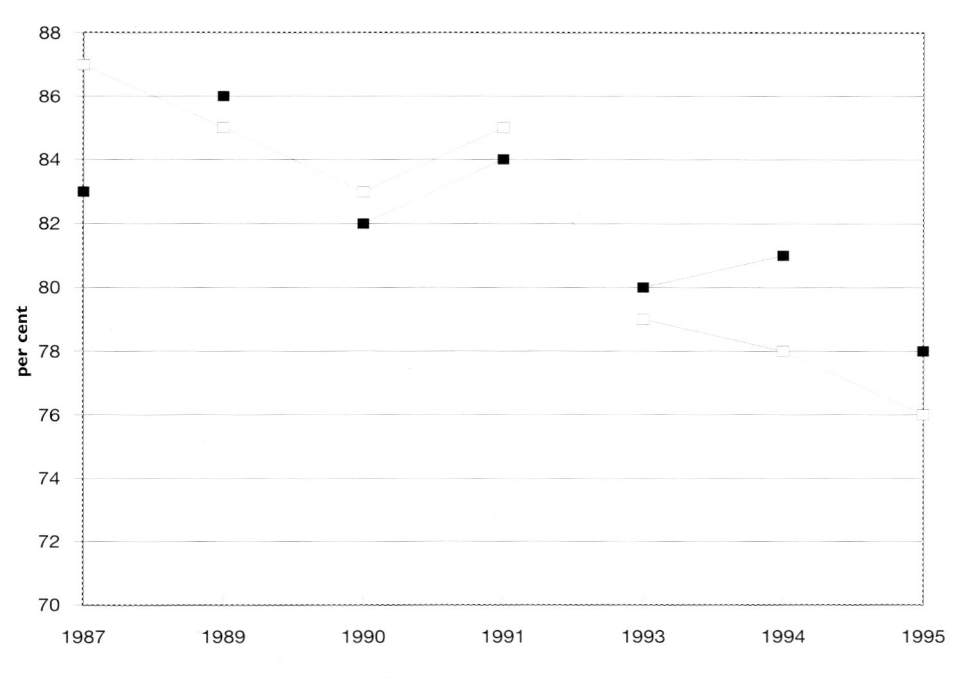

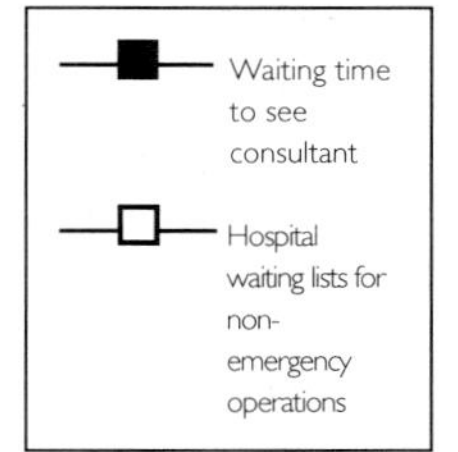

Source: British Social Attitudes Survey[5]

Figure 4 Aspects of the NHS thought in need of improvement: waiting times, 1987–1995

This suggests that the *Patient's Charter*, which set maximum lengths of time patients could expect to wait, has had at least some impact.

Primary care

Although dissatisfaction with the state of the NHS has increased, people have always tended to express more favourable views about services provided by the professionals within it. Respondents are inclined to reply to questions about specific services primarily on the basis of their own experience. By contrast, questions about the general running of the NHS appear to elicit more broadly-based views and so may be answered in terms of political opinion rather than personal experience. The BSA survey asked:

From your own experience, or from what you have heard, please say how satisfied or dissatisfied you are with the way in which each of these parts of the National Health Service runs nowadays.

Figure 5 shows trends in dissatisfaction with GPs and dentists. Dissatisfaction with GPs remains fairly low: in 1995 only one in ten respondents expressed dissatisfaction with the family doctor service. However, dissatisfaction with dentists has risen sharply during the 1980s. This supports the evidence presented in *Health Care UK 1995/96*[7] which suggests that up to 50 per cent of new patients were finding it difficult to get NHS treatment as an increasing proportion of dentists withdrew from the NHS.

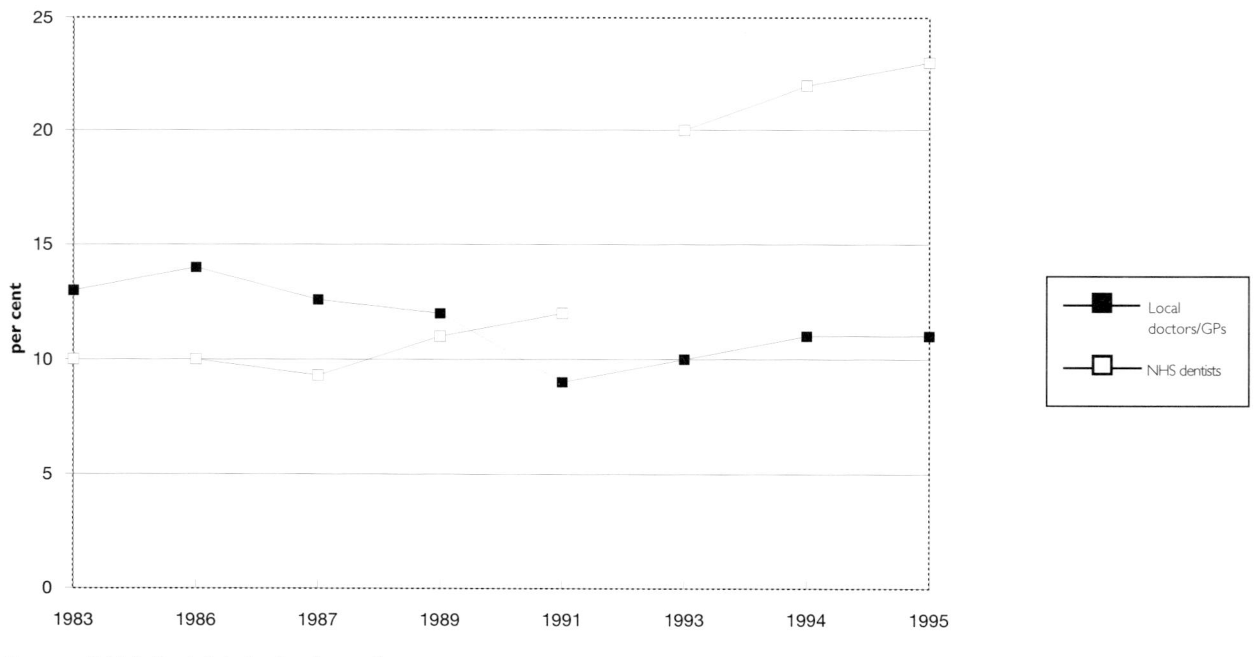

Source: British Social Attitudes Survey[5]

Figure 5 Dissatisfaction with family doctors and dentists, 1983–1995

European comparisons

How do these findings compare with the rest of Europe? In particular, is there a similar link between dissatisfaction and government spending levels on health at a cross-national level? A recent Eurobarometer survey conducted in the 15 European Union Member States in 1996 asked for views on health care systems and spending.

Figure 6 shows the relationship between per capita expenditure on health on the one hand and dissatisfaction with the running of health care on the other. The original question read:

> *In general, would you say you are satisfied, fairly satisfied, neither satisfied nor dissatisfied, fairly dissatisfied or very dissatisfied with the way health care runs in (country)?*

Eurobarometer Survey

The Eurobarometer health survey asked European citizens in the 15 Member States a number of questions related to the running of health systems in their countries, their views on the need for reforming the systems and the level of health expenditures. The findings of the survey were based on face-to-face interviews in people's homes and in the appropriate national language. Sample sizes ranged from 595 in Luxembourg to 2074 in Germany. National sample surveys were conducted from 27 February to 3 April 1996.

The inverse relationship between perceptions of dissatisfaction and per capita expenditure is evident (correlation coefficient = –0.63) and to an extent supports the BSA findings in Figure 2. It is interesting to note that the UK lies some way

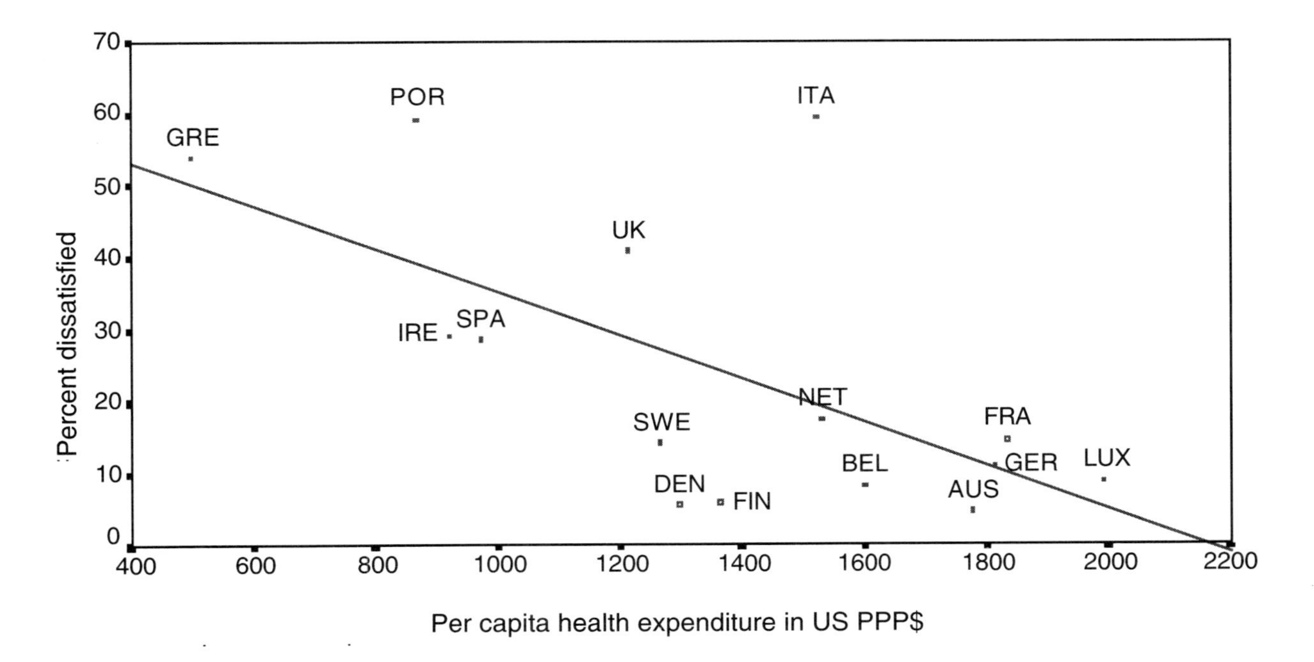

Source: Eurobarometer Survey[2]

Figure 6: Rates of dissatisfaction and health expenditure

above the regression line, implying that dissatisfaction (at 40.9 per cent) is greater than its level of health spending would predict.

These findings support earlier results reported by Blendon *et al*[8] who, in an analysis of ten nations, also found that public satisfaction was associated with higher levels of health spending. The authors commented that:

> *This may be a reflection of the availability of more sophisticated technologies, greater choice of physicians, less waiting and travel time for elective and specialised medical procedures, and the age and modernity of health care facilities.*

Blendon *et al* accept, however, that their data cannot explain the obvious exception of the United States which '.... *has the highest spending per person and reports the lowest level of satisfaction*'.

The results from the Eurobarometer survey also strongly indicate that high dissatisfaction is linked with support for fundamental changes or complete transformations of the health system (correlation coefficient = 0.98; see Figure 7). Furthermore, as Mossialos notes with respect to the UK:

> ... *the percentage of those asking for major changes or major transformations of the system (56%), 5 years after reforms were introduced, is much higher than that of those dissatisfied with the running of health care (40.9%)*[2]

Changes in public opinion: more recent data

The results from the BSA survey strongly suggest that once the honeymoon period immediately

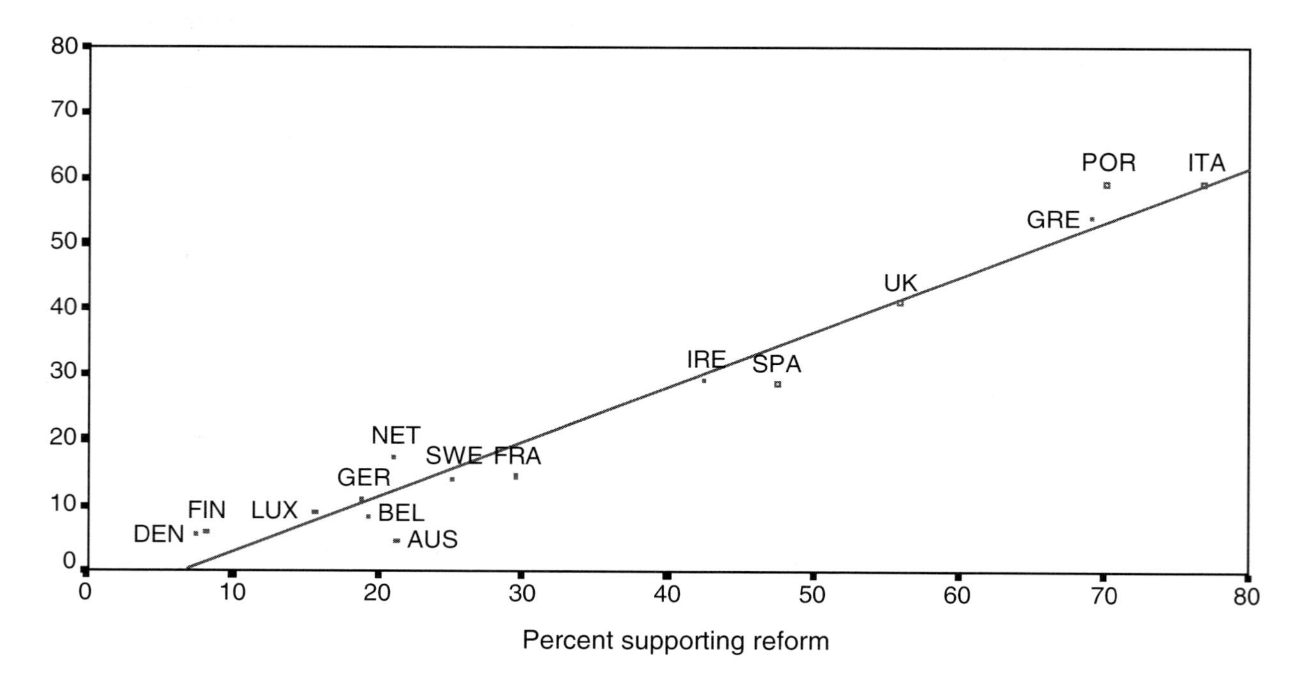

Source: Eurobarometer Survey[2]

Figure 7: Dissatisfaction and support for health reform

following the introduction of the UK reforms was over, dissatisfaction rose dramatically with the overall running of the NHS. However, it is quite difficult to assess changes after the reforms with these data, since the latest year currently available from the BSA is 1995. In view of this, the King's Fund commissioned a module in the Office for National Statistics (formerly Office of Population Censuses and Surveys) monthly Omnibus Survey for the three months covering December 1996 to February 1997. These data were combined with data from a similar survey in 1991/2 to provide a unique dataset which covers a period of significant policy change and which gives an insight into the state of public opinion in the months prior to a general election.

Data from the Omnibus survey have been used to examine variations in responses by age, gender, region and experience of health services. Multivariate analyses were also undertaken to explore whether or not individual characteristics of respondents were consistently associated with reported opinions in the two time periods.

Table 2 shows that dissatisfaction with the overall running of the NHS rose by over 55 per cent from 18.4 per cent of the population in 1991/2 to 28.6 per cent in 1996/7. It is important to note that although these trends are consistent with those in Figure 2, the reported levels of satisfaction are not directly comparable with the BSA data for methodological reasons.[1] Table 2 also shows that most satisfaction was expressed with GP services, with over 80 per cent of

The Omnibus Survey

The Omnibus Survey run by the Office for National Statistics (ONS) is a nationally representative sample of approximately 2000 adults conducted each month. Respondents are asked a set of basic classificatory questions covering their characteristics and household circumstances. The King's Fund first commissioned ONS (then OPCS) in 1991/2 to include in selected sweeps of the Omnibus Survey a module of questions concerning individuals' health status, health care utilisation and attitudes towards the Health Service. These questions were repeated in 1996/7 and we now have data for the months November 1991, February 1992, December 1996 and January 1997. The respondents were aggregated into two broadly similar samples – 4256 in 1991/2 and 3738 in 1996/7 – which are representative of the non-institutionalised population of Great Britain. The questions on satisfaction are identical to those employed by the BSA.

Table 2 Satisfaction* with health services 1991/2, 1996/7

	1991/92				1996/97			
	Satisfied	Neither	Dissatisfied	Don't know	Satisfied	Neither	Dissatisfied	Don't know
	%	%	%	%	%	%	%	%
Running of the NHS	66.7	12.4	18.4	2.6	55.1	13.5	28.6	2.9
Local doctors/GPs	86.5	4.3	8	1.2	83.4	5.8	8.9	1.9
Hospital inpatient services	61.2	7	9	22.7	55	11.6	13.9	19.5
Hospital outpatient services	57.2	8.6	17.5	16.7	56	13	17.5	13.6

Source: King's Fund

respondents expressing positive opinions in 1991/2 and 1996/7. This supports the BSA results and other findings of consistently high levels of satisfaction with GPs.[9,10] On the other hand, dissatisfaction with inpatient services rose by 54% during the five-year period so that the gap between dissatisfaction with outpatient services and inpatient services has narrowed. This also concurs with the latest BSA survey which showed an increase of 18 per cent in dissatisfaction with inpatient services between 1993 and 1995.

Figure 8 shows the regional variations in levels of dissatisfaction with the running of the NHS. In both 1991/2 and 1996/7 the highest levels of dissatisfaction are observed in London. Respondents in the capital also recorded the largest absolute increase in dissatisfaction from a little under one-quarter in 1991/2 to almost 40 per cent in 1996/7. In fact, the latest data show that substantially less than one half of respondents (42%) in the capital were in any way satisfied with the running of the NHS.

Determinants of dissatisfaction in 1991 and 1997

What might have accounted for the increases in dissatisfaction in London and elsewhere? Are they widespread or are they more commonly found among certain sub-groups of the population? In order to investigate these questions the correlates of reported dissatisfaction with health care for 1991/2 and 1996/7 were also examined (see box: multivariate analysis, opposite). The factors possibly associated with dissatisfaction with health services are likely to include a range of demographic, socio-economic and health status characteristics.[1] Although we acknowledge that other factors such as variations over time in media coverage of the NHS and differences in ideological beliefs may affect opinions,[11] we do not have data about such potentially important influences. Given the relatively high level of

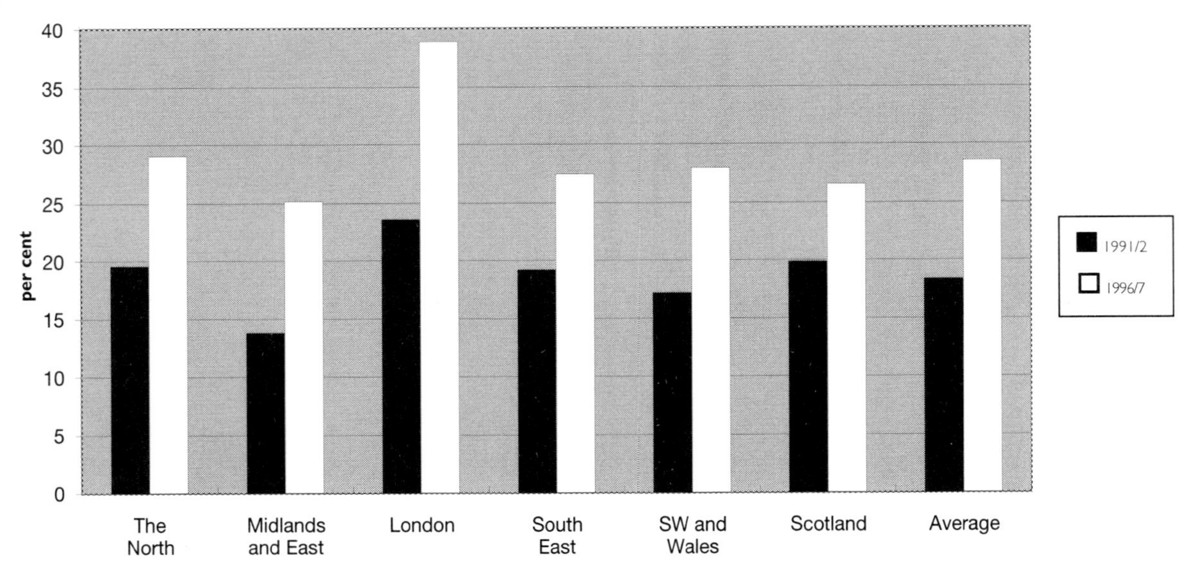

Source: King's Fund

Figure 8 Dissatisfaction with the overall running of the NHS by region

dissatisfaction and the marked rise since 1991/2, the empirical analysis has been confined to the first question on the overall running of the NHS.

Table 3 shows the odds ratios (see box) and their levels of statistical significance for all of the explanatory factors that were significantly associated with dissatisfaction in both 1991/2 and 1996/7, after adjusting for a number of other potentially explanatory factors.

The odds ratios in Table 3 suggest that there is an inverted U-shaped relationship between the age of respondents and perceptions of dissatisfaction. Young people between the ages of 16 and 24 and those respondents who are retired have a relatively low probability of reporting dissatisfaction compared with those of middle age. Another finding is that women are less likely than men to be dissatisfied with the running of the NHS, and the same is true for respondents who have been hospital inpatients during the 12 months before interview. In contrast, people living in London are about one and a half times more likely to be dissatisfied than others in Great Britain, and the odds ratio has increased between 1991/2 and 1996/7. However, none of the

Multivariate analysis

Logistic regression is the most appropriate statistical technique to investigate those characteristics of respondents that are significantly associated with a dichotomous dependent variable: dissatisfied or not with the running of the NHS.[12] It is used to estimate the probability of the event in question occurring, given certain characteristics or circumstances of the respondents. A range of demographic and socio-economic characteristics of respondents, together with measures of health status and recent experience of using services, were analysed to identify whether they are associated with dissatisfaction.

Odds ratios

The odds ratio can be interpreted as an indicator of the relative importance of the independent variables included in the model. Specifically, it expresses the increased or decreased odds of an expected event associated with a particular characteristic after controlling for all of the other variables in the equation. For example, an odds ratio of 1.52 implies that an expected event (e.g. dissatisfaction) is approximately one and half times more likely to happen whilst controlling for other characteristics.

Table 3 Logistic regression model of dissatisfaction with the overall running of the NHS*

	1991/2 (n=4256)		1996/7 (n=3738)	
Independent variables	**Significance**	**Odds ratio**	**Significance**	**Odds ratio**
Age 16–24	**	0.58	**	0.63
Retired	**	0.57	**	0.57
Female	**	0.72	**	0.84
Recent inpatient stay	**	0.69	**	0.67
London	**	1.48	**	1.72
Chi-square χ^2	83.963		90.031	

Source: King's Fund
* Controlling for ethnicity, economic status, recent contact with GP, occupational class and health status
** $p<0.05$

differences between years in the size of the odds ratios is statistically significant.

Discussion

Two findings stand out from the analysis presented above. First, the increases in dissatisfaction with the general running of the NHS and with the quality of hospital inpatient services since the General Election of 1992; and secondly, the statistically significant relationship between spending and dissatisfaction. The multivariate analysis suggests that there is also some consistency of relative perceptions of satisfaction by distinct subgroups of respondents over time. People living in London seem especially likely to be dissatisfied with the NHS, whereas retired people, women and those respondents with recent experience of having been a hospital inpatient are all more likely to report higher than average levels of satisfaction in both 1991/2 and 1996/7.

Nonetheless, the rise in dissatisfaction with some aspects of the NHS seems to be a fairly general phenomenon. It is not confined to one or more sections of the population. Even among some of the groups (e.g. women) that are more likely to express satisfaction one can observe increases in dissatisfaction during the past five years. What might explain these trends? There is certainly no shortage of possible explanations because the NHS has experienced such a considerable amount of policy change in recent years. The contenders might include:

- the introduction of the internal market;
- the battles over much loved hospitals such as Bart's and Guy's and the continuing reduction in the number of hospital beds in London;
- the de facto privatisation of nursing care for the elderly;
- more explicit rationing of access to health care;
- growing concerns about the financial viability of the NHS.

Others might add to this list of possible contributors to growing public disquiet about different aspects of the NHS. However, we tentatively suggest that a combination of local service issues such as the threatened rationalisation of hospitals in London, specific concerns about the quality and availability of hospital inpatient services and more widespread anxieties about the level of public expenditure on health care may have contributed most to growing pessimism about the state of the NHS.

London

People living in London are much more likely to be dissatisfied with the running of the NHS than the rest of the British population. There may be several reasons for this finding. Londoners might be more dissatisfied with life in general and/or have higher social expectations. It is at least as likely, however, that the discussions surrounding the reconfiguration of London's acute hospitals during the early-to-mid-1990s, which were widely reported in the media, contributed to growing dissatisfaction. Pressure on health services also appears more acute in London than elsewhere with increased demands being made on the hospital system through emergency admissions resulting in temporary closures of A&E departments and trolley waits for patients. Furthermore, several reports have shown that specific services in London such as those for people who are mentally ill and the primary care sector are still relatively poor in London despite numerous initiatives to improve the situation.[13,14]

Quality and availability of health services

Although the majority of respondents expressed satisfaction rather than dissatisfaction with both inpatient and outpatient hospital care, there has been a significant rise in the numbers of those who reported dissatisfaction with in-patient services. This is also reflected in the latest BSA survey which reported a fall in satisfaction with inpatient services by 7 percentage points (from 64% to 57%) between 1993 and 1995.[5] One possible explanation could be a perceived decline in the quality of inpatient services. Further evidence from the BSA shows that the proportion of respondents who thought that they would be discharged from hospital before they were ready to leave grew from 32 per cent in 1991 to 44 per cent in 1995.[5]

An obvious alternative way of interpreting these results is to point to the fact that people with recent experience of the health service are much less likely to be dissatisfied with both the overall running of the NHS than those without. This might be thought to indicate that the standard of care received by users is very high. However, Judge and Soloman[1] have suggested other explanations:

> *For instance, people who have received care may simply be grateful that they received any service free of charge. They may also be relieved that they are no longer waiting to be seen or treated. They may have forgotten the negative, organisational aspects of waiting while remembering the more personal 'caring' side of their treatment. This so-called 'gratitude barrier' cannot be ignored.*

Of course, we acknowledge that all statistics about satisfaction with complex services should be interpreted with caution. Respondents are asked to answer questions based on what they *think* would happen and we know that beliefs about the Health Service can, rightly or wrongly, be influenced by the media as much as by personal experience.[11] However, the fact that there appears to be a growing disillusionment with specific health services might, in the longer term, undermine support for the basic principles of the NHS.

Health spending and public expectations

Perhaps the most compelling explanation is that rising dissatisfaction could reflect increasing anxieties associated with media stories of a looming crisis in the NHS.[15] The international evidence strongly suggests that in many countries there is a link between levels of spending and satisfaction with domestic health care systems. In Britain there also seem to be strong associations between priorities for public spending, levels of dissatisfaction with the NHS and the generosity or otherwise of the annual public spending round. In short, the public appears to want to see sustained levels of reasonably generous funding for the NHS. Most people cannot easily vote with their feet and 'exit' to alternative health care suppliers but they can 'voice' their preferences in public opinion surveys and their views can influence their votes in general elections.

Growing disenchantment with Conservative management of the NHS may have been one of the factors influencing the outcome of the 1997 election result. If this has any substance the shifts in public mood could pose problems for the new Labour Government as well.

Despite the unexpectedly generous funding settlement for the NHS announced in the July 1997 budget, the Chancellor of the Exchequer is still committed in principle to sticking to the tight spending plans inherited from the Conservatives. The latest *Green Budget* from the Institute for Fiscal Studies (IFS) estimates that total NHS spending is planned to grow by 1.5 per cent in 1997-98, 0.3 per cent in 1998–2000 and zero in 1999-2000. These plans allow for much lower growth in current spending on health services than has been the norm over the last decade. But how realistic is this whilst maintaining the provision of front-line services at a level and standard that the public expects or needs? IFS are sceptical.[16] The authors warn that the Chancellor faces three options:

> *Either the government meets people's aspirations for better services, in which case large areas of public spending will need to rise as a share of GDP and taxes will eventually need to rise. Or we go along the Conservatives' 'pensions route' where people are encouraged to make their own provision in certain areas, with the government guaranteeing a basic minimum. Or we can go on as we are, trying to stretch a limited amount of resources ever wider.*

Most commentators believe that whatever the intentions of Labour to keep within its fiscal straitjacket, the NHS will, at a minimum, share in the growth of the economy. Yet it is by no means clear that this will be enough to meet demands for improvements in the NHS. Moreover as Harrison and colleagues note, the influence of the media can complicate expectations further by running stories of the application of new technologies in the NHS alongside gloomy tales of hospitals running out of funds.[17]

Conclusions

Between the 1992 and 1997 General Elections there was a marked increase in the proportion of British people who are dissatisfied with the Government's stewardship of the NHS. In the run up to the 1992 election very substantial injections of public expenditure were made available to ease the creation of NHS trusts and GP fundholders and to introduce an internal market into the NHS. In contrast, during 1996/7, the NHS found itself in such a tight financial straitjacket that media coverage of persistent pressures on health services was almost ever-present. We have shown that the link between dissatisfaction and health care expenditure is supported by evidence from cross-national comparisons in Europe. Therefore, it is almost inconceivable that such a regular diet of doom and gloom in the UK should not have heightened concerns among survey respondents about the future viability of a publicly funded and comprehensive National Health Service. If the British public are losing confidence in the ability of the NHS to provide for them then this finding alone represents a significant challenge to the new Labour Government.

Acknowledgments

Material from the Omnibus Survey was made available through the Office for National

Statistics and was used by permission of the Controller of Her Majesty's Stationery Office and ONS.

References

1 Judge K, Soloman M. Public opinion and the National Health Service: patterns and perspectives in consumer satisfaction. *Journal of Social Policy* 1993;22:299-327.

2 Mossialos E. Citizens' views on health care systems in the 15 member states of the European Union. *Health Economics* 1997;6:109-116.

3 Dixon J, Harrison A. A little local difficulty? *BMJ* 1997:314:216-219.

4 Dixon J, Harrison A, New B. Is the NHS underfunded? *BMJ* 1997:314:58-61.

5 Bryson C. *Trends in attitudes to health care: 1983-1995*. London: Social and Community Planning Research, 1996.

6 Bosanquet N. *Improving health*. In British Social Attitudes, 11th Report. eds Jowell R, Curtice J, Brook L, Ahrendt D. Aldershot: Dartmouth Publishing Company, 1994.

7 Harrison A, *Health Care 1995/96: an annual review of health care policy*. London: King's Fund, 1996.

8 Blendon RJ, Leitman R, Morrison I, Donelan K. Satisfaction with health systems in ten nations. *Health Affairs* 1990; Summer:185-192.

9 Jacoby A. *User surveys of general practice, vol 2*. London: Institute for Social Studies in Medical Care, 1989.

10 Williams S, Calnan M. Key determinants of consumer satisfaction with general practice. *Family Practice* 1991;8:237-242.

11 Judge K, Soloman M, Miller D, Philo G. Public opinion, the NHS and the media: changing patterns and perspectives. *BMJ* 1992;304:892-895.

12 Aldrich J, Nelson, F. *Linear probability, logit and probit models*. London: Sage Publications, 1984.

13 Johnson S, *et al. London's mental health: the report to the King's Fund London Commission*. London: King's Fund, 1997.

14 Boyle S, Hamblin R. *The health economy of London: a report to the King's Fund London Commission*. London: King's Fund, 1997.

15 Dixon J, Boyle S, Harrison AJ. Financial meltdown for the NHS? *BMJ* 1996;312:1432-143.

16 Dilnot A, Giles C eds. *The IFS Green Budget: Summer 1997*. London: The Institute for Fiscal Studies, 1997.

17 Harrison A, Dixon J, New B, Judge K. Can the NHS cope in future? *BMJ* 1997;314:139-142.

A new constitution for the NHS

King's Fund Policy Institute

The pressures on the NHS from demography, new technology and rising expectations are familiar, as are the successive crises to which the NHS is subject. But while the basic nature of the NHS has not changed, the world in which it operates has, both nationally and internationally. The attempt to roll back the state, once seen as a British, Thatcherite phenomenon, is now worldwide. New Labour is no sooner elected than it begins on a restructuring of social security, led by a businessman, designed to reduce the costs to the state and to limit its role, not to ensure, as its predecessor which established the NHS intended, that want should be abolished. More generally, it promised in Opposition and kept that promise in its first budget, not to raise the level of personal taxation. Against this background, it is not surprising that many argue that the NHS is unsustainable: either it *cannot be afforded* because taxes cannot be raised sufficiently to pay for it; or it represents a form of provision – almost entirely state financed and state provided – which is no longer in tune with the times.

The first part of this article describes the pressures to which the NHS is subject. It then goes on to set out the areas which need to be examined if effective ways of meeting those pressures are to be devised. The central assumption which underlies the discussion is that what is required to preserve the essential features of the NHS is a range of measures involving all the interest groups which the NHS comprises – taxpayers, users and the professionals providing the service.

The form of the original NHS was a compromise, largely between professional interests and the broad policy objectives of the then Government, which was reached after intense negotiation during which positions were changed and options abandoned which their proponents had initially been unwilling to give up. Out of all this emerged an implicit NHS constitution with financial powers clearly with the Government and service delivery clearly with the professions.

The events of recent years have begun to break down this implicit constitution: the Conservative policies of the early 1980s could be seen as the first determined attempt by the Government representing taxpayers to impose their interests in a systematic way through, for example, cost improvement programmes and competitive tendering for support services. The NHS and Community Care Act 1990 represented a continuation of that policy. The Conservatives also, through the *Patient's Charter*, took the first steps towards recognising users as an interest group in their own right, while the introduction of medical, later clinical audit, albeit as a professionally led activity, represented the first step of what has since become a centrally, ie Government, directed programme focused on clinical effectiveness.

In these ways the implicit NHS constitution has been changing incrementally, as the result of a series of separate initiatives, each taken in its own right. This paper argues that if the NHS is to continue as a tax-financed, publicly provided service for the nation as a whole, a new constitution has to be negotiated.

Any such re-negotiation should be based on two principles:

- that all interest groups, consumers, as well as taxpayers and professionals, should be involved, and:
- that much of what was left implicit when the NHS was established must now become more explicit.

We begin by outlining the nature of the new pressures bearing on the NHS and after briefly considering the NHS overall aims and objectives, we examine what each of the interest groups – taxpayers, users and professionals – might ask of the NHS in the future. We then go on to consider the internal constitution, ie the balance between central control and local discretion. Finally, we consider what should happen next. There are some areas where technical improvements are required but there are also awkward tensions facing both users and professionals which require political rather than technical skills to resolve.

Pressures

Since its inception, the NHS has seen itself under pressure from increasing demands on the one hand and limited resources on the other.

This tension remains essentially unchanged and indeed is inherent in any system of health care provision to which access is not limited by price or any other explicit mechanism for controlling use. Although the tension is not new, a number of new features have become prominent in recent years:

- continuous change;
- growing complexity;
- the transition from patient to user/consumer
- the changing role of the health care professional.
- growing public awareness of failures.

Taken together these suggest that the old way of resolving it, largely through implicit rationing imposed on an ill-informed public, will no longer work as they once did.

The first feature is continuing change. The policies pursued by the Conservative Government have been regarded with cynicism but here we accept them at their face value, as a series of attempts to preserve the nature of the NHS while changing the institutions which comprised it. Labour, by proceeding cautiously, has in effect recognised that there is no return to the old institutions, even if it is not clear what the new institutions should be.

In our view, the search for new institutional forms should continue. One of the indirect results of the implementation of the NHS and Community Care Act 1990 is the recognition that there are many possible forms of health service which are compatible with the basic objectives of the NHS. The approach set out in *Choice and Opportunity* which was welcomed on both sides of the House of Commons in the

January 1997 debate and now has the statutory framework to allow it to be developed, should ensure that there is greater scope for new forms of provision to emerge, at least within primary care.

The 'pilot first' policy set out in *Choice and Opportunity* means that new forms of provision will emerge but not always at the same rate over the country as a whole. This way forward will inevitably lead to tensions. It will create diversity between areas and will increase the tension between central departments and localities. That in turn will lead on to questions about what it means to have a national health service. As argued below, there may well be a case for introducing the concept of a 'local NHS', but this will only work if there are a set of ground rules which define the essential elements of a national health service and a central capacity based on accurate intelligence which can monitor local developments and a capacity to intervene if the national ground rules are broken. And it will only be acceptable if there is public understanding of the need for innovation and its concomitant diversity.

The second feature is growing complexity. The NHS has always been a complex organisation which over the years has struggled to find the right balance between local discretion and central direction. In the past decade, the search for the right balance has grown more difficult at both local and national level, in part because of growth in clinical knowledge, in part because of changes in the outside world to which the Service has had to respond and in part because of the increasing range of central policies and the introduction of explicit performance objectives.

These developments have also had the effect of bringing to the surface the degree to which the various elements of health care provision are interdependent both with each other and with other policy areas, including social care, clinical training and clinical research. The growth in emergency medical admissions to hospitals and the appropriate policy responses can only be comprehended and devised by looking across all the relevant actors and considering how they are currently responding to the pressures on them, the incentives they face and the constraints to which they are subject, and how they might respond if those incentives and constraints were altered.

Recognition of complexity requires new skills on the part of those managing the Service, both nationally and locally. In particular, it requires a new way of policy-making which acknowledges the limited knowledge available about the future pattern of health care delivery and of the impact of specific attempts to shape that future.

The third feature is the transition of the user from patient to consumer. The passive patient is developing into a potential partner in the process of deciding the way that care should be provided. The previous Government recognised that in the *Patient's Charter* but, despite its extensive development, the Charter remains an *ad hoc* response to particular failings rather than a coherent attempt to define what the rights and responsibilities of users should be. Although in itself welcome, the *Charter* and other initiatives such as *Patient Partnership* have increased the tension between the professional view of what constitutes health need or ability to benefit and that of the individual patient/consumer and hence who should judge whether a service is or is not well designed. More fundamentally still, development of the user/consumer role undermines the professional's role as allocator of resources; ie the principal means of implicit rationing. If that role is undermined through challenges to the authority of clinical judgement, it must be performed in other ways. But there is as yet no obvious alternative.

The fourth feature, the changing role of the health care professional, follows from the third. The 1948 implicit constitution effectively left responsibility for the provision of services to the professions. That area of discretion is not only being eroded by consumers seeking to establish their own role in determining how services should be provided, it is also being attacked by taxpayers seeking to establish that the resources they have trustingly handed over to the professions have been properly, ie cost-effectively, used.

It is nearly a decade since Sir Raymond Hoffenberg concluded that clinical discretion was dead. Since then a series of further initiatives such as those relating to clinical effectiveness have emerged designed to circumscribe it. From the viewpoint of professionals, the NHS is becoming a more demanding environment but, at the same time, their view of what is an acceptable career pattern is itself changing. Professional commitment to the Service must be retained but it cannot be taken for granted in the way it once was.

The final feature is growing public awareness of failure and expectations of what can be done. The media have been significant agents in this process, in part because of their fascination with the new and in part because of their focus on the personal and particular, rather than the general. While this may be regretted, there is very little to be done to modify the behaviour of the media directly.

This means that the NHS must have a strategy for ensuring that the public at large understands the issues it has to deal with. What has been missing entirely is any effective means of presenting the issues from the viewpoint of the NHS as a whole. Attempts to involve the public in decision-making have been tentative and incremental, focused on the individual intervention or the specific decision. The Service has been, both at local and national level, very reluctant to engage the public in the difficult issues which managers and clinicians have to deal with. The politicians ultimately responsible have been equally reluctant, preferring to emphasise positive achievement rather than hard choices.

In our view, however, greater public understanding and involvement are required if the NHS is to continue to enjoy widespread support. If the issues and choices are not explained, the result will be a general but uncomprehending disillusion, which might in turn lead to the NHS becoming unsustainable. To prevent such a development will require new forms of engagement with the public of a kind not yet attempted. Any such attempt will entail risks of its own but the risks of not making an attempt now seem greater than the alternative of continuing with the *status quo*.

The central conclusion we draw from consideration of these pressures is that the NHS must continue to adapt, develop and innovate. Such a course is not without risk. Conservative Ministers found it hard to evade the charge that the reforms introduced by the 1990 Act were undermining the NHS by introducing commercialism and other values and processes deemed by their critics to be incompatible with what the NHS stood for. But the greater risk is to leave things as they are in the hope that the Service will cope.

In the White Paper *A Service with Ambitions* the Conservative Government attempted to rebut the charge that they were dismantling the

NHS but signally failed to do so. In part, this was because the White Paper was too unambitious a document: to those in the NHS it offered nothing and to those outside it appeared irrelevant since it offered no specific commitments, merely aspirations. In part, it was because the previous Government could never shake off the charge that they were intent on privatising the NHS. Because of this fundamental lack of trust, change of any sort appeared to bring that threat a little closer to realisation. In part, and perhaps most fundamentally of all, it was because the White Paper smoothed over the pressures and tensions set out above and failed to tackle the central issues which the Conservatives policies had raised.

But despite this central weakness, the White Paper did contain within it the beginnings of an explicit attempt to set out what the NHS stands for. For this to be done properly, however, there are two basic requirements:

- explicit recognition of the pressures and tensions set out above
- development of a coherent and comprehensive response across the NHS as a whole.

That response may be seen as a reworking of the implicit NHS constitution in the light of the changes set out above. The question therefore is: how should a deal on a new constitution be struck in the conditions of the 1990s? The rest of this article sets out the broad areas which would have to be considered in its development.

Towards a new NHS constitution

The statutory framework for the NHS is very broad and, like the British Constitution itself, is largely filled in by administrative action taken within the very wide discretion enjoyed by the Secretary of State under the 1977 NHS Act. Although none of this is secret, it is uncodified. Even the relatively informed outsider can find parts of this implicit constitution hard to establish, be it the precise way that finance flows from the Treasury down to the local level or the nature and range of the services which the user can expect to enjoy. The increasing use of the courts in health as elsewhere is one response to that, reflecting as it does a lack of clarity as to what the NHS should provide and the way that decisions should be made.

The notion of a written constitution designed to provide such clarity is vulnerable to the charge that what is most important cannot be written down and that general rules will never fit the infinite variety of circumstances to be found within the field of health care. These charges are valid and powerful but we believe there remain many areas where explicitness is both valuable, achievable and necessary.

A new constitution for the NHS, as for the nation as whole, would in practice involve a consolidation of much of what exists. The new Government will want to adopt much of what the previous Government has done in respect of corporate governance, equal opportunities and other areas relating to the corporate behaviour of the NHS. There, at least at the level of form, there have been massive improvements in recent years in the way in which NHS officers and organisations conduct their public lives. What is needed here, therefore, is consolidation followed by re-presentation in a more accessible form.

But a new constitution would also have to break new ground in a number of areas and go further than the previous Government went, covering:

- NHS aims and objectives;
- Interest groups;
- The NHS internal constitution; and,
- The private sector.

Aims and objectives

The starting point must be a statement of the core values which the NHS should embody. Some of this would be straightforward. For example, *A Service with Ambitions* sets out the following four broad principles for the NHS:

- universal in its reach
- high quality
- available on the basis of clinical need
- responsive to patients and carers.

Those set out in the annual *Priorities and Planning Guidance* by the NHS Executive are slightly different: they run as follows:

> *equity – improving the health of the population as a whole and reducing variations in health status by targeting resources where needs are greatest;*
>
> *efficiency – providing patients with treatment and care which is both clinically effective and a good use of taxpayers' money;*
>
> *responsiveness – meeting the needs of individual patients and ensuring that the NHS changes appropriately as those needs change and medical knowledge advances.*

While these are largely uncontroversial at this broad *system* level, they are incomplete. In addition, they are imprecise and there are conflicts between them.

Incompleteness

In the present context two types of values are missing from these summary statements: those relating to the corporate behaviour of the NHS itself and other organisations which receive finance from it, and those relating to the workforce and the values it embodies in the way that it deals with users: we pick up on both of these below.

Conflicts

Our earlier analysis has suggested that equity and efficiency may conflict if the means chosen to develop the Service lead to differences between areas, eg in the availability of drugs or the availability of finance such as that offered in challenge funds or other special sources of top-sliced finance which are used to stimulate innovation. Greater responsiveness to users may also, if effective, promote greater variety in provision. Such potential conflicts must be acknowledged rather than evaded. That may mean that boundaries to the extent of diversity have to be defined.

Lack of precision

Imprecision can only be reduced by commitment to specific policies and to monitoring whether or not they are achieving their intended aims. In the case of equity, the broad principles of resource allocation present no serious difficulty. But there are still tough issues to be addressed. The most difficult relate to a meaningful commitment to defining the NHS role in reducing inequalities of health status where this involves a commitment over and above that already recognised in the geographical resource allocation formula. Another is the availability of services. Evidence cited elsewhere (p xx) reveals the variations that already exist between areas. While, in principle, these should be reduced if not removed if the NHS is to be genuinely equitable, the practical implications of doing so are considerable, implying as it would a national set of service designs and suggested service levels.

The question of what is meant by clinical need must also be addressed. This can no longer be left as a self-explanatory justification for determining the way NHS resources are used. It begs the question of the place that cost, on the one hand and personal factors such as time spent waiting on the other, should play in clinical decision-making. That of course can never be reduced to a simple formula no more than evidence-based practice means that clinical judgement is out of date. Rather it is question of determining what considerations are relevant when such decisions are taken.

Statements of objectives such as those made in *A Service with Ambitions* risk being seen as meaningless since such a wide range of policies is consistent with them. That in itself is not a bad thing: commitments to particular institutions or specific forms of service would risk fossilising development and consequently it would be unwise to consider *constitutionalising* commitments of this form. The challenge of leaving value statements in their general form is to create means by which either their achievement can be measured or recognised and their infringements can be detected. That will in turn require technical and institutional innovation to find new ways of monitoring how resources are actually used. Some ways of doing this are suggested below.

Interest Groups

Although there might be general agreement on the broad values which an NHS should pursue, any NHS constitution must recognise the different interests of those involved in it. The original constitution was primarily negotiated between the medical profession and the state representing the taxpayer and the patient. Now the nature of this deal has changed: the patient/user is now a distinct *interest* group in its own right. In what follows, therefore, we look at these interest groups in turn, taxpayers, users and professionals.

Taxpayers

Users and providers would like taxpayers to make a commitment to stable funding combined with reliable increases year on year. The previous Government made an election commitment, eventually matched by Labour, to a real terms increase year-on-year, an expression which still left open substantial room for manoeuvre. Others have urged that through hypothecation of particular revenue sources, the issue should be taken outside the standard public expenditure planning process. But there are serious objections to this approach – in particular, it is hard to ensure stability of revenues this way; moreover it does not assist in the process of defining how much should be spent on health services.

We have argued elsewhere that there is no right way of defining how large the health budget should be and hence no formula to define either its current level or its rate of increase. This leaves the task to political judgement and while that is entirely appropriate, it begs the question of the basis on which this judgement should be made.

Level of funding

In recent years, the financial deal has, in effect, been that the NHS will get more as long as it becomes more productive. While the nature of the deal may be right, its form is not, in that the main way in which productivity has been measured is wrong. The Purchaser Efficiency Index is perverse and the new Government's intention to abolish it is welcome. Yet, it is idle to suggest that alternatives can be quickly found which provide a useful measure for the productivity of the NHS as a whole. More fundamentally, the centre, be it Treasury or Department, is not in a position to assert that any particular level of productivity gain is achievable since its knowledge of the production side of the NHS is insufficient for it to do so with any confidence.

Without major technical developments it is hard to see a quick and significant improvement in the existing process. One way forward may be to introduce an NHS Business Case – which sets out the areas where in the centre's view there should be a growth in spending combined with an explicit statement of where cost reductions can be made. At the moment, the negotiations surrounding the annual determination of the NHS budget are shrouded in the usual budget secrecy, so it would be a small step forward if the nature and content of the current debate were made known.

This approach might be supported by the development of the existing programme budget for health services by subdividing some of the large block items such as acute care into service or other groupings which might be genuinely informative about how resources are being used and where increases or reductions are taking place.

These are in themselves modest changes and not enough in themselves to protect the taxpayer's interest – there is a limit to what can be done at the overall level. That interest is best protected by appropriate policy-making and by rigorous audit processes. We make suggestions about both below.

Rate of increase in resources

The hard question here is the extent to which the NHS can be isolated from the general pressures on the public purse on a year-by-year basis and given a secure medium term future. In the past, governments felt able to make long-term commitments in real, ie service-specific, terms, under what was known as the Plowden system. This process came unstuck in the economic crises of the 1970s, which led to introduction of cash limits and the abandonment of any commitment to real terms increases.

Expenditure plans for the second and third year of each planning period have systematically been set for the health programme below the level actually achieved so it is arguable that all that is required are realistic plans, not financial shadow-boxing. Ironically, the tougher and more confident the Chancellor is towards public spending as a whole, the easier it should be for a realistic medium-term commitment to be made. However, any such commitment would have to be earned by improvements in the evidence offered to justify an increase in resources.

Even without that however, there is scope for improving the way that charges are justified – here the user is in effect the taxpayer. The existing pattern of charges lacks rationale and increases are made on a yearly basis without explicit justification. The Government should accept that the existing structure of charges and changes to them require explicit justification based on evidence.

Users

In the 50 years since the original NHS constitution was formed, it is arguably users whose position has changed most. In those more paternalistic times, it was assumed that how services were provided was exclusively a professional matter even though it was recognised even in the early days that demands would outstrip supply. This position is already recognised as untenable, but while the NHS has changed a great deal in recent years so as to become more user responsive it has done so in a piecemeal manner.

The interests of users have to be explicitly recognised in a number of different ways. We take first issues relating to the scope and role of the NHS: just what is the deal that the NHS intends to offer; we then go on to what patients might expect at the point of use and how decisions affecting both these might involve them and others.

Range of services

The bundle of services which the NHS comprises should be defined. Before considering what these might be, we need to reflect further on the record of the Conservative Government. Although the focus of commentary has been on the 1990 reforms, the most serious changes it brought about were arguably to long-term care and to dentistry. Unlike the 1990 Act, however, these changes were made without the benefit of a White Paper or intense political argument–until it was too late. One result has been an undermining of the NHS as a whole as its image of comprehensiveness has been damaged.

Other developments have had the same effect. In the case of expensive drugs, for example, differential access between patients from different parts of the country has been revealed, which appears to make a mockery of a national health service. The term 'rationing by postcode' has become rapidly understood. Again, the issues have never been centrally explained: it has been left to local purchasers to defend their actions often on the basis of limited knowledge. Stephen Dorrell when Secretary of State confirmed that no medically necessary treatment should be excluded from the NHS, thereby acknowledging that whether a treatment was cosmetic or not depended on circumstances. Experience elsewhere such as in New Zealand suggests that any attempt to rule in and rule out of a public health care system will result in little change. There are only a few areas, such as IVF, where a decision might make a difference in terms of whether services are in or out of the NHS, but the very definition of a clear bundle could itself reduce concerns about whether or not the Service is equitable.

A statement on the *bundle* involves two main things:

First, a commitment to justifying changes such as those that have occurred in long-term care, dentistry, and foot care where types of service or need may be judged to be outside the range of the NHS. Experience in other countries has shown that exclusions are difficult to achieve for whole classes of treatment; eg some forms of cosmetic surgery may be judged *purely* cosmetic and hence outside the bundle, but others may be judged to have therapeutic value, such as the treatment of gross deformities.

Second, an explanation of how new services or treatments should enter the bundle. This is largely a question of the criteria relevant to admitting new ways of providing services within the basic bundle. The Conservative Government made significant progress in this direction through the introduction of health technology assessment, but more could be done both in respect of drugs and new surgical procedures where the recently introduced arrangements (see page 62) rely on voluntary compliance.

A good example of failure to grasp the nettle of service restriction arose under the previous Government in relation to ambulance services. The notion of a category of call which would not attract an ambulance response was rejected, no doubt because Ministers wished to avoid the charge that they were cutting back services and also the risk that they would be blamed if a patient in urgent need did not receive a rapid response. But such non-essential calls, which amount to some 15 per cent of the total, are often trivial; some form of gatekeeping is required, based ultimately on the judgement that certain forms of need can and should be met outside the NHS.

Within the accepted bundle, the same issue of defining the threshold for treatment arises. At present, acute hospitals are rebalancing the pattern of their activity towards emergency and away from elective care. While this general trade-off is apparent, its detailed implications, in conjunction with continuing attempts to remove long waits for any form of elective treatment, are not. Equally, the implicit trade-off between the extent of the bundle and the threshold for treatment within it needs to be brought out: what if, for example, the nursing element of long-term care was reclassified as being within the NHS bundle? The previous Government's response to the Health Select Committee report on long-term care suggested that this was not a current priority, but the basis of that judgement is completely obscure.

Distribution of service

It is one of the greater ironies of social policy that while the prime aim of the NHS is seen as ensuring that access is equitable, the Service itself does virtually nothing to ensure that it actually is. The key requirements here are:

first, reaffirmation of the principles on which resources are allocated to areas. This is primarily a technical issue but significant changes may be required to ensure resources are distributed equitably.

second, tighter definitions of what equity in practice is intended to mean. The current Planning and Priorities Guidance while asserting the objective does not suggest a means of ensuring it is achieved. A system of equity audit is required on the lines proposed by Michaela Benzeval (see *Health Care UK 1994/95*)

third, as part of the previous requirement, an explicit commitment should be made in relation to differences in health status. The new Government has indicated that it will take inequalities seriously and that will demand action outside the NHS itself. But the potential role of the NHS should not be underestimated. Improved access to health care could make a real difference to many disadvantaged groups as could joint initiatives with local authorities and voluntary organisations to develop innovative forms of health promotion, as well as ensuring take-up of existing services such as infant health and immunisation and screening programmes.

Quality of services

Quality is so elusive a concept and services are so diverse that specific quality standards such as those in the *Patient's Charter* are likely to remain rare. But audit reports, be they from the Confidential Inquiry into Peri-Operative Deaths, the Audit Commission, the Clinical Standards Advisory Group and the National Audit Office, typically identify basic shortfalls in the way that care is provided which put lives or recovery at risk.

Equally difficult are the less tangible aspects of the patient's experience. New models of audit may have to be developed drawing on and extending features of current arrangements. In mental health, for example, the Mental Health Act Commission inspects premises in both an announced and unannounced way, and members talk to patients directly on the ward. They do this on behalf of a vulnerable group subject to a very restrictive regime. Their manner of operation could be extended to other categories of patient. Similarly, it is some time since the Audit Commission began to consider the user viewpoint, eg in relation to day surgery, but monitoring of this type by auditors remains rare while the NHS in general continues to ignore it apart from *ad hoc* studies.

What is needed is a systematic approach to monitoring the patient's experience. Satisfaction surveys are commonplace as are surveys of users' views of particular services and their non-clinical components, eg hospital food or waiting times. A broader approach is required. One element of this should be audit across interfaces; ie NHS audit should not typically be provider-based, as it is now, but patient-based, wherever the patient goes. This simple suggestion could lead, at the same time, to a much more fruitful form of clinical audit than is currently practised.

User rights

The Patient's Charter requires a fundamental re-appraisal, the need for which has already been recognised by the new Government. It has grown up in response to a political imperative in relation to waiting lists, built on existing standards, eg in relation to ambulances, and responded to events as they have emerged, eg A&E standards. It lacks coherence and underlying philosophy.

The Association of Community Health Councils for England and Wales has recently put forward a set of proposals (see p 57) which would extend the Charter into new areas. These bear on access, rights to care, choice and information, advocacy, quality standards, confidentiality and redress.

For reasons set out elsewhere (see p 108), the current system for dealing with clinical negligence fails most users completely. Lord Woolf's report on Civil Justice made a number of proposals for improvement working more or less within the current framework. More radically, the link between accountability and compensation might be broken. In his recent book, *Medical Negligence*, Andrew Phillips has argued that this link might be broken in a way which is beneficial both to patients and to professionals – though possibly at the cost of further burdens on the taxpayer. He also shows that there are a number of ways forward reflecting different balances between professionals, users and taxpayers.

Users and citizens

The NHS has already begun to respond to the

transition from patients to consumers through the national *Patient Partnership* initiative as well as many local projects designed to involve users in service design. But it has scarcely made a start in improving the way decisions are made at a strategic level. The public at large usually oppose proposals for change, particularly where these involve relocation of services, in large measure because they associate change with loss and are sceptical of the claims for improvement that accompany it. Equally, the issues which are emerging around the availability of new drugs are perceived simply as denial of care rather than a sensible response to what are often still untried techniques.

As noted above, these issues are not new but they are now more visible and hence they must be tackled explicitly. At the very least, better ways must be found of explaining the issues and choices to those immediately affected and to the public at large. But it may be necessary to go further than this and involve both users and citizens in decisions more directly. There have been some experiments with citizens' juries but these have been directed at local rather than national issues. The proposed *People's Panel* (*Guardian*, 14th July 1997) appears to be a move in this direction, but the task is not simply to *sample* public opinion but to inform it and, if possible, give it a greater role in decision-making.

Professional interests

The original NHS constitution was a compromise between the ambitions of the Government of the day and the power of the medical profession. The implicit deal was that the profession should enjoy day-to-day discretion and security, in return for accepting a form of Service that many of its members did not want. Subsequently, important further elements emerged, for nurses and other professionals as well as doctors, such as the establishment of independent Pay Review Bodies which could be seen as offering the professionals some confidence that their aspirations for higher incomes would not be arbitrarily blocked by the Treasury.

Over the past decade or so, this deal has begun to fall apart, in part because the professions themselves have made new demand, (eg for more flexible careers and less demanding workloads), but more significantly because pressure from government for better performance in clinical and financial terms has undermined it.

There are many tough issues to tackle, resolution of which would again threaten or appear to threaten professional power. The hardest lie at the intersection between services, training and research, in the definition of professional roles, the boundaries between professions and professional privileges, particularly the position of the Royal Colleges. These issues have scarcely been tackled by previous governments and they are largely unexplored by research.

A start has been made with the JM Consulting Ltd report into the 1960 Act system for regulation of the professions allied to medicine (see page 14) and the same process should be extended to the other professions in the light of the University of Manchester/Institute of Health Services Management report on the future of the NHS workforce (see page 79). This latter set out a radical agenda for all parts of the workforce, but it did not directly address the existence of the professions as such and the awkward issues of where they are properly independent and self-regulating and where not, and what the practical implications of recognition of the flexibility in the boundaries between professions would be for the current structure of professional governance.

There seems to be little joy in this for the professions, appearing as it does to promise a future in which restrictions on clinical practice grow and the notion of professional status is undermined. But there are opportunities as well as threats. These lie in three main areas:

First pay. After the last round of pay settlements, it appeared that local pay was dead, even if the Pay Review Bodies and previous Government had not abandoned it. But that aside there remain significant differences between the Treasury and Department of Health on the one hand and the professions on the other as to the principles which should govern pay determination. The professions could well argue that the affordability criterion which the central departments consistently attempt to impose is inappropriate in the form it is currently presented and also that central judgements are based on an insufficient understanding of what is actually happening within the service.

Second, there may be scope for greater flexibility than currently exists in respect of time commitments, career structures and roles. While the professionals concerned would welcome this, there would be a price to be paid, reflecting the massive cost to the taxpayer that their training gives rise to.

Third, as the development of fundholding has shown, some doctors have grasped the chance to innovate both clinically and organisationally: the clinical leadership role may be developed further and not just by doctors and not just at local level. A recent *BMJ* editorial by Donald Berwick (*BMJ* 314 31 May 1997), addressed to the US health care system rather than the British, nevertheless raised issues relevant in this country. The main point it made was to urge the medical profession to change its role in the light of the new economic and social environment in which it is now operating, away from its old (restrictive) guild status, to a new role which extends beyond the sectional interest of the profession. To take one example, Berwick points out that:

> *Doctors, like others, tend to regard measurement of performance as a threat. In their role as system leaders, both individual doctors and medical associations will need to embrace the measurement of performance as a step in their own learning.* (p 1565)

The transition that Berwick argues for will of course be difficult to make but it is an essential one that is required in the UK as well. Change is already under-way, e.g. through opening up the General Medical Council to greater lay participation. What is needed, however, as the JM Consulting Ltd report into the professions allied to medicine proposed, is a thorough overhaul of the regulatory framework, designed not only to update it, but also to make it fit for the changes in professional roles that are bound to emerge in future. That overhaul might well lead to more external monitoring of performance, but equally it might also lead to a clearer definition of the proper exercise of professional discretion and, indeed, leadership.

The central challenge that Berwick throws out is for doctors to choose between becoming citizens in system improvement or to play the role of victims. In the context of this article, the question is whether or not doctors and the other professions can be pro-active in the renegotiation of the NHS constitution which this paper argues is necessary.

The internal constitution

For nearly 50 years, the NHS has struggled to find the right balance between centre and periphery. The present balance results from a muddle: the 1990 Act regime was presented as a decentralising policy which has turned out to be the reverse of that. What is needed now is a renegotiation of the internal constitution in the light of a proper appreciation of the growing complexity of the NHS and the factors underlying it. Such a renegotiation might involve imposing restrictions on the role of the centre and the explicit creation of scope for local initiative.

Limiting the role of the centre might involve a number of changes. First, new policies should be piloted and appropriately monitored and evaluated. *Choice and Opportunity* pointed the way and the present Government appears to have accepted the approach. The hard part is to recognise what it involves in terms of investment in the requisite skills to make this approach work – as the current cliché has it, to make the NHS a 'learning organisation'. Some of the elements of such as system such the Centre for Reviews & Dissemination exist, but experience with trying to learn from the London Initiative Zone programme shows that many are not.

Second, where piloting is inappropriate and nationwide policies such as the Calman reforms of medical education are introduced, they should be properly costed and their implications drawn out. The Reagan administration in the USA adopted the notion of a policy impact statement, with the explicit intention of cutting down the role of the federal government. The same principle should apply to the NHS Executive and the Department of Health. Such a 'statement' would require that the implications of any central initiative, particularly but not exclusively the resources needed to implement it, should be systematically identified before implementation began.

As for extending the scope for local initiative, there is no way of drawing simple and permanent lines around the central role. Accordingly, any statement of the areas where local choice might be exercised must be partial and be limited to critical areas. It might include:

- first, a statement on how decisions on exclusions from the basket of NHS services should be taken and under what conditions new services can be introduced, i.e. whether the roles set out above should be national or local;
- second, a statement of the circumstances in which there may legitimately be variations between areas in the level and type of services on offer. Some such as those deriving from ethnic or demographic mix will be obvious, but others are less so. For example, it is arguable that, as now, national (minimum) programmes should exist for school health, screening at all ages and specialised paediatric facilities, as well as a consistent approach to maternity and cancer care. In others, the case for national levels and standards of provision is less clear. In the case of emergency care, geography alone is likely to dictate a wide variety of ways of providing a service and such variety might be further encouraged by the kind of pilots the 1997 Primary Care Act allows for. If standards are

set, then they should bear on outcomes rather than provision itself. In yet others, levels and standards of care may be deemed a purely local matter. For example, in respect of services meeting needs which vary widely between areas, the national role may simply be to ensure that accreditation is properly conducted;

- third, identification of the factors considered relevant to choosing between patients, eg in the determination of clinical priorities and waiting lists;
- fourth, a definition of the price of greater local autonomy in terms of either sanctions in the event of failures or specific monitoring or external audit requirements.

This list is, of course, indicative rather than exhaustive. Defining precisely what it should cover would be the prime focus of any negotiations between central and local interests over what a National Health Service should comprise and which areas are the proper subject for local choice.

Reporting

The previous Government made a commitment to openness and signalled its intention to begin reporting on clinical outcomes. This needs to be reaffirmed in the light of the Health Service Ombudsman's comments (see p 107) and both must also be applied to private suppliers of services, as we note below.

More significantly, a commitment must be made to systematic reporting on the quality of performance, both in terms of the service provided and the broad objectives of the NHS as a whole. The NHS Annual Report as it stands should be discontinued. A really radical government would hand the process over to an independent body which would combine the powers of existing institutions such as the National Audit Office, the Audit Commission and the Clinical Standards Advisory Committee, which would, given the resources, allow a reliable judgement to be made on how the NHS was performing. This should include a systematic commitment to monitoring the patient's experience of services and should focus not simply on the episode but on whole patterns of treatment.

It was a Labour Minister, Richard Crossman, who insisted on the creation of what became the Health Advisory Service to report on standards in long-stay institutions, against very strong professional opposition. While the atmosphere is much better now, there are still vested interests to be faced. Clinical audit remains a professional preserve even if the results are of wider interest: against the background sketched out above, this seems indefensible – part of the *old* constitution which does not fit the *new*.

Consideration of how monitoring and audit should be reformed and extended must be seen in the context of the ideas set out above for altering the balance between central and local roles and also for demonstrating to the taxpayer that the Service deserves the money it gets. If there is to be more local freedom, there must be greater openness and better reporting. Although these are ultimately political issues, there is a large technical agenda here stemming from the key question of what the sources of genuine efficiency improvement are, how they are best pursued and what the respective national and local roles should be.

Private sector

The private sector could be said to form the fourth part of the post-war settlement, but its terms of participation have largely gone by default. A new constitution should set out what is seen to be the appropriate role for private finance and provision. The issues are to some degree issues of principle, e.g. as with private education, choice of sector could be seen as a right. This right in effect underpins a two-tier service which the present Government has argued is unacceptable for the NHS itself. That right could be rejected, e.g. in Ontario the right to insure privately is limited to services for which the province does not insure *or*, it could be accepted, but provided within the NHS by, for example, extending the amenity bed concept. Alternatively, rules might be introduced which limited the scope of private insurers to pick and choose both the people they insure and the packages they provide: the most extreme form of this would be to only permit policies which spanned the full spectrum of emergency and elective care.

The issue of private provision turns largely on setting proper ground rules for *fair* competition between public and private providers. This would require that a number of detailed issues were addressed bearing on the equity and efficiency of the current arrangements such as training of staff by the NHS and other factors which distort competition between private and public provision, eg in long-term care. At present all forms of private provision rely on the NHS to bail them out if things go wrong, but they pay no price for this service. Alternatively, it is often argued that the existence of private insurance and provision reduces the burden on the NHS. It may well do so, but the precise nature of the inter-relationships is poorly understood. How far, for example, can the private sector expand before it begins to reduce the ability of the NHS to supply services? The Royal Commission on the NHS made a start nearly 20 years ago to consider the mutual impact of public and private provision, but there has only been intermittent interest since and little substantive research.

Finally, it would be reasonable to expect that any private provider to the NHS accepts the same terms of corporate behaviour as the NHS itself, including access to information, audit and other procedures which are applied within the NHS.

Overview

The starting point of this paper is that the NHS faces a series of new pressures which will make it harder to sustain in its present form. The task, for those who wish to see it survive, is to devise new ways of responding to these pressures. To this end, we have put forward a number of specific proposals bearing on:

- justifying increases in NHS expenditure and charges;
- definition of the scope of the NHS and changes to that scope;
- the definition of equity between areas and between people;
- monitoring users' experience of the service;
- the roles of central and local management;
- reporting and audit.
- corporate behaviour in the private sector.

These proposals stem from the two basic principles from which we started:

- that all interest groups, consumers as well as taxpayers and professionals, should be involved, and;
- that much of what was left implicit when the NHS was established must now become more explicit.

But implementation of these proposals will not be enough. The outcome of the 'negotiation' of a new NHS constitution cannot be specified in advance since it must stem from interaction between the interest groups involved. Such a 'negotiation' is not of course one that can be conducted formally, round a table. Rather, it would have to take the form of a sustained and lengthy dialogue, during which positions are changed and amended in the light of whats learned during it.

This will be a slow and difficult process, but a start has already been made. Donald Berwick's article in the *BMJ* is one of several published during 1997 which have addressed the future role of the medical profession.

The ACHCEW proposals exist: the King's Fund has launched a separate and more wide-ranging initiative designed to define the interests of users and citizens. But other interest groups and stakeholders have yet to enter the field at such a general level.

The wide debate that this would lead to is just as likely to generate tensions as consensus. The Government will have to face some hard choices and defend some unpalatable decisions. If the argument set out in this paper are right however, not to face up to the issues now will make them harder to tackle later. Indeed, it could lead to a decline of trust in the NHS which will ultimately make it unsustainable. If there is one point which underpins all our analysis, it is that the NHS cannot do everything its users may want and this must be openly acknowledged.

The present Government does at least possess the great advantage over its predecessor of being perceived as supporting the NHS. The greater the efforts it makes to prepare the ground for – 'getting its justification in first' as it were – the greater the chances of success.

Housing, health and community care: the inter-agency dimensions

Bob Hudson

The debate on the housing dimension of community care has moved on considerably since Sir Roy Griffiths' somewhat dismissive verdict that housing agencies should be limited to arranging and sometimes managing the 'bricks and mortar' of housing need for community care purposes. His report[1] was widely condemned for taking such a narrow perspective, and this criticism seemed to penetrate the subsequent community care White Paper, *Caring for People*,[2] which took the view that suitable good quality housing was essential to social care packages, and urged social services authorities to work closely with housing agencies of all types in developing plans for a full and flexible range of housing. However, only one of the 106 pages was actually devoted to the housing dimension, and the emphasis upon adaptations, 'Staying Put' and 'Care and Repair' initiatives seemed to reduce the housing role to one of immediate practicalities rather than that of strategic planner in partnership with social services and health.

More recently, the tripartite agenda seems to have been more properly acknowledged. In 1992, the Departments of Health and Environment brought out a Joint Circular[3] on housing and community care which began with the declaration that: 'Adequate housing has a major role to play in community care and is often the key to independent living. The Government wants housing authorities to play a full part, working together with social services departments and health authorities, so that each can effectively discharge their responsibilities'. However, the Joint Circular contained no fresh initiative for delivering this declaration. Again, in 1997, new joint guidance[4] from central government sought to provide a framework to help social services, housing and health agencies to establish strategic co-ordination. Overall, it seems reasonable to conclude that there is now a consensus of opinion around the need to create a central role for housing through collaborative planning with social services and health authorities. This, however, does not mean that there is agreement upon precisely what this role is and how the three parties might most effectively work together.

There are essentially five major issues upon which housing, health and community care intersect. These are:

- supporting those without a home;
- helping people with care needs to remain in their own homes;
- assisting a move to more supported accommodation;
- facilitating a move from institutional to community living;
- assisting a move from supported to ordinary living.

In considering a strategy to address these dimensions, an important starting point is to recognise the potential contribution of all three parties across health, social care and housing. The roles of health and social care staff tend to be more widely recognised and understood than those of housing staff in this respect, but when the health or social care needs of tenants are not being met, it is often housing managers who first become aware of the problem. But although the principle of inter-professional and inter-agency working is one which commands wide acceptance, *realpolitik* at the interface can be a very different matter. It is important that these inter-agency dilemmas are identified and addressed, otherwise strategies for progress may fall well short of expectations.

Inter-agency dilemmas

There are several ways of analysing the inter-agency dilemmas affecting health, social care and housing agencies. In this review, a distinction is made between three types of fragmentation – *externally* driven, *locally* driven and *culturally* driven.

Externally driven fragmentation

Externally driven fragmentation refers to those sources of fragmentation which arise externally to local inter-organisational networks, typically from economic factors or from actions taken by central government which, intentionally or unintentionally, impact upon local relationships. These forces will be examined under two discrete but related headings: central government fragmentation; and intra-organisational preoccupations.

Central government fragmentation

Central government is fragmented in organisational, policy and financial terms, and this inevitably influences the degree of attainable cohesion at local levels. Centrally, the Department of Environment takes the lead on housing matters and the Department of Health on health and community care issues, but neither seems to have prioritised community care housing. Indeed, in so far as government attention has focused upon community care-type housing, it has been directed by the Department of Environment to the Housing Corporation for implementation by housing associations outside of the local government system. This fragmentation can not only lead to a failure to focus upon issues of mutual concern, but can even result in the pursuit of diametrically *opposed* policies. The Department of Environment, for example, has been charged with cutting back public expenditure on social housing; the Department of Health is committed to the resettlement of people from long-stay institutions; and the Department of Social Security wishes to reduce the range and level of financial support for people living in the community.

More recently, the Housing Act 1996 has been making significant changes to social housing provision which may prejudice the position of vulnerable people in the community. From January 1997, local authorities will no longer have a duty to provide permanent housing for homeless people in priority need. Instead they will be obliged to provide temporary accommodation for up to two years, or assistance to find accommodation in the private sector. The only way to secure permanent rehousing will be through the council's housing register. Charities have expressed concern that that this could lead to vulnerable people being shunted between unsuitable temporary properties or simply being handed estate agents' property lists. The Act has also created the category of twelve-month 'introductory tenancies', giving councils the right to evict any new tenant who they feel is not behaving satisfactorily. Although designed to deal primarily with 'neighbour nuisance', the provisions may be misused against tenants whose behaviour is unusual or against whom there is prejudice.

This organisational and policy fragmentation is mirrored in financial and planning fragmentation, with no direct link between central government expenditure programmes concerning housing, health and community care: the Housing Investment Programme (HIP) allocation is outside of the Revenue Support Grant and Standard Spending Assessment mechanisms; the HIP allocations to local authorities are based upon one index of need, while the Advanced Development Programme allocations by the Department of Environment to housing associations, are made via the Housing Corporation and based upon a different index of need. Separate negotiations apply to each programme, and there appears to be no cross-referencing at local level. Even for 'special needs housing', the Department of Environment manages the Housing Corporation which in turn creates national priorities for housing associations to implement, but these have not been couched in terms of an explicit set of national community care priorities agreed with the Department of Health.

All of these features influence the existence and effectiveness of local planning systems. Housing associations are expected to interpret their responsibilities for local needs, and these are not necessarily based upon local community care needs as determined by social services. Health authorities in their turn still tend to separately produce purchasing and business plans which reflect their own priorities. Currently, health, housing and social services authorities are all required to submit annual plans to their respective government departments, and although there is an expectation that each will consult one another, this amounts to little more than central exhortation. In such circumstances, localities tend – at best – to fall back upon bilateral discussions about one-off projects, and at worst engage in a game of 'pass-the-parcel' over responsibility for funding specific elements of care and support.

Intra-organisational preoccupations

There is a tendency to treat barriers to collaboration as though they exist only within an *inter*-organisational field, and this has resulted in a neglect of the internal processes and structures of each of the organisations involved. The reality is that any potential collaborating partner may be facing such a heavy range of intra-organisational preoccupations, that inter-agency working may be relegated to the margins. The main such preoccupations will tend to be organisational change and budgetary shortfall.

Local housing authorities have seen their role transformed from one in which they were responsible for co-ordinating a directly owned and managed capital and revenue-intensive service, to one in which they manage a residualised public service. Where previously they possessed a number of powers of direct intervention, they have now become more like 'enabling' authorities – a shift which equally affects health and social services authorities. Although such a change *does* require an inter-organisational approach, the requisite relationships tend to be with agencies *other* than health or social care. Reid,[5] for example, identifies the following:

- private finance for social housing;
- local authority support for housing associations;
- local authority support for housing associations;
- leveraged private sector investment for urban and housing renewal.

The arguments are also applicable to both health and social services agencies. For health care organisations, the priority has been to respond to pressure to reduce their waiting lists and speed up hospital discharge procedures – a strategy which makes demands upon both housing and social care agencies, but not within the framework of a rational inter-agency approach. At the same time, social services authorities are faced with higher levels of need and increasingly tight rate support grant settlements. For all three parties then, constant structural change and financial constraint have precipitated an inward-looking preoccupation with organisational survival. On top of this, managers and staff are often changed, their responsibilities redefined and their agencies merged or divided. All will have difficulty in working out who they might be working with across agencies, as well as understanding the objectives and priorities of the reshaped organisations.

Locally driven fragmentation

Local fragmentation can be of two types: that which arises as a consequence of central fragmentation, and that arising from local circumstances. In exploring these issues, a distinction is made between strategic boundaries and barriers and operational boundaries and barriers.

Strategic boundaries and barriers

Several obstacles to strategic collaboration can be identified: different strategic schedules; different strategic approaches; and the cumulative effect of shifting boundaries and conflicting priorities.

Different strategic schedules

In looking for integration or convergence across housing, health and social care commissioning, it would seem to be a minimum requirement that commissioning strategies and other planning documents are explicit about the relationship of each to the other, and the extent to which any one of them reflects and expresses the aims, objectives and actions set out in the others. It might even be argued that they should be as explicit about those parts of health and local authority business which are perceived to be solely within the remit of one authority and therefore *beyond* the scope of integrative mechanisms. The different strategic timetables of the parties make this difficult, with housing authority and health authority business plans falling well in advance of the normal publication date for community care plans. Indeed, not all social service departments even *have* an identifiable purchasing plan to align with those of the other agencies. The growth of GP fundholding or other forms of GP commissioning further complicate the picture, partly because of the increase in the number of interfaces to be managed, and partly because GPs tend to be the weakest link in inter-agency terms. Even excluding GPs, where health, housing and social services authorities are not coterminous, there can be as many as ten authorities involved, each with a purchaser-provider split, as well as scores of housing associations, voluntary organisations and user groups.

Different strategic approaches

Underlying these scheduling variations is the more fundamental problem of different *approaches* to strategic thinking. Watson and Conway[6] sum it up in the following way: '... in housing, thinking is oriented primarily around properties and usually around different tenures; in social services, thinking centres on different client groups; while in health, it is frequently the location and type of service which provide the focus.' The problem is exacerbated where the commissioning role itself is narrowly and inwardly focused upon procedures, costing mechanisms and contract specifications, rather than outwards on assessment and strategic planning across agencies.

Shifting boundaries and conflicting priorities

There is nothing new about shifting boundaries between organisations – there was, for example, a long debate in the 1950s about which elderly people needed residential care because of their welfare needs under the National Assistance Act 1948, and which required long-term hospital care under the NHS Act 1946. However, there has recently been a more pronounced attempt to define vulnerable people as having welfare rather than medical needs, with social services now funding people in nursing homes and home care staff performing roles that were once the province of district nurses and other primary health care staff.

Means[7] identifies three equally important boundary issues between housing and welfare. First, most people define housing associations as housing agencies, but this can serve to obscure their role as social care providers of nursing homes, residential care and domiciliary services – activities which account for over a third of their expenditure. Second, the Department of Environment and Housing Corporation have long been concerned to distinguish the additional housing management costs associated with 'special needs' housing schemes, from the costs associated with the provision of care and support, with the latter seen as the funding responsibility of health and social care agencies. And thirdly, there has been a debate about the appropriateness of funding the welfare (as opposed to housing management activities) of sheltered housing wardens through housing revenue accounts.

Cumulatively, these factors result in local arrangements which are both fragmented and complex. The 1994 Department of Health study[8] of housing and homelessness could find little evidence of effective joint working, noting that although there were examples in relation to particular projects (such as young single homeless people and people with challenging behaviour) there was not yet a shared vision leading to co-ordinated planning. Moreover, those schemes which *do* get off the ground are often characterised by a bewildering degree of complexity and consequent high negotiation costs

On a broader front, Arblaster *et al.*[9] suggest that there is unresolved tension surrounding the mutuality of the competitive and collaborative imperatives behind so many of the social policy reforms of recent years. They note that whilst a market economy of welfare may result in a diversity of agency providers, the emphasis is on the agencies' own specialism, and agencies continue in business by gaining the next contract. Within these competitive arrangements, inter-agency collaboration is difficult and the focus upon intra-organisational performance indicators has encouraged a narrowing of the services provided.

Operational boundaries and barriers

In this case the concern is with those working practices at the level of individual service users which fragment the services and diminish the effectiveness of the support they receive. There are two significant dimensions to this problem: marginalisation of non-social care personnel from the care management process; and the budgetary barriers associated with targeting strategies.

Marginalisation from care management: housing

In their study of the housing, health and social care needs of people in ordinary housing, Arblaster *et al.* found housing agencies expressing frustration about the difficulties involved in obtaining formal assessments by social service departments for people housing staff perceived as having care support needs. Social service departments were seen as increasingly restricting assessments to certain people in key groups, and not assessing people in other groups. The former category included some people with mental health problems and frail elderly people, while the latter included homeless people with mental health problems, some families with complex problems and people with drug/alcohol related difficulties. It was felt that some assessment processes did not properly take into account the ability to cope at home, and housing staff were not involved in assessments even when it seemed appropriate that they should be. Goss and Kent[10] see part of the reason for this to be the different approaches to assessment taken by the respective agencies. Social services expect to conduct assessments based upon individual needs, whereas housing agencies look at equity across their stock and use need on a *relative* rather than an *absolute* basis – a difference which makes joint assessment at an individual level a problematic exercise.

Marginalisation from care management: health

The involvement of community nurses in the care management process was a prominent feature of both the White Paper, *Caring for People*, and the subsequent Policy Guidance,[11] but again there is only limited evidence that GPs and other members of the primary health care team (PHCT) have secured an effective role. The attitude of GPs towards the community care reforms in general, and assessment and care management in particular, has often been far from positive and a range of obstacles to the involvement of other PHCT members have arisen from some of the early investigations: difficulties with cross-agency referral and assessment; limitation of the care management role to social care staff; the concentration of community health services staff upon hospital discharges rather than those needing retention in the community; the resistance of primary health care team staff to an involvement in care management; the existence of separate 'assessment cultures'; the potentially restrictive nature of NHS contracts on community health services' staff activity; and the reluctance of primary health care team staff to engage in financial assessments.

Budgetary barriers and targeting

As budgetary constraints have increasingly affected all of the agencies relevant to this review, so each has sought to narrow down its respective priorities and target support to those in the 'greatest need'. One of the consequences of this uncoordinated response is that the holes in the welfare state 'safety net' get increasingly bigger and more people fall through them. Community care support is now explicitly aimed at people with high level care needs, but the unmet need amongst those with medium and low level difficulties is causing concern to housing managers and other professionals, who are often the first to pick up the high level needs of tomorrow, yet are themselves under pressure to cut management costs through the process of compulsory competitive tendering of the housing management function and by the Housing Corporation's policy of revenue funding housing management functions but not care and support functions. One way of reducing costs is to eliminate support roles for vulnerable tenants. The policy paradox, then, is that whilst there is a growing acceptance of the use of general needs housing with support for vulnerable groups, this support is being so tightly targeted that most vulnerable tenants are having to cope unaided.[9,10,12]

Culturally driven fragmentation

The term cultural fragmentation is used to refer to the absence of a *shared understanding* between those who have been socialised into different professional roles and subsequently employed by separate organisations with different cultures – a development which can give rise to separatism and rivalry, rather then integration and co-operation. For Cunningham and Spencer,[13] the limited role of housing within the context of the changing relationship between health and social services professionals can be in part explained by the fact that housing's image as a profession is generally weaker than that of health or social work. Housing has long been associated primarily with the management of property, rather than the more holistic needs of vulnerable individuals and groups, and division still remains on what should constitute the 'proper' role of the housing manager. This can have implications for the way in which housing is perceived by the other partners.

In a study of housing issues for people with HIV, for example, Molyneux[14] reported that those drawing up the agendas for joint planning came from health and social care backgrounds, and tended to think of housing as a separate and less important issue – the housing staff who did attend were underrepresented and felt marginalised. By the same token, social care concerns often fail to penetrate the world of housing. In a study of housing services for disabled people in 21 authorities, Morris[15] found that only three had a written policy on meeting the needs of disabled people, most had little data on their housing need, and disabled people were not integrated into mainstream allocation policies. Where such developments *have* arisen, there may be a further conflict of cultures. Goss and Kent[10] suggest that the health model may be seen as one with high clinical standards and a strong commitment to patient safety, while social care and housing agencies often place greater emphasis upon independence and a normal living environment.

For Arblaster *et al.*[11] all of this adds up to the lack of a basic conceptual understanding of the different functions of the various agencies. It is not clear what responsibilities health agencies have, for example, for funding accommodation schemes for people who would have been in hospital before the number of hospital beds were reduced, and for those who have been discharged from hospital. Widespread confusion exists about the role of housing management and its responsibility for social care. Housing authorities are told that the Housing Revenue Account should be primarily a landlord account,[16] most housing managers would wish to see housing as a *personal* as well as a *property* service, yet it is becoming increasingly difficult to raise rents sufficiently to cover the costs of care support.

If anything, the NHS role may be slipping further away. Traditionally, many public health physicians were involved in decisions about an individual's priority for rehousing on medical grounds, but the Acheson Report[17] recommended that they should no longer be so involved, thereby diminishing the already small opportunity for a health input into housing issues. The future pattern of the NHS is thought to be one which is 'primary care-led'[18, 19] in which general practitioners will use their influence as commissioners to determine what is provided by the health care system, yet GPs themselves are typically seen as the weakest link in the collaborative chain.[20]

Inter-agency options

The exhortatory model of collaboration typically begins by calling for an integrated service based upon a shared vision of care, but it is usually unclear what this shared vision actually looks like. This lack of clarity is one of the reasons why there is a temptation to begin joint working with a discussion of structures and processes, as well as a tendency to regard notions of value and principle as platitudinous and effete. This is unfortunate, for unless there is some consensus over values and principles, there can be little hope of agreement on forms of collaboration.

Vision and values: the current paradigm

If there is a dominant paradigm to which all three agencies currently subscribe, it is the notion of 'special needs housing'. The Housing Corporation recognises the following groups as having 'special' housing need: people with learning difficulties; people with mental health problems; physically disabled people; elderly people with support needs; young people at risk and/or leaving care; people with HIV/Aids; people with drug misuse problems; people with alcohol problems; women at risk of domestic violence; ex-offenders; vulnerable mothers and babies; and refugees. If there is a shared characteristic, it is that all are seen as potentially requiring some form of specialist accommodation or supported housing.

Although the inspiration for this model may well be benevolent, it has come under increasing criticism in recent years. Means,[21] for example, raises the following objections: the housing need of some people in the special needs categories is simply for affordable housing; some need only temporary housing provision, while longer-term arrangements are organised; some people need social care, health care, personal assistance and a home adaptation if they are to avoid drifting into a housing-with-support scheme or a residential setting; and some live in supported housing not because they need specialist housing, but because this is a mechanism by which their personal assistance and health care needs are met. These points relate to the concern of Arnold and Page[22] that it is inherently difficult to even estimate the need for 'special needs' housing. They lodge four objections: that there is no useful consensus about what the term covers; there is no reliable evidence on whether people either want or need special needs housing; much existing special needs accommodation is not used effectively – some people do not need the amount of care provided, while others remain there for lack of 'move-on' housing; and the concept carries the assumption that people require on-site surveillance or care. It is in the light of such arguments that support is gathering for a new paradigm.

Vision and values: an alternative paradigm

The emerging alternative to the special needs paradigm is one centred around the concept of *supported living* – an approach which has been developed initially in relation to people with a learning difficulty, but which may be applicable to other people. Bradley and Knoll [23] see this as the latest of three recent paradigm shifts which have shaped service systems. The period up to the 1970s was characterised by an *institutionalisation/ segregation* model ; this was followed by a *deinstitutionalisation/developmental* model in which people were viewed as needing to be trained and assessed through a continuum of settings; and finally the emerging *community membership/ functional supports* model. This new approach recognises that the second approach has often resulted in little more than the transfer of institutional practices to smaller community locations, and that the real challenge is to move support to where people live, and to adapt this to the needs of each individual. At its simplest, it is about enabling people, regardless of their disabilities, to live in the community where they want, with whom they want, for as long as they want, and with whatever supports they need to do that.

From this sort of definition there follows a number of important *principles*. Smith[24] identifies nine:

- people should be supported in living arrangements which are typical of those in which other people live;
- the services that a person receives should change as his or her needs change, without having to move elsewhere;
- a person should exercise choice over where and with whom he or she lives; people should have control over their own living arrangements;
- the aim of services and supports is to assist an individual to take command of his/her life, while building critical and durable relationships with others;
- the services and supports furnished to an individual should be tailored to individual needs and preferences;
- services and supports should be furnished where a person lives and within the context of day-to-day activities;
- supports must be extremely flexible, not restricted to particular types or categories of service;
- people should not be excluded from supported living arrangements because of the nature or severity of their disabilities.

The breadth of this approach requires a more integrated policy framework which makes appropriate connections between housing, health and social care. This requires assessment of people's housing needs as part of their assessment for health or care services, and the integration of housing provision with other forms of care and support so that the package as a whole meets people's needs more effectively. For housing agencies, the essential prerequisite will be to shift the primary focus from the management of property, to one which incorporates the health and well-being of tenants. Fletcher,[25] for example, argues that the success of the housing sector depends upon two approaches to community care. The first is to focus upon *communities* as well as the individual or family. This could lead to a goal of ensuring well-being by enabling people to remain in control and be confident of staying in the community, which implies the development of a locality model for community care alongside an assessment and care management model. The second approach is to involve care users and their relatives and neighbours in what would most help them support a vulnerable person – an opportunity to make the most of the informal community care network as recommended by the Barclay Report back in 1982.

For social services, the challenge is to rethink the current focus of community care around the delivery of *personal care* as the first choice[26] – for some, the concept of personal care represents loss of control, particularly where it is based around negative ideas of minimising risk and managing dependence. The association of this approach with the narrow targeting of a relatively small number of individuals with high support needs, means that the focus is skewed towards the individual at the expense of the community in which they live. For the NHS, the challenge is to jointly develop with housing and social care agencies a strategy that moves outside traditional health interventions and contributes instead to an improvement in people's general well-being – a movement in line with the notions of '*health gain*' and '*healthy alliances*' between a range of different agencies.

Conclusion

At a general level, the starting point for any inter-agency collaboration has to be an acknowledgement of inter-dependencies. Without this, joint working makes no sense. Although the inter-dependencies between health, housing and social services are considerable, this may not necessarily be the perception of any configuration of local actors. For example, Arblaster *et al.*[9] reported that some housing agencies were resentful that they were peripheral to community care and joint commissioning processes, and felt that in order to become involved they had to take the initiative in organising inter-agency activities. The links between health and housing are often particularly weak, with health agencies possibly acknowledging both the theoretical and practical impact of housing upon health, but not acting upon this recognition.

If the prerequisite is that all three parties see some benefit to themselves of collaborative working, then the logical practical starting point is to identify problems which all recognise they need to address. The resolution of these problems could then be expected to meet the needs of:

- health agencies requiring access to an appropriate range of housing with support
- social services agencies for realistic management of their community care budget
- housing managers for access to health and

social care professionals for vulnerable tenants.

Once policy aims have been established, setting targets and standards will be the next key element. In the case of the *Health of the Nation* policy, for example, the Department of Health has set targets expressed as a percentage increase or reduction in the incidence of specified problems as a basis for assessing progress. No such targets have ever been set nationally for other community-based policies affecting health, housing and social services, and it could be a useful exercise for all three partners locally to consider the extent to which they might reach a consensus on what these might look like. Harker *et al.*[27] for example, suggest the following three-year national targets:

- reduce the level of street homelessness by at least 50 per cent
- complete a national assessment of housing requirements across all government department programmes
- ensure the production of joint strategies on housing for community care, based upon local housing, community care and health plans
- require information on the housing options for people assessed under the Community Care Act and discharged from hospitals.

Means[19] sees several grounds for optimism: at the local level, practitioners and managers from housing agencies, social services and health are now in much more regular contact than was once the case; there is more of a shared language relating to such notions as the mixed economy, purchaser-provider splits, user empowerment and so on; there is widespread agreement on the need to foster people's independence in whatever setting they live; and there is growing acceptance that nobody should be expected to change their permanent residence simply in order to obtain the services which they need. But a shared vision will only begin to mean something when it is translated into practical action on the ground.

References

1 Department of Health, *Community Care: an agenda for action* (Griffiths report), HMSO 1988

2 Department of Health, *Caring for People: community care in the next decade and beyond*, HMSO 1989

3 Department of the Environment/Department of Health, *Housing and Community Care*. Circular 10/92 and LAC(92)12. HMSO 1989

4 Department of Health /Department of the Environment, *Housing and Community Care: Establishing a Strategic Framework*. Department of Health 1997

5 Reid, B. Interorganisational Networks and the Delivery of Local Housing Services. *Housing Studies* 1995; Vol.10, No.2, pp.133-149

6 Watson, L. and Conway, T. *Homes for Independent Living: housing and community care strategies*, Joseph Rowntree Foundation 1995

7 Means, R. Housing and Community Care for Older People: joint working at the local level. *Journal of Interprofessional Care* 1995; Vol.10, No.3, pp.273-283

8 Department of Health, *Housing and Homelessness: report of the community care monitoring special study* 1994

9 Arblaster, L., Conway, J., Foreman, A. and Hawtin, M. *Asking the Impossible? Iinter-agency working to address the housing, health and social care needs of people in ordinary housing*, The Policy Press 1995

10 Goss, S. and Kent, C. , *Health and Housing: working together?* The Policy Press 1995

11 Department of Health, Caring for People:

community care in the next decade and beyond. Policy Guidance. HMSO 1990

12 Hoyes, L. Supported Housing and Community Care, The Policy Press 1996

13 Cunningham, R. and Spencer, S. The Role of Housing Managers in the Implementation of Community Care. *Social Policy and Administration 1995*; Vol.30, No.3, pp.227-243

14 Molyneux, P. Bringing housing back on to the agenda. *Care Plan* 1995; September, pp. 23-25

15 Morris, J. *Our Homes, Our Rights: housing, independent living and physically disabled people*, Shelter 1995

16 Department of the Environment. *Housing Revenue Account*, Circular 8/95, HMSO 1995

17 *Public Health in England: Report of the Committee of Inquiry into the Development of the Public Health Function* (Chair Sir D Acheson), HMSO 1988

18 Department of Health. *Primary Care: the Future: choice and opportunity*, HMSO 1996

19 Department of Health. *Primary Care: delivering the future*, HMSO 1996

20 Hudson, B. General Practice and Community Care: developing the links. *Health and Social Care in the Community* 1994; Vol.2, No.5, pp.309-312

21 Means, R. From 'Special Needs' Housing to Independent Living? *Housing Studies* 1996; Vol.11, No.2, pp.207-231

22 Arnold, P. and Page, D. Housing and Community Care: bricks and mortar or foundation for action? Joseph Rowntree Foundation 1992

23 Bradley, V. and Knoll, J. *Shifting paradigms in services to people with developmental disabilities*, Cambridge MA. Human Services Research Institute 1991

24 Smith, G. A. Supported Living: new directions in services to people with learning disabilities, National Association of State Mental Retardation Programme Directors 1990

25 Fletcher, P. House Rules. *Community Care*, 30th May-5th June 1996, pp.6-7

26 Fletcher, P. The relationship between Housing and Community Care Journal of Interprofessional Care 1996 Vol. 10, No. 3, pp. 249–56

27 Harker, M., Kilgallon, B., Palmer, J. and Tickel, C. *Making connections: policy and governance for community care*, National Federation of Housing Associations 1996

Challenges in promoting clinical effectiveness and the use of evidence

Gifford Batstone and Mary Edwards

There are challenges at all levels in the NHS as far as achieving clinical effectiveness* is concerned and in the greater and more overt use of research evidence in making decisions which influence patient care and population health. In this paper, these challenges will be discussed at three main levels:

- at national level;
- at a corporate level, which includes the purchaser and provider interaction;
- at the clinician level, which is influenced by a wide range of factors, some of which may appear conflicting. (Clinician in this context is used to refer to any health care professional involved in providing clinical services to patients and clients in all areas of health care.)

One thing that can be assumed is that everyone involved in the business of health care, whether policy-maker or direct care provider, has an interest in ensuring that the optimal level of care is provided. The challenge to be met, however, is how to turn this overarching objective into reality.

* In this paper clinical effectiveness is defined as the application of interventions which have been demonstrated to be efficacious to relevant populations in an appropriate fashion.

National challenge

The national challenge for clinical effectiveness is given in that deceptively simple phrase – 'to secure, through the resources available, the greatest possible improvement in the physical and mental health of the people of England' which is the main objective of the NHS. This theme is echoed in the introduction to *Promoting Clinical Effectiveness*.[1] The policy documents issued by the Department of Health in this area are aimed at chief executives of health authorities and trusts and appear to suggest a rather centralist view of clinical effectiveness with its three main messages of

- inform
- change
- monitor.

Even the useful publication which followed on sources of information for clinical effectiveness indicates that its purpose is to provide 'guidance about clinical and investment decisions' on 'specific clinical topics'.[2]

Inform

Considerable expenditure has been devoted to creating an information flow for the NHS. The processes of the R&D strategy, health technology assessment and the roles of bodies such as the Centre for Reviews and Dissemination are some of the products of that deployment of resources. *Promoting Clinical Effectiveness* compiles information from Effective Health Care Bulletins, Effectiveness Matters, Epidemiologically Based Needs Assessments, systematic reviews of research evidence, clinical guidelines and health technology assessments on a variety of topics. In addition, a useful reference list to organisations involved in this type of activity is given. The aim, according to all these policy statements is to co-ordinate many areas, such as the national R&D strategy, health authority purchasing intentions (including clinical audit) and the management of NHS providers and education programmes. This appears to be a positive approach; however, there is little indication of how it might be achieved, and it is laced with concepts which run counter to gaining the enthusiasm of clinical staff. For instance, the section on monitoring starts with the assertion that variations in patient treatment are not explained by population characteristics and continues that 'national indicators will be developed to highlight these and help given to investigate them'. This is frequently seen as direct criticism by health care professionals who feel they are doing their best. The recent publication updating the national R&D strategy[3] indicates a change in emphasis with the introduction of key functions such as:

- making knowledge available to decision makers through dissemination;
- promoting the use of research and development findings;
- promoting an evaluative culture in the NHS.

To some extent these targets have been met, for example with the publication from York University of the Effective Health Care Bulletins and Effectiveness Matters and the projected list of new topics.[4] In addition a number of local information sources, such as the Development and Evaluation Committee (South and West Region) and SIGN in Scotland, along with the growth of health service research organisations, such as ScHARR at Sheffield University, have supplemented and sometimes repeated the work of York. It is interesting to note, however, that although more than 90 per cent of health authorities and trusts recall receiving the Effective Health Care Bulletins, only 40 per cent of trusts confirmed having taken any action on the basis of the information.[5]

The Clinical Outcomes Group, set up by the Chief Medical and Nursing Officers for England and Wales, continues to co-ordinate issues around outcomes, clinical effectiveness, guidelines and clinical audit. Under this umbrella, criteria for appraising guidelines[6] have been determined; however, this has led to few guidelines being commended, primarily because of the variable quality of the guidelines. More recent approaches to guideline development, such as those for asthma[7,8] do appear to meet these criteria and represent a step forward in the quality of the style and evidence base of guidelines. Hopefully, other groups involved in the development of guidelines will take note of the success of this approach.

The Health Technology Assessment (HTA) programme is an important part of the national R&D programme and is the largest single initiative in the research side of the clinical effectiveness policy in terms of funding. By the end of 1995 over a hundred systematic reviews and research projects had been funded. However, the time course of this approach inevitably leads to the generation of practice based on current evidence of effectiveness, which is presumably less powerful than the one available when trials and reviews have been completed. The major issue here is that when all this evidence is finally issued through the HTA programme, clinicians will already have found ways of tackling the specific problem. They will then need to change their practice again based upon the new-found research evidence.

In technologically led areas of health service delivery the pressures to be in the forefront run counter to waiting to find the evidence for changing practice, and hence ways in which HTA may be bypassed are created. The rapid uptake of laparoscopic cholecystectomy based upon the perceptions of cost reduction, as a result of reduced length of stay, and a small amount of data and assumptions about improved quality of life immediately post-operatively, have led to comparative trials on safety and effectiveness being undertaken some years after the routine implementation of this technique.

The costs associated with undertaking large scale multicentre trials are escalating at an alarming rate. Combined with this, the patent life of some drugs may be very short (if the drug has been used for many years to treat one problem but it is thought it could be used for something else) and so the profitable return on the trial investment is very limited. This is therefore leading to drug companies restricting the trials undertaken. For the clinician, the problem is that they think a drug may be useful for a particular condition (possibly based upon one small trial) and therefore they decide to use the drug anyway, without strong evidence. These clinicians will be working by 'the best evidence available', although this is often far from optimal and may have considerable resource implications for the NHS.

HTA is currently catching up with the questions clinical practice is asking today, and perhaps this is an inevitable aspect of such an approach. However, clinical practice will not be limited by the availability of research data and HTA will need to look over the horizon to assess up-and-coming pharmaceutical and technological developments if it is to be of optimal benefit to the NHS.

Epidemiologically based needs assessments are aimed at supporting the developing roles of purchasers by summarising the population's health care needs within a typical health authority (normally 250,000 people) for a given disease or health care problem. The composition of the second series for 1997 is shown in Box 1.

Another substantial area that requires assessment is that of screening programmes. The NHS Executive has accepted the recommendation of the National Screening Committee that screening programmes should not be introduced or indeed expanded until they have been reviewed, evaluated and proven to be

Box 1

- Accident and Emergency Departments
- Breast cancer
- Low back pain
- Dermatology
- Child and Adolescent Mental Health
- Gynaecology
- Genitourinary Medicine
- Palliative and Terminal Care

effective, a massive undertaking to which to sign up.

Information on economic evaluations is held on the NHS Executive's Register of Cost Effectiveness Studies, which is updated by the Centre for Reviews and Dissemination at York University and accessible through its database. To date, however, there are only a small number of good quality studies available on cost-effectiveness, and this is a major gap in the information available to policy-makers and managers.

From the NHS policy level it must seem that enormous efforts are being made to promote the generation and availability of research data and technology assessments. While most purchasing authorities are aware of the breadth of these initiatives, there are suggestions[5] that this is much less so in provider organisations. As for the clinician, the plethora of sources, and difficulties with accessibility for those who are not familiar with information technology, leaves these resources virtually untouched. Little appears to have been done to target clinicians or even the library staff in their locality, who should be the vehicle for linking clinicians and information. The situation for staff working in community settings and general practice is even worse, unless electronic links to library services have been created to the locations where clinicians work.

The central efforts in dissemination of evidence seem considerable at first glance but dissemination must be more than merely publishing and mailing. The RCN definition of dissemination[9] indicates the limitations of current central approaches. It considers dissemination as 'the presentation of information and ideas to a variety of audiences needing to use information to improve practice and activity, in forms and media accessible to those audiences'. Perhaps looking at some successes, such as pain control in terminal care and the use of compression bandaging for leg ulcers, gives clues to a way forward. These issues were addressed to professionals through media which were essentially educational. However, the NHSE has done little to harness the considerable expenditure on medical and non-medical education to meet the needs of evidence-based practice. Its approach of targeting information at purchasers may have limited the potential impact for improved patient care.

Change

Following the introduction of the internal market into the health service in 1989, the route for implementing national policy has been through purchasing organisations. Purchasers are still struggling to find the best mechanism for implementing these changes; at present, the commonest one is the contract negotiated with provider organisations. There is growing acknowledgement, however, that the contract is a blunt instrument for achieving change and can simply engender stubborn opposition and numerous excuses for why change cannot happen. It would seem therefore that the current approach of sending policy messages to purchasers, thus avoiding clinicians, is at risk of sabotaging the clinical effectiveness initiative.

There are a number of initiatives looking at implementing and monitoring changes in practice and they highlight the issue of attributing the change. Walshe and Ham[5] consider factors in the uptake of the recommendations contained in the Effective Health Care Bulletins on cataract surgery, treatment of benign prostatic hyperplasia and pressure-relieving aids. From their survey it appears that where recommendations are way out of line with current clinical practice they have little impact (e.g. trans-urethral incision of prostate) and when they are close to current collective professional belief they merely confirm what is already happening (e.g. cataract surgery and pressure sores). They conclude that information on clinical effectiveness needs to target topics which are between these two extremes if it is to have an effect on clinical behaviour. Similar results were found by the GRiPP project implemented in the Oxford Region.

The barrage of acronyms associated with clinical effectiveness indicates the priority it now holds. The majority are associated with specific areas of clinical practice within volunteer organisations and aim to implement the lessons learnt from implementing research findings (see Box 2). Some take an educational approach to learning skills associated with the implementation of evidence and at least one has looked at a number of topics associated with prescribing in general practice.

Box 2

GRiP	(Getting Research into Practice)
FACTS	(Framework for Appropriate Care throughout Sheffield)
ACE	(Assisting Clinical Effectiveness)
PACE	(Promoting Action on Clinical Effectiveness)
ARIF	(Aggressive Research Intelligence Facility
CASP	(Critical Appraisal Skills Programme)
NETRAG	(North East Thames Research Appraisal Group)
EMU	(Evidence supported Medical Union)
TRIP	(Turning Research into Practice)

Initiatives such as those in Box 2 require careful evaluation to show:

- that there was a change in clinical practice;
- that any change is attributable to the implementation intervention;
- that it was the external expert input that generated the change and not simply the allocation of funding;
- that the projects were cost-effective or at least cost-neutral for the patient benefits gained;
- that these project sites were able to take the lessons from a specific clinical topic and develop a widespread improvement in the use of evidence across the whole organisation.

Sadly, to date, there is no objective evidence from evaluation of these projects to satisfy these requirements although the FACTS project in Sheffield probably has the most convincing findings. Many of the projects are relatively new, and their evaluations are awaited with interest, although most appear to have been organised in a fashion which makes it unlikely that they will meet the above criteria. Research projects using quasi-experimental block designs and multiple time frames to show changes in practice are being undertaken and should meet these criteria. Experimental approaches take longer and are more expensive but may in the long run be a more cost-effective way of determining the best ways of changing practice based on evidence.

The unkind but necessary question of whether any success in implementation projects is due to the funding that comes with the project remains unasked. The ability to fund local facilitation for implementing change in clinical practice appears critical to success, as indicated by the Royal College of Nursing's DySSSy (Dynamic Standard Setting System) project, although success cannot be guaranteed. This must raise questions of cost-effectiveness when many projects have been reported informally as barely saving their consumption of resources.

Monitor

This element of the national strategy is characterised[1] as measuring and demonstrating health benefit at both individual and population level. However, there is also an emphasis on 'variations in the way in which people are treated that are not explained by population characteristics'. This promotes monitoring not so much of processes but of resultant health outcomes. While this is necessary to show improvements in health, it is not the way in which those responsible for immediate patient care relate to the health benefits of those patients.

Another monitoring process is that of clinical audit. The NHS has republished *Using Clinical Audit in the NHS: a position statement*, which now includes the government's response to the criticisms of the Public Accounts Committee. Centrally there appears to be an increasing interest in national audits as a way of addressing the factors which influence clinical decision making and variations in clinical practice. This is seen as being complemented by the work of the Clinical Standards Advisory Group which has been charged with taking a detailed look at the standards of care across the NHS.

The issue of monitoring has now become bound up with outcome indicators which come from a range of sources. Those for psychiatry (Health of the Nation Outcome Scales) appear to have a reasonable professional acceptance. However, many of those in the recent government proposals seem to be at odds with scientific information. There is for instance an emphasis on wound infection rates when research findings indicate that these are more closely correlated with the physiological state of the patient and the seriousness of the condition requiring surgery than any other factor. For some conditions, such as breast cancer, the mortality and morbidity rates are more likely to be affected by patterns of referral, uptake of screening and trust funding for a full breast care service than the ability of a surgeon to use a scalpel. Appearing to monitor professionals within trusts by such methods is bound to discredit the move towards a wider use of outcomes information. Tanenbaum[10] in her study of this indicates that physicians regard outcomes research as being as much political as scientific and empowering the research community relative to practising doctors. Current policy seems to be more influenced by researchers than by practising clinicians from district hospitals.

Corporate challenge

The Priorities and Planning Guidance for the NHS 1997/98 presents six medium-term priorities, of which one is clinical effectiveness. Through this, health authorities are charged with 'securing the greatest health gain from the resources available through decisions on the evidence of clinical effectiveness'. To achieve this it is anticipated that they will:

- get information about evidence of clinical effectiveness to decision makers;
- encourage changes in practice;

- measure and monitor the results – for example through clinical audit;
- implement a progressive shift in investment from less effective interventions towards effective ones.

The contractual arrangement between purchaser and provider is a very blunt weapon in this area. Initial approaches, such as not purchasing grommet operations, have fortunately been short-lived. The question which taunts purchasers is how good does the evidence have to be before entering into discussions with provider organisations. Part of this quandary is to determine ways of approaching issues where there is little clinical evidence but high levels of expectation, such as aroma therapy and other complementary therapies. Increasingly, there is a recognition that absence of evidence does not equate to evidence of absence.

Walshe and Ham[5] report that while approximately 60 per cent of health authorities said that they had discussed the Effective Health Care Bulletin on cataract, only 33 per cent of trusts said they had discussed it with their health authority. The figures for the Bulletin on benign prostatic hyperplasia were only 42 per cent and 26 per cent respectively. This disparity must generate concern about the effectiveness of these interactions, so important in meeting the challenge within the Priorities and Planning Guidance.

Attempts to prioritise evidence in order to generate an action list have had a strong tendency to rate only systematic reviews and randomised controlled trials as being worthy of generating any response by purchasers. Another approach has been to calculate the numbers needed to treat (NTN – a calculation made from the absolute risk reduction caused by an intervention rather than the relative risk reduction) to give priority to certain clinical areas.

Despite these approaches to determining how to use resources, legal and other challenges by patient advocacy groups have persuaded purchasers to agree to therapies which have a less strong evidence base than other developments purchasers wished to buy. Moral dilemmas around the drug treatment of multiple sclerosis and motor neurone disease or the use of genetically engineered Factor VIII in haemophilia have challenged interpretations of evidence by purchasers in a very public fashion without generating an appropriate national debate. The system of approval for use of medicines via the Committee on Safety of Medicines is based on safety rather than efficacy. To date, the Department of Health has indicated its unwillingness to consider a two-stage approach which firstly concerns safety and secondly looks at efficacy and suitability for use by the NHS. Similar systems in use in Australia have overcome some of the problems of drug use within their health service. In an era of evidence-based practice the uptake of such a system in the UK has considerable advantages to both purchasers and clinicians, as well as giving a significant message on the importance of effectiveness and cost-effectiveness.

From a population perspective the link between evidence-based practice and clinical effectiveness is indicated in the definition of clinical effectiveness frequently quoted by the Department of Health as the 'application of interventions which have been shown to be efficacious to a population'. This may appear to take a very public health view; however, it accepts that efficacy relates to trials and effectiveness to real practice and hence rather different outcomes may be anticipated. We consider[11] that clinical effectiveness has three pre-requisites – firstly, clinical professionals with up-to-date knowledge and skills and appropriate attitudes; secondly, that these professionals work collaboratively and cohesively in clinical teams; and thirdly, that these teams are supported by management structures which are responsive to both patient and strategic needs. All three are required for clinical effectiveness and any one of these may limit the ability of the others to generate greater clinical effectiveness. Therefore to achieve the targets in the Priority and Planning Guidance, health authorities will need to address all three areas in conjunction with providers.

To help meet the evidence needs of individual clinicians, an increasing number of trusts have worked to increase the accessibility of evidence by providing computer access to Medline, Cochrane and CINAHL from ward/department workstations by linking the library CD–ROM with the hospital intranet. Combined with educational sessions to help clinical staff gain rapid access to the data they need for everyday clinical practice, this tactic gives a clear message to clinicians of the importance managers ascribe to the greater use of evidence. This approach is necessary for the use of evidence in 'real time' to solve clinical problems and enhances overall use of evidence as judged by frequency of accessing databases.

The evidence needs of clinical teams occur in rather different contexts, such as reviewing current practice in response to unexpected clinical patterns or the development of team protocols, care pathways or guidelines. In these contexts of use of evidence, greater concentration may be given not only to systematic reviews but also to organisational and social impacts. For this a wider range of databases will be needed.

Managers will use evidence in the area of prioritising options and may have a greater emphasis on cost-effectiveness data. This, if anything, requires a higher level of searching and appraisal skills than those needed for most clinical decisions, yet the push for education is targeted largely at clinicians and those with public health roles. If purchaser and provider managers wish their clinical colleagues to 'live by the evidence', they must undertake to recognise the disciplines of the use of evidence in prioritising the deployment of resources. Methods such as that described by Guyatt *et al.*[12] do not seem to be used widely.

In their interactions with provider organisations health authorities need to determine whether to take a topic-based approach to clinical effectiveness or try to attempt a more systematic approach to enhancing the use of evidence. Information on the extent to which trusts which undertake an implementation project on one particular topic are able to use this experience and the learning gained to change practice in other clinical topics has yet to be shown. The alternative or supplementary approach to promote a more general increase in the use of evidence involves provision of the necessary databases and educational programmes to increase the use of these. Few health authorities appear to have co-ordinated their activities with those responsible for education such as education consortia (for non-medical education) and postgraduate medical and dental deans. However, linking clinical effectiveness with clinical audit funding appears widespread and has helped audit processes to use research evidence rather than group consensus to create the criteria and standards for audit. The belief that continuing education does not work needs to be dispelled if health and education authorities are to work together. The systematic review by Davis *et al.*[13] indicates that continuing medical education works but the range of clinical behaviours in the trials reviewed seems very limited. Perhaps more informative are the data presented in a different format[14] which indicates that more interactive, locally or workplace-based approaches are more likely not only to change the knowledge base and practice but also improve patient outcomes.

For both health authorities and trusts considering whether or not to invest in a new service (e.g. a stroke unit), a very wide range of information comes into play. Local prevalence data, population demography, length of stay, mortality and morbidity, patient satisfaction surveys and focus groups, cost per case, information gained from visits to see different models of work, organisation of existing services, all have a role. These influences are not from experimental research but are needed to interpret the findings of systematic reviews. Further, they are not as rigorous as experimental research and may have in-built assumptions, such as the discounting rate in economic models. Educating clinical staff in appraising and assessing such a wide range of information and collating the overall findings require more than just one-day courses on critical appraisal skills. Evidence that acquisition of such skills influences clinical behaviour of established clinicians is lacking.

The range of evidence on changing clinical practice (see [15,16,17]) does not seem to be widely used by those wishing to generate those changes. This gives a poor impression of the determination to use evidence by those clinicians who are aware of this data.

The clinician's challenge

The challenge for policy-makers is to present clinical effectiveness in a fashion which helps clinicians to detect, accept and use evidence to improve clinical effectiveness. Clinicians are more likely to be influenced by their colleagues, their professional bodies and the requests of their patients than they are by commissioners of clinical services. This section will address these issues and ways in which policy-makers may harness the considerable efforts of the professions.

Professional bodies

The main discussion point in the professional literature has concerned the definition and purpose of demands for the greater use of evidence and increasing clinical effectiveness. Responses polarise according to the source of the challenge to implement research findings into routine practice. For example, a hierarchy of acceptability can be developed so that if a local respected peer thinks change is needed, that is preferable to the view of the Royal College, which in turn is more acceptable than the view of the local purchasing authority. To many, clinical effectiveness is seen, at best, as a slight to professional practice and at worst as the end of clinical freedom and the Hippocratic oath. To some extent these discussions focus on the definitions of evidence-based practice and clinical effectiveness.

Issues around definitions

Evidence-based medicine has been defined as the 'conscientious, explicit and judicious use of current best evidence in making decisions about the care of individual patients',[18] an approach which has become closely associated with the implementation of randomised controlled trials in medicine. By comparison a different emphasis is given by McKibbon *et al.*,[19] who describe evidence-based practice (EBP) as ' an approach to health care that promotes the collection, interpretation, and integration of valid, important and applicable patient-reported, clinician-observed and research-derived evidence. The best available evidence, moderated by patient circumstances and preferences, is applied to improve the quality of clinical judgements'. This definition indicates the range of evidence and factors which influence decisions taken in the clinician–patient interaction when determining appropriate care. The yet wider definition, that of evidence-based health care, by Hicks[20] is a functional one: 'evidence-based health care takes place when decisions that affect the care of patients are taken with due weight accorded to all valid, relevant information'. This approach involves not just clinical practitioners but also managers and policy-makers and accepts information as the resource, providing it is both valid and relevant. As such it has a greater level of acceptability as it removes the perceived stigma that clinical effectiveness is something managers expect or demand of clinicians rather than being a corporate way of behaving.

Central initiatives on clinical effectiveness and the use of evidence, which work through professional mechanisms, need to take account of the use of language and the covert messages it gives to practitioners. The frequent use of the term 'evidence-based medicine' is perceived as being exclusive to medical doctors and has implications that only randomised controlled trials can indicate how clinical practice may be improved. For this reason the wider use of Hicks' definition will be welcome to the majority of providers of care.

Actions of professions in health care

Professional bodies have always recognised their role in enhancing the clinical practice of their members – indeed this is their major role. This has been demonstrated in the production of professional standards and many clinical guidelines. Over time, guidelines are becoming more evidence-based and less the consensus opinion of the celebrated few. Moves to require and monitor continuing education (e.g. continuing medical education for doctors and the UKCC post-registration system (PREP) for nurses) recognise the rapidly changing evidence base of clinical practice but without overtly specifying the need for this continuing education to be based upon research findings.

Professional bodies have in various ways incorporated in their examination systems the skills of critical appraisal of research as well as promoting research activities to ensure their members have appropriate skills as part of their preparation for professional practice.

Currently, the importance of evidence-based practice and clinical effectiveness is demonstrated by the development of centres dedicated to these issues for a range of clinical specialities including those listed in Box 3.

In addition there is now an increasing range of publications to promote professional interest in the use of evidence and enhancing clinical effectiveness, as shown in Box 4.

Box 3

Centre for Evidence-based Medicine

Centre for Evidence-based Child Health

Centre for Evidence-based Nursing

Centre for Evidence-based Pathology

Box 4

Evidence-based Medicine

Evidence-based Nursing

Evidence-based Cardiovascular Medicine

Evidence-based Health Policy and Management

Bandolier

Journal of Clinical Effectiveness

Journal of Evaluation in Clinical Practice

Journal of Health Services Research and Policy

Journal of Quality in Clinical Practice

(A much more detailed list may be found in Booth A, *The ScHARR Guide to Evidence-based Practice,* Sheffield: ScHARR, 1997)

These publications fulfil a number of needs for professionals. Some give summaries of research evidence or systematic reviews with a commentary to indicate the importance of the findings and consider issues of implementation. Others review a variety of aspects of clinical practice and have an educational role in helping readers understand more of the techniques involved in interpreting the significance of research findings. Most concentrate on experimental approaches; however, a few now include qualitative data. Those concentrating on clinical effectiveness cover issues of implementation, patients' views of changes in care and the roles of monitoring and audit.

Other developments have been using information technology. The development of the Cochrane Library brings over 65,000 references to clinical trials and systematic reviews into a single CD-ROM easily used on a personal computer. For those more competent technologically there are many internet sources and at least four which give ready access to clinical material (see Box 5).

Box 5

MedFinder http://www.netmedicine.com/medfinder.htm

Cliniweb http://www.ohsu.edu/cliniweb/

OMNI http://www.ac.uk

IDEA http://www.ohsu.edu/bicc-informatics/ebm/ebm_topics.htm

One major route for the dissemination and promotion of good clinical practice and its organisation has been through clinical guidelines. Most professional bodies have taken this route to updating their membership, often funded in part by central funds for clinical audit. The end result has been a large number of publications which the NHS Executive has sought to endorse through the Clinical Outcomes Group. As indicated earlier, however, the appraisal system developed by Cluzeau *et al.*[6] has meant that many guidelines have not met the quality criteria required. This has acted as a stimulus to guideline development groups and recent publications, such as that on asthma by the Newcastle group,[8] indicate the evidence on which recommendations are based and fulfil the other criteria.

Most professional bodies do not appear to have made overt links between their guideline development activities and their role in training and continuing professional development. Better co-ordination of systematic reviews of evidence, guideline development, education and clinical audit is required by the professional bodies if they are to use their full potential for enhancing clinical practice and patient outcomes. One organisation that has made a start in this co-ordination is the Royal College of Nursing that published its Clinical Effectiveness Strategy in 1996 indicating that they were seeking to make exactly these links.

The Department of Health has invested in the roles of professional bodies in clinical audit but this does not seem to have generated the co-ordination of the legitimate role of professional bodies in generating a high level of clinical practice by their members.

Clinical team challenge

As most improvements in patient care involve a wide range of individuals developing and optimising a system of care based on research findings rather than just a single intervention by a single professional, the dynamics of the multi-professional team are a key factor in developing effective clinical practice. Selection of topics where research evidence might be sufficiently important to consider by the clinical team is an essential starting point. Various members of the team will have different priorities influenced by their professional pressures and interests but probably little by overall population needs. With respect to guidelines Batista and Hodge[21] have suggested a route to determining topics which could be considered:

1. Feasibility
   adequate data and likelihood that implementation will make a difference
2. Population
   prevalence of the condition being considered, whether implementation will improve patient quality of life, and the target group of clinicians who see patients with the condition
3. Costs
   resources needed for implementation both in individual cases and for the population as a whole, for both current and unrecognised needs
4. Effects on population, costs and practice
   chances of improving patient quality of life, development and implementation costs, considering both positive and negative potential

These factors are essentially a *population dimension*, and health authorities working with specific clinical teams need to recognise this and that members of the team are likely to offer a variety of research approaches to any particular clinical issue. While randomised controlled trials remain the gold standard of scientific enquiry into clinically effective practice, observational and qualitative data should not be automatically dismissed as lacking validity and reliability. Observational studies are often more sensitive to context – 'and also most likely to have lessons for real health care in real situations'[22] which take account of context, history, culture and values. Teams will be more successful if they accept a plurality of research data recognising that professional groups may have traditional preferences for qualitative and quantitative approaches and use them both to develop new clinical practice. Part of this process involves the mutual recognition of roles in delivering patient care and as such may be used as an approach to team development. Issues around the applicability of systematic reviews have been addressed by the Cochrane Collaboration[23] and need to be considered by both clinical teams and health authorities.

Policy-makers will assist in this process if they accept a hierarchy of evidence which is more wide ranging than that traditionally used. We suggest that the evidence bearing on clinical practice can be set out in the following hierarchy, which ranges from the most to the least reliable.

Experimental
- Systematic review
- Randomised controlled trial

Quasi-experimental
- Cohort study
- Case controlled study
- Survey
- Block design study

Qualitative
- Interview
- Observation (participant, non-participant)
- Grounded theory

Opinion
- Consensus approach (Delphi, nominal group, etc.)
- Expert opinion

Individual challenge

There is often a set of rather negative responses to concepts of evidence-based practice. Many clinicians will argue that they have always used evidence in determining the nature of their clinical work. However, this begs the question of the availability of all the relevant evidence and how effectively this has been sought or whether practice is based on a limited or even selective search for information. Frequently, those espousing such views are not aware of developments in databases, searching strategies, systematic reviewing and meta-analysis. The issue is, therefore: are the changes needed attitudinal, technical or both? Many professionals are not just computer-naive but essentially IT-phobic. Local strategies to help clinical staff learn the basics of searching and appraising data may be led locally involving library staff and a variety of health care professionals with sufficient expertise. These may be interested doctors or nurses; however, it is interesting to note that pharmacists have many of the necessary technological and searching skills needed to help other clinical colleagues. Further, the need for continuing professional development, such as PGEA in general practice, CME/CPD for hospital doctors, PREP for nurses and similar approaches for therapists, may be used as levers to introduce more staff to the necessary skills.

The genuine use of research in determining routine clinical practice and problem solving will not happen until research evidence is more readily available to clinicians in their workplace and clinicians are sufficiently confident in using the skills of searching, appraising and applying evidence.

The powerful role of social influences on changes in clinical practice has been shown in a number of studies,[24] yet there appears to be little use of these approaches in clinical effectiveness policy, although they are used widely in the pharmaceutical industry. Presumably the use of influential peers is cost-effective or alternatives would have been sought by industry.

Another source of information are studies on how clinicians change their practice and what approaches they take to this. These show the wide use of education and learning and that this is more deliberate and extensive as the changes to be made are more complex.[25,26,27]

Patient challenge

There are challenges in the use of evidence for both individual patients and patient advocacy organisations. Many advocacy groups are increasingly proficient in acquiring and appraising a wide range of evidence in their field of interest. Further they have a ready audience to assimilate their conclusions and are therefore influential in patient's expectations of appropriate interventions. Challenges by health care professionals and purchasers to these expectations are regarded as being cost based and hence rationing of services.

For the individual patient there is increasing recognition that 'in order for autonomous authorisation to be genuine both the doctor and the patient need access to good quality information'.[28] For instance, the use of video to present information on prostate disease and help patients understand how various options might relieve their specific symptoms, and with what risk of side-effects, has modified patient expectations and reduced the frequency of surgical procedures. Further, as many patients are more adept at searching the internet and finding relevant information, the concept of the special body of knowledge associated with the professional diminishes, altering the clinician–patient relationship.

Changes which will happen in the professional role as patients have access to clinical research information need to be addressed by educationalists. When patients have access to information which runs counter to the contents of clinical contracts with health authorities, it is the clinician who is left in a difficult position. From their current behaviour, commissioners of clinical services seem at best unaware of the difficult position in which clinicians are placed. Again policy seems to be top-down and no efforts appear to be made to help clinicians deal with these situations.

Conclusions

The role of policy in promoting clinical effectiveness accepts a model of change indicated in Box 6.

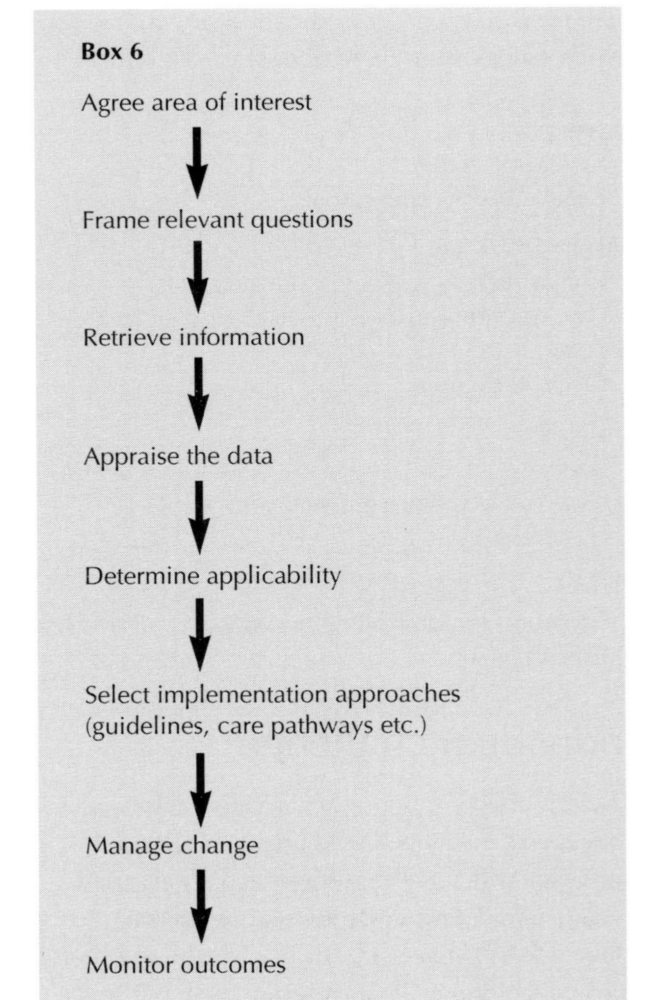

This generic process requires the information being produced through both departmental and professional efforts but there is still a large gap between information producers and information users. Much of this echoes the differences between views of researchers and clinicians indicated by Tanenbaum.[10]

Firstly, clinicians need answers to questions as they arise in clinical practice. The fact that some health technology assessment or systematic review will give the necessary information at some point in the future merely increases their frustration. For this reason these processes need to anticipate to a much greater extent than currently the future needs of patients and clinicians.

Secondly, there is the question of the population versus the patient focus of clinical effectiveness and the wider use of research evidence. While health authorities and government rightly focus on populations, clinicians even with wide experience rarely achieve numbers of patients or treatments which reach statistical significance. This is the strength of the approach of clinical audit in that it allows clinicians to set standards based on the evidence and monitor the process of care anticipating these standards will be met in full. This is a correct professional approach providing the standards are evidence-based.

To overcome the issues and generate a true clinician interest policy needs to be reviewed from the viewpoint of clinicians working in clinical teams and how it can help them overcome the dilemmas they face. A greater concentration on enabling clinicians to access the data already available in a fashion which meets the immediacy of clinical issues will create a greater sense of ownership rather than these data being solely for the research community and those fascinated by information technology. The considerable efforts of professional bodies and groups need to be co-ordinated more effectively, not only with government policy, but also their own educational roles and those of education consortia and postgraduate deaneries.

More use should be made of both recognising that systematic reviews give good information on how to apply evidence and the range of evidence that is needed to generate changes in clinical systems delivered by clinical teams.

The sole use of service contracts is far too blunt an instrument by itself to change the attitudes of clinicians towards clinical effectiveness. Health authorities need to use the evidence on changing clinical practice much more widely if they are to achieve their aims. As social influences appear so important in determining changes in clinical practice, the question as to why they are not used more must be addressed. Similarly, health authority and national approaches to using clinical audit as a monitoring tool need to recognise the differing approaches of clinicians and researchers to outcomes measurements.

References

1 NHS Executive, *Promoting Clinical Effectiveness, A framework for action in and through the NHS*, Jan 1996

2 NHS Executive, *Clinical Effectiveness Reference Pack*, Oct 1996

3 NHS Executive, *Research and Development in the new NHS: functions and responsibilities*, 1995

4 Sheldon TA, Melville A, Providing intelligence for rational decision making in the NHS: the NHS Centre for Reviews and Dissemination, *J Clinical Effectiveness* 1996; 1, 51–4

5 Walshe K, Ham C, *Acting on the evidence, progress in the NHS*, The NHS Confederation, 1997

6 Cluzeau F *et al.*, Appraising clinical guidelines: results of a pilot study, *J Inter Professional Care*

1995; 9, 227–35

7 Eccles M *et al.*, North of England evidence-based guidelines development project: methods of guideline development, *BMJ* 1996; 312, 760–2

8 North of England Asthma Guideline Development Group, North of England evidence-based guidelines development project: summary version of evidence-based guideline for the primary care management of asthma in adults, *BMJ* 1996; 312, 762–6

9 NHS Executive, *Report on the Task Force on the Strategy for Research in Nursing, Midwifery and Health Visiting*, 1993

10 Tanenbaum SJ, Knowing and acting in medical practice: the epistemological politics of outcome research, *J Health Politics, Policy and Law* 1994; 19, 27–44

11 Batstone GF, Edwards MB, Achieving clinical effectiveness: just another initiative or a real change in working practice?, *J Clinical Effectiveness* 1996; 1, 19–21

12 Guyatt GH *et al.*, User's guides to the medical literature IX. A method for grading health care recommendations, *JAMA* 1995; 274, 1800–4

13 Davis DA *et al.*, 1995, Changing physician performance. A systematic review of the effect of continuing medical education strategies, *JAMA*, 274, 1836–7

14 Davis DA, The dissemination of information: optimising the effect of continuing medical education, In: Earl VD *et al.* (eds), *Disseminating research/changing practice*, Thousand Oaks: Sage, 1994, pp.139–50

15 Oxman AD *et al.*, No magic bullets: a systematic review of 102 trials of interventions to improve professional practice, *J Canad Med Assoc.* 1995; 153, 1423–31.

16 Funk SG, Tornquist EM, Champagne MT, Barriers and facilitators to research utilisation. An integrative review, *Nurs Clin N Amer* 1995; 30, 395–407

17 Lomas J, Teaching old (and not so old) docs new tricks: effective ways to implement research findings, In: Earl VD *et al.* (eds), Disseminating research/changing practice, Thousand Oaks: Sage, 1994

18 Sackett DL, Richardson WS, Rosenberg W, Haynes RB, *Evidence-based medicine: how to practice and teach EBM*, London: Churchill Livingstone, 1996

19 McKibbon KA *et al.*, The medical literature as a resource for evidence-based care at *http://hiru.mcmaster.ca/hiru/medline/mdl-ebc.htm*

20 Hicks N, Evidence-based health care, *Bandolier* 1997; 4, issue 5, 8

21 Battista RN, Hodge MJ, Setting priorities and selecting topics for clinical practice guidelines, *Can Med Assoc J* 1995; 153, 1233–7

22 Carr-Hill R, Editorial: Welcome? to the brave new world of evidence-based medicine. *Social Science and Medicine* 1995; 41, 1467–8

23 Glasziou P, Applicability and recommendations, *The Cochrane Collaboration Methods Working Groups Newsletter* 1997; June, Oslo

24 Mittman BS, Tonesk X, Jacobson PD, Implementing clinical practice guidelines: social influence strategies and practitioner behavior change, *Quarterly Review Bulletin* 1992; 18, 413–21

25 Fox RD, Mazmanian PE, Putnam RW, *Changing and learning in the lives of physicians*, New York: Praeger, 1989

26 Allery L, Owen PA, Robling MR, Why GPs and consultants change their clinical practice; a critical incident study, *BMJ* 1997; 314, 870–4

27 Soumerai S, Avorn J, Principles of educational outreach to improve clinical decision making, *JAMA* 1990; 263, 549–56

28 Hope A, Editorial, *J Med Ethics* 1995; 21, 259

Minding the gap: design, practice and expectations in emergency care

Thomas Judge

Social and technological changes along with the effect of world-wide economic competition will continue to force re-appraisal of our social contracts across all areas of public expenditure, but especially in health care. This re-appraisal presents an unusual dilemma particular to medicine. Unlike other public systems in which strategic planning goals can be established, at least in theory, on the basis of projected demographic changes, in health care, near infinite demand, a lack of defined therapeutic endpoints, and moving targets in the forms of care provision present a never-ending conflict between desire and public finance.

Perhaps the most visible service in the re-appraisal of health care – and one service which, because of its special features, illustrates the problems of design and practice – is the provision of emergency medical care. As with every other sector of health care, utilisation of emergency services is growing year on year, but there is no consensus as to the factors responsible for this growth and hence whether or how it can be controlled. While the lack of evidence-based practice remains an issue across medicine as a whole, it is particularly visible in the emergency sector owing to the pervasive influence of the media. Almost as soon as new interventions are reported, they become the dramatised in both documentary and fictional media, thereby creating demand for application. The high emotive content also attracts the majority of media and public attention when mismatches between resources and services result in delivery failures. Currently, it is nearly impossible to find a single report on health care in general not incorporating the sounds and visual images of the ambulance service and/or the hospital A&E department.

Moreover emergency care by definition does not respond to traditional strategies for controlling utilisation through scheduling or for delaying utilisation, such as GP appointments or the waiting lists used for elective procedures. With both budgets and responsibility resting with a range of organisations, emergency care sits on 'the fault line of the tectonic plates of primary and secondary care.'[1] In all, the rapid growth, high visibility, and the complexity of system attributes allow emergency care to serve as a useful surrogate in understanding larger system problems in health care and the public decisions required to provide services into the future.

Taken together, growth in demand, high visibility, with corresponding political sensitivity, provider reluctance to change practice, and the complex and changing function of the emergency care system present a huge challenge to the sustainability of the NHS. The inter-relationships between these four issues are producing a widening gap between demand and resources. While year-on-year growth in demand against fairly flat resources is perhaps the easiest way to define the gap, the real issue is one of system design, practice, and expectations. This article argues that although there are some factors such as an ageing population which cannot be controlled, many of the factors contributing to the mismatch *are* within provider control and are the result of traditional paradigms of emergency care. If the current mismatch between demand and resources is to be brought back into balance, providers must change their fundamental understanding of emergency care.

Foundations

Historically, the provision of emergency medical services arose primarily from developing a community level 'rescue' type response to injuries from fire, drowning, and road traffic accidents with additional limited roles developed from war time experience for managing mass casualty incidents and disasters. Ambulance care attendants were minimally trained, if at all, and care was essentially defined as transport, often described as a 'hair-raising horizontal ride to the hospital.' The UK transport system, developed in the contingencies of the Second World War, illustrated the need for a response structure to catastrophic multi-casualty incidents whether natural or man-made.

Prior to 1974 ambulance transport was organised at the local council level and hospital level services were described as 'casualty units' in the UK reflecting the war years' element of trauma. Units were small; typically a room or several rooms (hence the concept of the 'ER' in the USA), sometimes staffed by a nurse, with back-up from whatever physician was most available whether trained in resuscitation or not. Routine, resuscitative interventions today performed by paramedic and technician crews were strictly within the province of physicians if they were available at all and most were unavailable.

Two key issues predominated in the developing emergency care system. The first problem was life-taking trauma. In the era before universal automobile ownership, this was primarily a military problem revolving around triage and transport from the battlefield. The trauma ethos of the military experience had several effects on the development of emergency medical systems (EMS). Beginning with Larrey's introduction of triage and mass deployment of ambulances in 1797 and evolving through Thomas's significant development of the traction splint used for femoral fractures in the First World War, the concepts of early evacuation, triage, and field treatment of battlefield casualties have steadily reduced battlefield mortality with the mean evacuation time from the battlefield in hours roughly reflecting the percentage of mortality. The US experience in Vietnam, introducing wide deployment of dedicated medivac helicopters, reduced the previously formidable ratios of earlier wars to the 2 per cent level, nearly matching mean evacuation time frames from the battleground of roughly one hour to two hours.

The other great EMS dilemma, the management of cardiac arrest, arose from efforts to overcome near-universal mortality from these events. Efforts to reverse the effects of arrest began with demonstrating the efficacy of mouth-to-mouth breathing in the USA by Safar in the late 1950s and the introduction of public resuscitation training in the early 1960s. Simultaneously, in Belfast, Pantridge and Geddes, observing increased morbidity from acute myocardial infarction and poor survival rates in out-of-hospital cardiac arrest, decided to take the physician and newly portable cardiac monitor/defibrillator, then a dramatic advancement in cardiac care, to the patient hoping to better salvage hearts rather than wait for yet another non-viable patient to arrive at the Royal Infirmary. These early efforts were systematised in Brighton by Chamberlin and Baskett over the next ten to fifteen years with dramatic positive results in resuscitation.

In addition to trauma and cardiac arrest, it is important to appreciate two other key ingredients, both again originating from the military experience. First, the concept of using non-clinician staff to provide advanced resuscitative skills. Second, a trauma care model of problem stabilisation followed by rapid transport, by road or helicopter, to distinct trauma units staffed by specialist trauma surgeons. In the civilian context this became the core of the modern EMS system with technicians and paramedics providing increasingly sophisticated field resuscitation and stabilisation followed by transport to specialist physicians at the A&E.

System design: the mortality model

While brief, this short history is essential in understanding both successes and failures in the current system, as the originating ethos and understanding of what constitutes emergency care continue to define the system today. It is also essential to understand that the last three decades have witnessed a complete transformation in emergency care, but this has taken place through piecemeal adaptation, in response to new clinical technology and opportunities rather than as a result of conscious system design. New providers and technology have been widely deployed with tremendous knock-on effects in other areas of medicine. Resuscitation theories, assisted by the ever-increasing portability of advanced technology, have defined an emergency care system in its own right almost overnight. Common causes of mortality, considered untreatable barely more than a generation ago, are today considered treatable public health problems with, in particular, an expectation the health care system be capable of reversing cardio-pulmonary arrest.

Throughout this evolution, the primary objective of 'saving lives' has remained at the core of the service. This makes sense on one level in that, despite the implementation of a sophisticated emergency care system in the UK, the impacts of cardiac arrest and critical trauma remain substantial. Despite the investment in a highly developed emergency care system, 250,000 people per year experience acute myocardial infarctions[2] with estimates of potentially reversible premature cardiac death in the realm of 75,000 per annum.[3] With primary focus on sudden death, the newly introduced ambulance standards have been almost wholly justified by anticipated gains in 'lives saved' in cardiac arrest. The case of life-taking trauma is similar, with a 1988 report from the Royal College of Surgeons estimating that in comparison with the USA up to 33 per cent of 514 trauma deaths were avoidable in a 1000 case cohort.[4]

But although dramatic results in resuscitation have been managed in some settings, success in one setting has not been broadly reproducible in other environments despite continuing growth and deployment of resources. The demonstrated 'gold standard' of an out-of-hospital 30-40 per cent success rate in cardiac survival is achieved in only a handful of communities world-wide and estimated reported survival rates in the UK – no standard reporting format exists – range between 2 and 11 per cent.[5,6]

Central initiatives to improve services have not necessarily improved the situation. While the Government delayed the widespread introduction of cardiac defibrillators in the ambulance service until 1984, less than ten years later, in 1993 without any specific evidence as to the efficacy of paramedic level care, the call came for trusts, with great fanfare of *Patient's Charter* standards, and at significant expense, to provide a paramedic on every ambulance, primarily to treat cardiac arrest and life-taking trauma. Lost in the fanfare are science and design. In both cardiac arrests and critical trauma, paramedics are only part of the solution. Current strategies for dealing with cardiac arrest have been overtaken by technology and are out of date. Paramedics were originally conceived as 'equaling' defibrillators, now a technician skill. And while the ongoing debate in the pre-hospital community revolves around who is better at managing cardiac arrest, successive studies have shown little difference in survival rates for these patients whether treated by paramedics or technicians.[7,8,9]

More fundamental in responding to cardiac arrest is a system to get a cardio-defibrillator to the patient as quickly as possible, with survival decreasing by 10–12 per cent in each successive minute of ventricular fibrillation, the most common lethal cardio-electrical event.[10] Again, technology has moved on and the advent of automatic defibrillators means this therapy, originally strictly the province of physicians, is now a component of public cardio-pulmonary resuscitation (CPR) training. If there is an eight-minute window of opportunity at maximum to reverse sudden cardiac arrest, and four minutes are necessary to achieve best practice results, it is not the current EMS system that will likely make the major difference. At minimum, defibrillation should be available from every public safety response point such as the fire brigades and police services. If the current technology of interpretative, automatic defibrillators, usable with minimal training had been available in 1967 rather than 1987, the emergency care system of today would likely look very different.

Why is this important? Clearly, cardiac arrest and critical trauma remain primary challenges in emergency care systems as these clinical conditions must be reversed within minutes. However, these two issues are only a small component of care delivered outside either the GP's surgery or the A&E department. In a financially constrained system, 'gold standard' performance – the ability to deliver care at all times and in all places in less than 8 minutes for the fraction of patients experiencing these life-taking dilemmas, comes at the expense of the vast majority of problems encountered by emergency care providers. The reverse is also true, answering the common condition efficiently and effectively makes it more difficult to respond to the extraordinary.

In any case, reversing cardiac arrest is a narrow measure of system performance. While neurologically intact resuscitation is the ultimate positive result for an emergency care system, achieving this success only affects a narrow subset of the population at great expense. Moreover, what can be achieved in this way is much less than it is often suggested. A survival rate even as high as 30 per cent also means 7 out of 10 patients do not survive, but this is seldom acknowledged, indeed the opposite is more likely. A recent review of US media by the *New England Journal of Medicine* found a 67 per cent survival rate of patients with cardiac arrest on prime-time television series in the USA, far in excess of the current 15-30 per cent discharge rate experience.[12] No comparable review has been made in the UK but the results are unlikely to differ.

Increasing experience also shows that some patients do not benefit from resuscitation and further significant numbers do not want resuscitation, primarily patients with terminal disease. Although a patient's primary physician may write a 'Do Not Attempt Resuscitation' order, there is no consistent universally accepted format in place. Further, although recent recommendations by the Royal Colleges Ambulance Liaison Committee[13] have begun to address the futility issue, requirements remain conservative, with limited options for either not starting or terminating resuscitation efforts. By and large this means the continuing practice of often futile resuscitation followed by transport to the hospital.

Strategies targeting cardiac arrest have meant a large investment with dramatic but limited results for a small cohort of the population. It is not that managing cardiac arrest is not important, it is the manner in which it is undertaken in the face of other issues. The much larger health care issue is to focus on rethinking the much larger role the Ambulance Service Trusts, technicians and paramedics must play in co-ordinating and delivering not only resuscitation but a much wider spectrum of emergency care in the community.

Changing the model: from mortality to morbidity

At the end of the day, treating cardiac arrest is palliative care at best: chasing improvements in mortality statistics may slow down proven success in reducing morbidity from left ventricular failure and cardiogenic shook, a far better economic investment. Recent work in Grampian demonstrates the value, in these terms, of better management of acute myocardial infarction (AMI), a common precursor to cardiac arrest. The recognised treatment pathway is early recognition, access, immediate intervention with oxygen and nitrites, opiate analgesia, and thrombolysis. Despite years of evidence that maximum benefits of treatment must be achieved 'in the community at the first opportunity; [as] coronary care initiated in hospital can only have limited impact on mortality'[14] the benefits of early opiate and thrombolytic administration remain largely unrealised until entry into the hospital. GP involvement in acute cardiac care is limited in most places, and paramedics are not allowed to administer either the opiate or thrombolytic agents. With increased survival rates nearly double the rate of salvage from arrest states, the economics are overwhelming not only in the immediate term but in reduction of long-term disability. Recent efforts by a number of ambulance trusts to 'fast track' AMI patients have showed good results in reducing 'door to needle' time, but these efforts are limited in scope and even where operational, they are not widely reproduced; definitive care still waits until some point after hospital arrival.

Meeting the objectives of the best treatment being available at the right time and place needs a range of strategies which will require more training and equipment, and most important completely changed relationships between GPs, paramedics, and A&E staff. Obviously the costs of implementation are substantial, but as Rawles points out in his analysis of costing 'by giving any thrombolytic agent half an hour earlier we gain as many lives as we would from giving alteplase (r-tPA) instead of streptokinase – at no additional cost and without the penalty of two additional strokes per thousand.'[15] In addition to the benefit in terms of lives saved, this half an hour saving represents nearly £1,100 savings per patient available to spend on either an improved drug regimen, as suggested by Rawles, or other care.

The traditional emphasis on cardiac arrest may also come at the expense of overall community health care. The emergency care system, both pre- and in hospital, measures success by, and requires resources for, the reversal of cardio-pulmonary arrest and critical illness or trauma. In practice, however, its role has become the management of all types of medical and trauma problems, minor to life-taking, serving as the public safety net for a myriad of what may be defined as 'non-medical' problems incurred by the homeless, mentally ill, poor, transient, and immigrant populations with language and structural access problems to NHS and social services.

In brief, although the system is built around the critically ill and injured, emergency care in fact serves a great variety of needs. It encompasses a very wide range of providers, but while every provider has some responsibility, it is difficult to pinpoint where the responsibility for emergency care as a whole lies. Without a strategic design for the system, resources and efforts will continue to be wasted through duplication, while opportunities to improve services for the public will continue to slip by. It is to this issue we turn next.

Recent policy: problems in understanding practice

Rapidly rising demand and costs, publicly heralded emergency care delivery failures, and unclear results have lead to calls for a comprehensive review of the emergency care system. *By Accident or Design*, the Audit Commission review of A&E services and the current Audit Commission review of ambulance contracting and performance are indicative of this effort.

The introduction to the 1994 Scottish Office Policy Review calls for an even wider approach to looking at the entire system of emergency care.

> *The Report takes as its starting point the needs of patients who require urgent healthcare without having been able to make any prior arrangements. It has therefore had to take account of the complete spectrum of patients' A&E health care needs. That approach involves recognition of the fact that such patients require the services of a wide range of services and medical specialities, including A&E departments, associated specialities such as orthopaedics, anaesthetics, and coronary care, ambulance services, and primary care services. The report gives the name 'A&E Service' to the totality of these components. It is important that this should not be regarded as synonymous with the speciality of A&E medicine.*[16]

It goes on to detail how this system should be implemented.

> *Health Boards, as the primary agents of change in the NHS, through the contracting process and as purchasers of services on behalf of their populations, should plan to secure an A&E Service which:*
>
> - *meets the identified needs of the population, both resident and visiting;*
> - *takes account of public wishes and expectations;*
> - *provides the most effective intervention possible within the timescale required;*
> - *makes optimal use of the resources available;*
> - *provides the most appropriate form of care in the most cost effective manner, by striking the correct balance of provision between primary, hospital and major trauma care, with appropriate ambulance support;*
> - *is accessible to the population to a degree commensurate with the right treatment being available at the right time and place.*

The envisioned system, however, may exist more on paper than in practice, even in Scotland, which probably has one of the most organised 'systems' of emergency care in the UK.

Problems however emerge even in the description. The call for a comprehensive service composed of many specialities does not include, at least by name, providers usually considered as part of the 'social care' system, despite their clients overwhelming the A&E department on a regular basis. Further, it defines what 'A&E medicine' is not, although in fact providing a comprehensive primary, social and specialist care

Table 1 Event-driven care attributes

occurrence outside care point
24-hour occurrence
seasonal variations
minor to life-taking misfortune
time and not time sensitive
unpredictable
unexpected
unplanned/scheduled care
expected
planned
chronic care crisis
health maintenance

Table 2 Emergency-driven care attributes

unplanned and unexpected
unpredictable +/-
crisis – extremely time sensitive
first few minutes to hour are crucial
critical and potentially life-taking
< 3-5% of volume
some patients will not survive despite interventions
resource and technology intensive
expertise in handling volume sensitive
concentration of resources and specialists necessary
must be managed on specific site through transport

Table 3 Urgent-driven care attributes

time sensitive +/-
first minutes to hour are crucial
minor to major problems
90-95% of volume
limited critical resource and technology
misfortune and chronic care based
after hours and access to care barriers
demographic and geographic considerations
unplanned palliative crisis
unplanned chronic disease management
social and psyche care problems
manageable in multiple settings

service is the essence of A&E medicine.

While the content and practice of both primary care and specialist care are well defined, the arenas of emergent or urgent care are not. A useful concept for thinking about them is *event-driven care*. This is illustrated in Table 1, which comprises an entire spectrum of problems, small to large, simple to complex, and urgent to emergent. Tables 2 and 3 illustrate the attributes of emergency in comparison with urgent care. Emergency care has evolved into the provision of short-term interventions in health crises with the important distinguishing feature of location – these events occur outside of established medical care delivery points. It is important to recognise the key differences in provider capability and location of where care can be delivered. Emergency care of the critically ill or injured requires constant exposure to a fairly small group of patients in order to maintain competence and needs to be delivered in the setting of immediate accessibility to specialised care, while the much larger group of patients may be seen in less specialised settings.

Even more crucial the practice boundaries between the social and medical care systems are also changing. Although budgets for social care, mental health care, and medical care are distinct, problems incurred by the affected populations are not. By default more than design, mental health crisis problems, clinical and social needs, crisis substance abuse, especially the effect of alcohol, and problems with the residential support system have become the default responsibility of the emergency care system to manage, especially after hours. Tables 4 and 5 list the more common problems seen by the emergency care system in both the pre-hospital and A&E setting. While some of these problems involve a level of complexity necessitating specialised care, equally many can be solved at a lower level of both services and providers within the community setting. This is especially true of the simple health maintenance and follow-up procedures and social care system issues.

Clearly, the distinctions between social and medical problems are blurring. The elderly patient suffering poor nutrition and without adequate heating may develop a range of medical problems as a result. Shared provider strategies are needed: effective links between health care

Table 4 Common emergency complaints

simple wound / soft tissue injury care
other uncomplicated minor trauma
'chest pain' triage and management
'shortness of breath'
asthma
left ventricular failure
seizures
hypoglycaemia/diabetes management
emergency detox and overdose
self harm and attempted suicide
'unable to care for self'
complications of falls in elderly

Table 5 Common reasons for A&E attendance

catheter changing
simple sutures
otitis media
throat cultures
after hours paediatric fever /n/v
wound checks
suture removal
unplanned medication maintenance
social care failures
• at risk psychiatric population
• at risk substance abuse population
• at risk geriatric population
• at risk homeless population

providers and local authorities to support patients at the community level both help prevent admissions and enable faster discharge to reduce acute bed 'blocking' at the hospital.

Rather than shared strategies between existing services, however, in response to the widening gap between rising demand and available resources, a variety of new initiatives are being developed. These range from expanding the availability of community-level care points with urgent care centres, minor injury units, and GP surgeries; expanding the scope of services provided by existing providers – GPs, paramedics, community pharmacists, and nurse practitioners; and adding new technology with prioritised dispatching systems for ambulances and health advice lines. Most of these have developed at the local level in response to financial issues. A call for restructuring emergency care has also been recently issued through a Chief Medical Officer's consultative document[17] emphasising self care and health information to help close the gap.

All of these initiatives will have some effect in restructuring care but all share the continuing pattern of development without a coherent strategy and evaluative process. While many of the ideas appear promising, they are being introduced without system-wide planning. One example is the proliferation of new forms of GP service. These may help the quality of life for the individual GP but it is unclear what effect they will have on the system. Further, in many localities co-ops are now competing with existing deputising services, thereby duplicating a service.

Responsibility for delivering services is also an issue. Currently, the only constant in the system is provided by the ambulance services purchased from multiple authorities by purchasers who may or may not have incentives to co-operate within a system of care. Who responds, the location of definitive care, and ECRs are all in a mix of both perverse incentives and disincentives focused on provider ease rather than patients. It is still far too easy to transfer problems to someone else's budget, with the A&E department and admission to hospital being the final catch-all. While competition might determine the best means of delivering the service, in the meantime scarce resources are used ever faster without corresponding demonstrable improvement in health gains. Although the problems with boundaries of service responsibility are universal, London is the ultimate example of this problem. The London Ambulance Service is the only constant and the only comprehensive emergency care system among 2 regions, 15 health authorities, 34 acute hospital trusts some 70 community Trusts, and hundreds of GPs.

Another of the many possible examples is the proliferation of medical helicopters. With the exception of Scotland with an integrated ground and air system, increasing numbers of ambulance trusts are developing air medical programmes. While much is made of the fact that in most cases funding is non-NHS, the first law of economics is in so many words, 'there is no such thing as a free lunch.' Helicopters still need to be staffed, supplied, and there is opportunity cost as well. While all of these programmes are innovative and there is clearly a role for air medical evacuation, evidence of clear demonstrable benefit is limited.[18] The question is not whether there should or should not be medical helicopters but how many, where deployed, and how tasked. In the geographic setting of England and Wales, using long-established methodology for placement, a case might be made for perhaps 3–4 helicopters in total without taking into account already deployed military assets. Again, there is a question of service design.

Most importantly, due to the political strength of existing institutions, the existing budget process, and resistance to change, it is likely the current delivery paradigms will remain the predominant means of emergency care access in the foreseeable future. But these paradigms as we show next, are increasingly unhelpful and indeed compound the problems the emergency care system has to deal with.

Out of date paradigms: problems with expectations and delivery

Whether access is through the 999 system or GP generally there are four stages to delivering care:

- access of the health care system;
- alleviation of symptoms including critical life support interventions;
- stabilisation of major problems;
- referral to secondary source for definitive care.

This makes sense for the critically ill or injured patient for whom appropriate care is unavailable from any other source than the hospital. In addition, the increased use of radiographic imaging and laboratory tests as essential components in the testing process requires the use of the 'central site' concept. What is less clear is whether or not this makes sense as the predominant pathway for all patients.

With a narrow window of time to treat cardiac arrest, any measure taken to improve access to the emergency care system makes sense, hence the introduction of universal three-digit emergency phone numbers facilitating rapid identification and location of problems. This might be seen as a 'big net' approach, gathering not only true clinical problems but poorly identified and potential problems as well. The inherent limits of technician and paramedic training require a conservative approach to medical risk management. These non-clinicians, despite excellent skills in identifying and treating what is 'wrong' with a patient, need to assume something is wrong with a patient causing the original access of the emergency system.

Although GPs respond to urgent and emergency problems and can treat minor problems, short circuiting the 'net,' most are not trained in resuscitation or have limited skills in this area. Further, they are poorly equipped and informed even when given new information on emergency care and resuscitation. With the exceptions of BASIC's programs, GP abilities to provide significant interventions in the pre-hospital phase of acute injury or illness are limited.[19] Furthermore policies on call-out are not universal and the extent of the role a GP is supposed to play in the emergent setting is neither well defined nor regulated. Consequently, GP-initiated care is widely variable in consistency and quality but generally confined to first-level interventions, diagnosis, and a subsequent call to the ambulance service for transport on to the hospital. Care of most acute problems primarily remains in the province of the hospital physician and setting.

The original focus on transportation after intervention in managing emergencies shapes the second paradigm, the ambulance as 'bus' service. Despite the advent of priority dispatching called for in the new performance standards, there is currently no option but to dispatch an ambulance to virtually every 999 request. Despite increasing skills and technology deployed on ambulances, the primary role of the ambulance service remains transport after limited but sometimes sophisticated interventions. Ambulance transport is not necessarily dependent on medical necessity despite a near 20-year debate over medical necessity and transport utilisation.[20] Further, there is no universal agreement as to what interventions should be performed out of the hospital and whether these interventions be allowed to delay the inevitable transport of patients to the hospital setting. Assumed throughout the debate is the transport paradigm.

There are also problems with identity. The general patient transport services run by ambulance trusts also add to both the perception and reality of the transport-defined role. In the absence of a legal description of what constitutes an 'ambulance', a wide variety of vehicles are described as 'ambulances', with the term used interchangeably from the most capable 'mobile intensive care units' to vehicles not more than a van with a cot or bench. Personnel descriptions are much the same. Ambulance staff are described in total as 'ambulance drivers' by both the media and clinicians. In the next breath they all become 'paramedics' with expectations of the ability to perform life-saving miracles. Further, as with vehicles, absence of regulation means anyone can describe themselves as a 'paramedic' with or without qualification.

The location of care points is the next paradigm, the 'one size' theorem. Not only is an ambulance dispatched to every call, but the outcome of virtually any 999 call is conveyance of any injured or ill party to the hospital. Although GPs are actively engaged in managing problems at the residential or scene level, unless the problem is so small as to preclude the need for diagnostic testing, the problem is gathered to the centre. Public access and education to use the 999 system coupled with increasing GPs' workloads and after hours coverage circumvent the GP's triage role and possible role as care giver. As with other system interactions, the lack of information regarding changes in non-office GP visits and utilisation of other care points makes it difficult to determine cause and effect.

Even more important, practice pathway paradigms create as many problems as they potentially solve. Traditional pathways from incident to A&E all serve to move problems from incident location and then concentrate the problems at the top of the care chain, the 'high rise' paradigm. This occurs whether the patient enters the system from either the 999 or the GP routes. The goal of having a specially trained senior physician to provide definitive assessment and treatment decision-making requires emergent problems – real, potential, and imagined – to be brought to a central care point as delivering this level of assessment on site is impossible to manage.

Utilisation of GPs at the residential level does not necessarily change the impact of these four paradigms on care delivery. Traditionally, GPs served as the primary gate-keepers for event-driven care. With GP utilisation also rising, complaints from GPs over terms and conditions have led to increased reliance on alternative approaches to after hour care such as deputising and co-op services. Increasingly, this results in GPs seeing unfamiliar patients with urgent problems or just re-directing the call to the ambulance service lowering the threshold for transport and admission.[21] Evidence is limited but most ambulance service trusts are experiencing a levelling of 'doctor's urgent' calls simultaneous with an increase in emergency calls.[22] This suggests a practice change away from the the gate keeping role by GPs with unfunded demand increases placed on the ambulance service and more patients following unnecessary pathways to care deliver points at higher acuity levels than needed. Combined with instructions to GPs to call the ambulance service directly for some problems such as chest pain, and slower response from GPs than the ambulance service, anecdotal evidence suggests the public increasingly is accessing the emergency care system directly for minor as well as critical problems, thereby adding to the problem of appropriate care at the appropriate delivery point.

In all, these four paradigms combine to bring problems, no matter how minor, from the community to the hospital-based clinician for definitive assessment and management. Often this is merely a determination that something is *not* wrong. The set of pathway paradigms just described make sense for relatively complicated clinical problems – the 1–3 per cent of life-taking insults along with roughly another 7 per cent of patients experiencing serious illness or injury – but as with all paradigms the problem is one of *a* paradigm becoming *the* paradigm.

The widening gap

Strategies for managing complex problems are not the same for managing less complex ones. In recent years there has been a steady trend of increasing utilisation of emergency care.[23] Emergency ambulance journeys increased 8 per cent in 1995/96 for the fourth consecutive year with activity levels 30 per cent higher than the late 1980s.[24] A&Es face much the same problem, with new A&E attendance in England and Wales up 2 per cent average year on year since 1981[25] and emergency admissions up 40 per cent since 1990.[26] Even more troubling is the case in Scotland where emergency ambulance utilisation increased 11.3 per cent last year[27] and A&E admissions have increased an average of 2.8 per cent per year since 1971, despite reductions of GP list sizes, down nearly 25 per cent, little change in resident population numbers, little change in amounts of violence, and a decreased mortality from heart disease. While the last factor and a 3 per cent increase in population aged 65 and over undoubtedly have some effect, it is not likely that the overall morbidity of the community has changed nearly as dramatically as utilisation. Far more likely to be responsible are changes in patient and system behaviour. With year-on-year increasing utilisation, the sustainability of the current pattern of provision is questionable.

As with the reversal of cardiac arrest, contracting performance requirements of journeys accomplished as a measure of success may also be a poor measure of overall system performance. The markedly improved response standards generated by the 1996 Ambulance Review[28] are likely to increase the problem as each 'success' in transport encourages further use of the system, however minor the problem. Why wait or pay for transport when calling for an ambulance service means rapidly accessible free transport. Further complicating this picture is the requirement to transport to the nearest hospital rather than to the hospital most capable of administering required care. With distance to definitive care measured in miles rather than time, a secondary transport of a critically ill or injured patient is often required, with a subsequent delay in definitive care and further utilisation of scarce resources.

Further, while the system is designed to

manage the most complex cases, increasing demand for urgent but not life-threatening health care overwhelms emergency care systems on a recurrent basis, most notably in the early winter months, with annual predictable crises in A&E departments and emergency admissions. On the less dramatic level there is the question of appropriate use – more commonly termed by health care providers 'inappropriate attendance'. It must be asked whether this is a question of inappropriate care seeking or inappropriate care delivery.

Efforts expended on managing low acuity problems intensively mean that fewer resources are available to deal with high acuity problems. The new prioritised dispatch of ambulances begins to answer the problem of shaping response to those most in need, but as the only option is to send an ambulance to any 999 access it will not begin to answer the 'appropriate' services issue.

The 1996 Ambulance Review calls for improving performance to 'life-threatening' calls (Category A) through the use of prioritised dispatch systems to 75 per cent reliability in eight minutes or less for 'life-threatening' calls by the year 2001. Originally the requirement for response within 8 minutes was for 90 per cent of these calls but this was dropped back to 75 per cent due to cost calculations. In addition to cardiac arrest, 'A' calls include adult chest pain, unconscious or seizing patients, severe respiratory problems, severe trauma, anaphylactic shock, severe obstetrical haemorrhage, and all calls for children under two years of age. The case for benefits of improved response standards put forth in the Review refers to the impact on reversing cardiac arrest by improving response time intervals. While improvements will undoubtedly have an impact on premature death, the requirement, as pointed out by one commentator 'really amounts to planning to arrive too late to make a difference.'[29] In the meantime other response time interval requirements (Category B) remained static at the 14/19 minute threshold. In addition to the 90 per cent reliability in the original drafts of the Review, a further allowance was made to create a new category C for non-urgent types of patients. Both the requirement to achieve a 90% rather than 75% reliability eight minute response and the addition of Category C were withdrawn after political review due to estimates of the cost of 90 per cent reliability and the possibility the public would see Category 'C' as a means of rationing access to health care[30] despite the opportunity to deliver care at more appropriate levels.

Looking at the system from the user's standpoint, delivery mechanisms may make things worse by not delivering care at the appropriate point by the appropriate provider. One has to wonder if, from the patient's standpoint, every time they call 999 they 'want' to go to the hospital in an ambulance; does the public really 'want' to attend an A&E and wait for hours for treatment of some fairly minor but immediate problem they do not know how to solve? Or do patients 'want' to either wait to see a GP during surgery hours, wait for a scheduled appointment for an immediate health need, or even call out a GP after hours? However, faced with a need and a limited number of choices, people will use the systems we design, but perhaps not as we have intended.

The total effect of the four delivery paradigms and current practice is to drive demand upward. Casting the widest possible net to prevent missing any potential problem, the ease and traditional use of transportation, and answering problems with one model of delivery, combine to move problems from one location to another, rather than to solve them at the lowest level possible. Similar to Roehmer's 'bed law,' the availability of the emergency care system, combined with a lack of incentives to care for problems at the lowest level possible, and the 'fuel' of intense media coverage (the stuff of miracles) may all combine to in fact stimulate demand.

In summary, current practices create as many problems as they solve. Traditional pathways from incident to A&E all serve to move problems from where they occur and then concentrate those problems at the top of the care chain. With this underlying design, it is not difficult to understand why there is a widening gap between resources and demand.

Despite the day-to-day delivery of excellent care by providers across the event-driven spectrum, failures in system design prevent the maximum realisation of resources while simultaneously making it more difficult for providers to deliver services on a daily basis. It is crucial to understand that not only is the gap between demand and resources widening, but also that the system of care contributes to that gap day by day and patient by patient. Perhaps one way to describe the problem is in fact a National Health 'Service' rather than a National Health 'System.' The issue becomes how to effect change and it is to this we turn next.

The way forward: closing the gap

First, better information is needed. Emergency or urgent care supplied by multiple providers is difficult to track. The lack of a common minimum data set, patient care reporting form, protocols, and shared information systems make it virtually impossible to track a patient event from start to finish. Social and medical care information must be linked. Without this capability there is no real means to measure pathways to see if intended results hold up in reality. League tables give some information about provider performance but do not begin to address system performance, much less anything regarding what happened to patients other than they moved through the system. Without a far more comprehensive information system there are no means of aligning provider incentives with system goals, leading to continued 'work shifting' rather than 'work sharing' between providers.

Second, in addition to better information gathering, clear benchmarking is needed to evaluate not only provider but system performance. Despite the lack of comprehensive system-wide information, wide differences are apparent in GP utilisation after hours, A&E admissions, emergency admissions, ambulance response reliability, and cost of providing ambulance services. As an example, initiation of the new prioritised dispatch study in four ambulance trusts is designed to help improve 8-minute response from 50 per cent to 75 per cent for Category A calls over a five-year period. Yet already, the Staffordshire Ambulance Trust, shadowing but not using the prioritised dispatch system, is achieving more than 90 per cent 8-minute reliability for 'A' calls and over 80 per cent reliability for all calls. Accounting for the difference in performance is essential. Cross-system benchmarking and best practice replication must become mandatory.

Third, more accurate assumptions and timing of research questions are needed. An illustration of this is the previously referenced Royal College of Surgeons' report on avoidable trauma death. In response, the Department of Health funded a pilot trauma system in Stoke-on-Trent. Experience was mixed at best in the evaluation as to whether or not the investment in a speciality trauma service actually led to a reduction in mortality. Three important findings did emerge, although to date mostly lost in the debate over the validity and timing of the Medical Care Research Unit study:

- a cross-comparison of trauma in the UK and USA is at best one of apples and oranges with a much lower volume of penetrating trauma in the UK, illustrating the problem of reproducing results across settings based on inaccurate assumptions;
- while the study site did not show a statistically significant improvement in mortality over the comparator sites, the data do indicate the need for a *system* of care. Unless pre-hospital, A&E, secondary, and tertiary care operate in tandem with the same script of protocols, patients who might benefit, will not, however sophisticated the service;
- also overshadowed was the apparent decrease in mortality due to neck of femur fractures at the Stoke site, far less glamorous than major multiple organ insults but far more important if the lessons to be learned are in health gain.[31] However, no definitive statement could be made as researchers found mortality determinations were not made uniformly, with attributions to the original insult in some settings, while other areas designated secondary causes, predominantly pneumonia, as the cause of death. The apparent improvement in mortality secondary to these injuries however clearly illustrates the value of protocol-driven system approaches.

Furthermore, the study was conducted too early and was limited to the trauma centre rather than the system. At the conclusion of both the pilot and study, the validity of the research is still not completely clear or accepted and the important lessons on protocol-driven pathways to management of complex problems remain lost in the continuing debate.

Fourth, the benefits of pathway management are also essential in the pre-hospital phase of event-driven care, not only at the individual provider level but also between providers. While any individual provider can measure reliability, the real value is to determine a prospective system plan incorporating all providers in managing events followed by rigorous and system-wide audit to measure results. Without this it is impossible to determine the value of health interventions either clinically or economically. Moreover, a shared viewpoint provides the base for the next step in improving and understanding the overall process.

Fifth, at the macro level the Government must set forth and enforce clear policy objectives to redesign and co-ordinate emergency care as a system which accounts for a continuum of care across boundaries and budgets. Accomplishing this is a long-term task. Consultations take time and the complexity of system interactions make it inherently difficult to identify effective change points even in the absence of tremendous resistance to change. Furthermore, consolidation as a means of efficiency is not in itself necessarily helpful. The question is one of how economies of scale can be achieved without provider units losing touch with the public at the community level, as individual community identity is important. This requires regional level planning but trust-level community interaction. Evidence of this can be seen in the problems of proposed hospital closures. In London, for example, health authorities in current form are probably too numerous and disconnected in terms of shared policy to ensure cross-provider synergy in the emergency care system.

Sixth, while the easy answer to calls for savings is always rationalisation at the unit level, projected savings and achievable savings may be quite different indicating the need for comprehensive system design. Savings by each unit are not only difficult to realise but savings in one unit may produce new costs in another unit. Recent suggestions of massive savings by reducing 'paperwork' are also likely to prove illusory.

Comprehensive costing information is essential, not only at provider level but for whole episodes of care running across several providers. Traditional reliance 'on cost equals price funding' compounds the reliable information problem. Costs need to be clear, and total price understanding is essential. If the recent improvements in understanding costs stimulated by the introduction of the internal market are lost in a move to dismantle the contracting process, it will become impossible to identify the most cost-effective solutions.

While changes must be made in the contracting process, such as elimination of single year contracts, the process does force accountability. The question is how to achieve administration and overhead savings while keeping services as local as possible. One means is to group provider trusts into more regional sized units sharing purchasing, overhead, and human resource efficiencies while retaining current trust identity and accountability. In effect this option would replace some health authority functions, in turn allowing health authority size and function to be consolidated to effect more coherent and comprehensive strategic responsibility, including, in particular, capital expenditure planning. In turn this would have effect at the regional level of system design.

Seventh, consideration needs to be given to the overall goals of system design. If problems are regional, is it even possible for health authorities and trusts facing immediate pressures to consider tackling them? Further, while additional calls are made to reduce the numbers of trusts and health authorities, amalgamation in the absence of a shared strategic plan is unlikely to reduce management costs, still less improve performance. Clearly, policy must come from the centre and regions must take a larger role in determining cross-boundary governance. The real change necessary is one of integration of efforts and thinking, including service design, budgets and governance.

Similar to the design questions, this process must incorporate all social and medical providers. Previous to the election, the policy quoted by Department of Health personnel reflecting ministers' views of 'our only policy is that we have no policy'[32] cannot be sustained. Guidance rather than policy will not change provider incentives. Systems need governance. A systems approach must be regional at minimum to realise critical mass. Clear goals are essential as well as performance standards measured in appropriateness of intervention rather than throughput. If the goal is to manage patients as close to home as possible, all providers in the emergency and social care system need to adhere to clear and shared strategies to prevent unnecessary admissions, to effect the earliest discharge possible to lower level care, and to manage urgent problems at the lowest level possible.

Eighth, we must better manage expectations. In addition to the need for comprehensive management information on the resource side of the equation it is absolutely essential to understand demand. It is unlikely that demand can ever be controlled but it can be significantly reshaped to more realistically align expectations with design. Clearly, one of the single major flaws at the resource and demand interface is the movement of solvable clinical conditions from one place and provider to another and almost universally higher level, rather than dealing with the problem at the lowest possible setting the first time. This results in not only increasing resource utilisation through multiple provider interactions but in driving up utilisation as well. Rather than the oft-heard complaint of 'inappropriate' attendance, the dilemma is more likely a question of inappropriate delivery.

During the course of an event-generated care request, there are numerous opportunities to rethink resource allocation. In each of the spaces of time between and interactions between providers there are opportunities to change delivery paradigms. In a recent working paper on managing demand Pencheon describes these opportunities as 'interfaces:'

> *These opportunities tend to concentrate where the significant resource dependent decisions are made: i.e. at interfaces. These are between self-care and professional care, primary and secondary care, across boundaries within secondary care, between secondary and tertiary care, and between health care and social care.*[33]

An effective emergency care system must be able to identify and respond to the wide spectrum of health care problems – from minor to life-taking – and allocate sufficient resources to comprehensively manage problems in real time on a reliable and reproducible basis. At the distinct points of access, response and management, multiple providers and options need to be available and utilised. This entails sophisticated communications and decision-making technology but at each of these interfaces the movement of the clinical problem can be evaluated in real time and directed on any of multiple care pathways.

This process is generally termed 'demand management' 'or computer assisted telephone triage (CATI).' On a smaller scale, these may be as simple as phone advice lines. Early evidence using the simple model appears positive. A trial undertaken by King's College resulted in high patient satisfaction and some redirection of patients to health care sources other than the A&E department.[34] Noted concerns included problems with 'consistency and reliability' consequent on the lack of formal training of and guidelines for call takers.

A fully integrated CATI system allows multiple options at point of access, response and management. While cost control has been the primary focus in many of these systems, the real value is to redirect the management of clinical needs to the most appropriate source and more importantly to manage demand downwards over time. Better educating the public as to the content of their emergent or urgent need and changing public expectations of delivery models in the health care system is possible, indeed the public is likely to adapt more quickly to these systems than health providers. The focus of efforts must be on patients rather than providers. Table 6 indicates common emergency and urgent conditions responsive to an alternative response

Table 6 Event-driven complaints with possible alternative care protocols

chest pain
asthma
left ventricular failure
hypoglycaemia
simple wound care
paediatric fever
back pain
abdominal pain
nausea and vomiting
psyche and social care
medication maintenance
minor orthopaedic
minor burns

and multiple options strategy.

Two large pilot CATI systems are currently planned for introduction in the autumn of 1997 by the Department of Health. However, these systems alone cannot be relied on to realign resources and demand. While use of the interfaces in order to better manage care is necessary, there is also great risk between the interfaces. Without full integration, inter-provider issues over allocation of patient responsibility and costs have the potential to derail projected benefits. Worse, patients can fall between the cracks. These systems not only need to co-ordinate allocation of the full spectrum of providers but need shared governance by all stakeholders.

What is to be done?

In the previous section some means of closing the gap are suggested. Underlying these efforts are four critical criteria:

- A review of the assumptions made in providing health care must be taken. If we do not understand the questions, a rational debate on the future is not possible and delivery will remain sub-optimal for both patients and providers.
- There must be clear policy and strategic planning from the centre with a shared 'script' and accountability at every level. A reasoned approach to restructuring must be initiated to align incentives among all providers while continuing to obtain efficiencies gains introduced by process improvements over the past years.
- The emergency care system must manage and integrate the interfaces in order to reshape the demand curve and deliver care at the lowest possible appropriate level. Provider and organisational boundaries must be breached not only amongst the medical community but between the medical and social care sectors.
- Changes must take the public into process to share hard decisions. After all, it is their system. Prioritisation should be considered positively rather than negatively. Managing problems at lower levels saves scarce resources for use in cases of greater need. The public understands and accepts this dilemma better than providers.

There are lessons to be learned from the intention versus the completion of design. The essence of emergency care is an imperative for action in the face of life-taking illness or injury, set against not only the sometimes unclear and ever-changing demands and abilities of resuscitation medicine, but also competing needs and goals of the other sectors in the larger health care system. The time-sensitive nature of decision making in emergency care coupled with the high emotive content of the immediate problem highlight the design and practice conflict on a daily basis. The resulting dramas are, unsurprisingly, prime time draws.

Faced with the challenge of increasing utilisation of demand and the narrowing, either relatively or in real terms, of resources, the sustainability of chosen approaches is at issue. Essentially, four strategies are traditionally employed in meeting this challenge:

- increase spending
- restructuring
- process improvement
- prioritise spending

Each of these strategies has been tried either singly or in combination on a continual basis over the years. Problems in funding are neither new nor unique and calls for increasing funding have occurred almost from the inception of the NHS. Work by the King's Fund Policy Institute argues that current funding levels, if permitted to grow at the rates achieved in the past, are adequate to sustain the NHS in its current form during the foreseeable future.[36] But recent expenditure settlements have not reached this level.

The second strategy is also likely to be of little benefit in the short term. The near constant restructuring of the administrative side of the NHS once or more a decade has never completely solved the demand – resource mismatch question. To date, evidence supporting the introduction of market dynamics and the purchaser – provider split into the NHS is mixed and, more importantly, it would likely take at least another few years of practice to establish the validity of these initiatives. Recent comments by the Secretary of Health acknowledge the problem of change for change's sake but the traditional pattern of continual restructuring without an overall strategy is likely.

By nature emergency care attracts the majority of media and public attention when problems of resources and poor service delivery arise. It is difficult to effectively plan and organise services in the midst of near constant crisis, especially in an arena as politically sensitive as emergency and resuscitation care. Real changes take time however, and providers, but more importantly for politicians, facing immediate problems call for action: it is at least better to 'seem' to be solving problems.

Continued reliance in the short term will be placed on the third strategy, continued process improvement. In itself, however, this strategy also remains problematic. While there is a debate on the value of the performance standards introduced by *The Patient's Charter* in measuring quality, attention over the past decade paid to process improvement measures more common to the industrial sector has proven there is untapped capacity within the NHS. If 'value for money' is important, reliance in some form on the accounting and performance efficiency measures introduced in the last decade must continue. Further, from the 'buyers' point of view, the public facing waiting lists, increasing efficiency of throughput is not an entirely unfounded measure of quality. However, the easiest gains have already been realised at the trust level.

This is not to say restructuring and process improvement are not necessary or worthwhile. On the contrary, they are absolutely essential. Lack of a coherent overall strategy for aligning system goals with provider performance and poor design will continue to swallow any gains in efficiency. However, as long as provider efficiency and quality are measured in volume throughput, it will be next to impossible to reduce utilisation. Every provider has cause to complain but little incentive to change, because at some point utilisation declines equate with budgetary losses, subsequent loss of function, and real or perceived loss of employment.

In the long run the only option is to focus on how available resources should be spent. Despite the 'rationing' political minefield, the economics of sustaining the NHS will force the first real debates on prioritisation in the next few years. Indeed work by the Institute of Public Policy Research on the use of citizen' juries and the recent NHS strategic planning discussion document, *Priority Setting in the NHS*, have initiated the process:

> *The Government recognises these pressures, not least in its commitment (which has been honoured each year) to real term increases in NHS spending. Even so, budgets will always be finite while demand is potentially open ended. There will always be a gap between all we wish to do and all that we can. Setting priorities is a fact of life.*[37]

Setting and accepting priorities is far from easy. While the oft-quoted distinction between health and 'sick' care might be considered mere semantics, it is absolutely crucial from the standpoint of administering budgets, as the provision of medical care is essentially a limitless task. While few would argue for the position of not extending the benefit of the gains made in medical science in the last half decade, the public needs to understand the enormous economic impact that doing so involves. As a commentator pointed out in the midst of the health care reform debate in the US 'most of our medical miracles are fiscal failures'. The public, however, will never be able to accept priorities unless health care providers lead the way.

Rethinking our assumptions and setting priorities will be difficult. Not only must we let go of cherished but flawed goals but inherent resistance to change by medical providers and the public must be overcome. Complicating the process is the absence of comprehensive system-wide information allowing for evidence-driven decision-making. This equates to the lack of a common set of data elements and the lack of a universal patient reporting system shared by all health care providers. It is difficult to understand and accept outcomes and limits if there is not a means to measure inputs. Further, until incentives in the current system change, work shifting rather than work sharing will continue with each group of over-utilised providers attempting to move responsibility for care on to other sector budgets.

While it is unclear what the answer(s) might be, there is already overwhelming evidence that current practice is not working. The goal of a comprehensive system capable of solving clinical problems at multiple levels has plainly not been achieved to date. Failed strategies are clearly apparent and further it is possible to understand a great deal about the cost of getting it wrong. Table 7 is a list of some lessons that should be well learned by this point.

Although the lessons in this paper are only a small part of the way forward, it is crucial to understand that the gap between demand for services and resources available is widening. More importantly, the paradigms of delivery and system contribute to the gap day by day and patient by patient with obvious results in sustainability. Massaging the system at the edges is no longer an option. The four traditional

Table 7 Strategies That Don't Work

Distinct budgets and accountabilities for medical and social care
Distinct provider identities and boundaries between professions
Attempting to continually meet increasing demand with current strategies
Measuring throughput as a proxy for system quality
Measuring provider rather than system performance
Work shifting rather than work sharing
Taking care of all problems at the top of the chain
A devolved system with performance guidelines instead of policy objectives
Lack of a universal patient care record required of all providers
Lack of cohesive and shared system vision
Resources that follow institutions rather than patients

means of bringing a system into equilibrium will not work unless other more fundamental changes occur. A more radical approach is needed.

This paper has argued that the real challenge to providers lies in their willingness to leave behind that which does not work: their traditional concepts of roles, identity, and practice paradigms in order to embrace a shared systems approach in sustaining emergency care into the future. Continued focus on the extraordinary, prevents better practice at the ordinary level. It remains to be seen if this is possible.

References

1 Pencheon D. *Emergency Care Handbook*. NHS Executive Oxford and Anglia. 10/ 95

2 Handley AJ. Defibrillation and the chain of survival. *Ambulance UK* 1995;10(2):23

3 NHS Executive. *Review of Ambulance Performance Standards*. CCOO23, 7/96, pp.32–38

4 Royal College of Surgeons of England. *The Management of Patients with Major Injuries*. London: Royal College of Surgeons, 1988

5 See 3

6 Goodacre S, Gray A, McGowan A. Collection of uniform cardiac arrest data by Ambulance Services in the UK. *Ambulance UK* 1996; 11(6):4–8

7 Nguyen-Van-Tam J, Dove A, Bradley M, Pearson J, Durston P, Madeley R. Effectiveness of ambulance paramedics versus technicians in managing out of hospital cardiac arrest. *J Accid Emerg Med* 1997; 14:142–148

8 Knapp M, Forsythe M, Wall B. *Costs and effectiveness of paramedic pre-hospital management of major trauma*. University of Kent, London School of Economics. Report to NHSE Health Technology Assessment Program. 1/ 97

9 Nicholl J *et al. The costs and benefits of paramedic skills in pre-hospital trauma care*. Sheffield: Medical Care Research Unit, The University of Sheffield; 1997

10 Communicore. *Sudden Cardiac Arrest: A treatable public health crisis*. 1996

11 Kuehl *et al. Pre-Hospital Systems and Medical Oversight*.St Louis: Mosby Yearbook, 1992

12 Cardiopulmonary resuscitation on television. *New England Journal of Medicine*; 335(21):1605–7

13 Baskett P, Fisher J. Recognition of death by ambulance personnel. *Ambulance UK* 1997; 12(1):13-16

14 Rawles J. Pre-hospital coronary care. *Pre-Hospital Immediate Care* 1997; 1(1):13–19

15 See 14

16 Health Policy and Public Health Directorate. The Scottish Office. *Emergency Healthcare in Scotland. Future Structure of Accident and Emergency Services. Report of a Policy Review.* 1994
17 Calman K *et al. Developing Emergency Services in the Community* Voll.1 and 2. NHS Executive, 11/96
18 Nicholl J, Snooks H, Bazier J. *The costs and effectiveness of helicopter emergency ambulance services. Information for purchasers in England and Wales.* Sheffield: Medical Care Research Unit. The University of Sheffield. 3/ 95
19 West RJ, Penfold N. A questionnaire survey of resuscitation equipment carried by general practitioners and their initial management of ventricular fibrillation. *British J of General Practice* 1997; 47:37–40
20 Multiple letters and editorials. *Ambulance UK* 1970–1995
21 Nicholl J, Coleman P, Parry G, Pickin M. *The provision of emergency ambulance services in South Yorkshire. Final Report.* Sheffield: The Medical Care Research Unit, The University of Sheffield. 8/95
22 Department of Health. Ambulance Services, England: 1995–96. *Statistical Bulletin* 1996; 11(7)
23 Audit Commission. *Management of Emergency Ambulance Services Project Specification.* 3/97
24 See 22
25 Audit Commission. *By Accident or Design: Improving A&E Services in England and Wales.* 1996
26 NHS Executive Oxford-Anglia. *Emergency Care Handbook* 1995
27 Scottish Ambulance Service, NHS Trust. *1996 Annual Report*
28 NHS Executive. *Review of Ambulance Performance Standards.* Final Report of Steering Group. 7/96
29 Roberts G. Improving the odds. *Ambulance UK* 1995; 4
30 See 28
31 Nicholl J *et al. The cost effectiveness of the regional trauma system in the north west.* Sheffield: Medical Care Research Unit, The University of Sheffield
32 NHS Executive, Department of Health, London (personal communication)
33 Pencheon D. *On Demand.* 16 January 1997
34 Dale J, Crouch R, Patel A, Williams S. Patients telephoning A&E for advice: a comparison of expectations and outcomes. *J Accid Emerg Med* 1997; 14:21–23
35 White M. Tony's Darlings join Tories on shifting ground. *Health Services Journal* 1997; 17 April
36 Harrison A, Dixon J, New B, Judge K. Is the NHS sustainable? *BMJ* 1997; 314(25 Jan):296–298
37 NHS Executive. *Priority Setting in the NHS: A discussion document.* 2/97
38 Lamm RD. Healthcare Heresies. *Healthcare Forum Journal* 1994; Sept/Oct:45–51

Age, renal replacement therapy and rationing

Bill New and Nicholas Mays

Rationing is now permanently on the health policy agenda and with the prospect of tight expenditure settlements for the next two years at least, the debate is likely to intensify still further. Some aspects of the debate, however, do seem to enjoy widespread agreement. The orthodoxy in reporting rationing issues is that it is possible, at least, to agree that older people should not be at a disadvantage in the competition for resources. However, this apparent consensus was shaken during 1997 when a leading health economist, Alan Williams, suggested that age *was* an appropriate criterion to take into account and that priorities should favour the young.[1]

In a separate development, the results of a national survey of renal units in England were published by the Department of Health in May 1996 after a two-year delay (henceforward 'the Department of Health Review'[2]). This confirmed that elderly people are less likely to receive renal replacement therapy (RRT) than younger age groups, even though the incidence of end-stage renal failure rises with age. Interest groups such as Age Concern were predictably outraged.[3]

The picture is further complicated by evidence from the rest of Europe. It is well established that our European partners treat more people for end-stage renal failure (ESRF) than the UK, and this is often taken as an indication that the UK is under-providing renal services. This lower provision is also associated with lower acceptance rates for elderly people as a proportion of all those accepted for RRT. But how can we establish what an appropriate level of provision is? And is the situation regarding elderly people quite as unethical as often suggested, or is the unequal distribution of RRT services in favour of young people justified?

The evidence

The Department of Health Review found that, on average, England accepted 65 patients pmp (per million population) per year for RRT, based on a survey undertaken in 1991–93. In contrast, the Renal Association had estimated that 'need' was running at 80 pmp.[4] Estimating need is fraught with difficulty. For example, a judgement about need in a particular locality is complicated by the particular socio-demographic circumstances prevailing, such as the age structure and the ethnic composition of the population: actual acceptance rates were found to vary between 19 and 128 pmp across districts. For now, though, it is enough to note that the best estimate of provision nation-wide in the early 1990s was well below that estimated as 'necessary' by professional organisations during the same period.

Most significant from the point of view of Age

Concern, however, was the disparity between the incidence of disease in older age groups and the number accepted for RRT in those groups. Figure 1 shows the results of the Department of Health Review's survey into England's renal service providers, combined with estimates from a previous survey published in the *BMJ* on incidence rates.[5] The clear implication is that as one gets older the likelihood of contracting chronic kidney failure increases but the chances of receiving treatment decrease. This is not the result of an explicit NHS policy, just the result of clinicians making difficult decisions in the context of limited budgets. Nevertheless, to Age Concern this constitutes a *prima facie* case of discrimination against elderly people.

Comparisons with European partners confirm this picture. Overall levels of RRT have long been considered relatively low in the UK, and the most recent data from the European Dialysis and Transplant Association (EDTA) show that the UK has lagged behind the mean of 16 European countries[6] since at least 1987, and that the disparity has been getting larger[7] – see Figure 2. All the data presented in this paper should be interpreted with caution, since there are significant problems of non-response at some centres, of data quality and of consistency over time. Nevertheless, using the data which are available, and making a simple adjustment for under-reporting from some centres in each country, the results are quite clear: the UK treats significantly fewer patients with ESRF than the European mean.

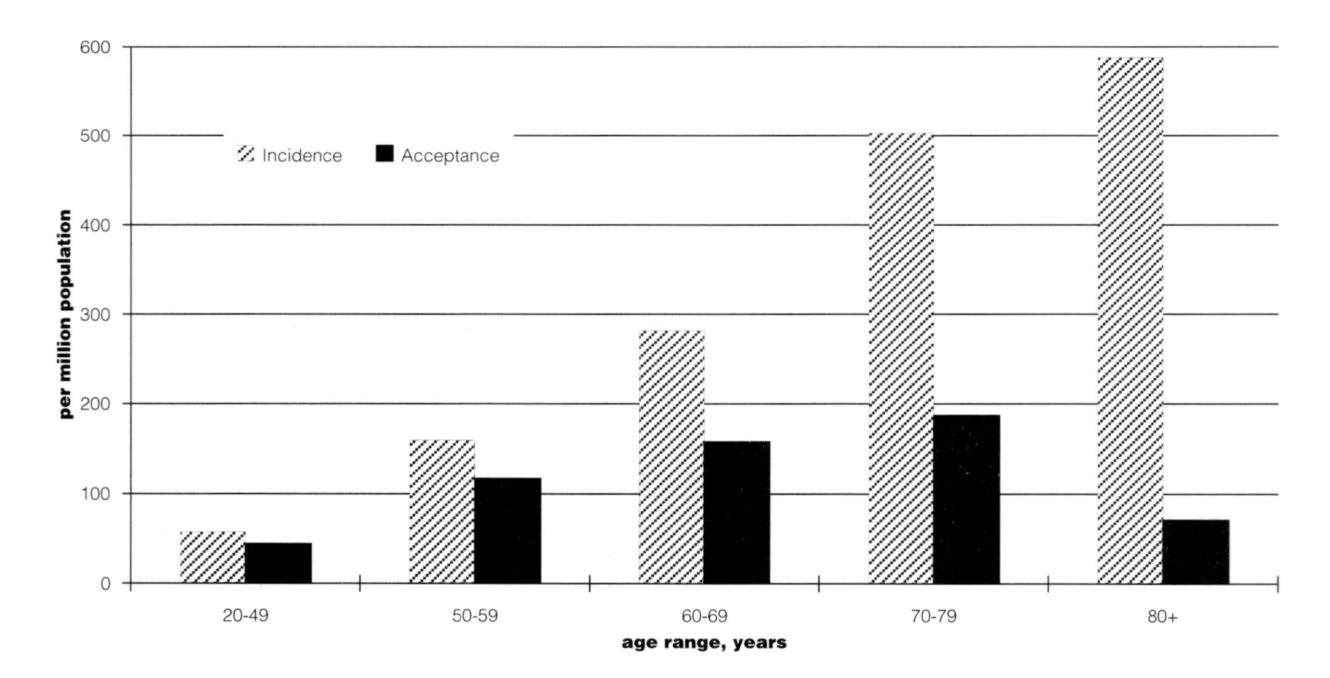

Sources: Department of Health (1996)[2] and Feest *et al* (1990)[5]

Figure 1 Age-related incidence and acceptance rates for chronic renal failure per year, England 1991–1993

The UK acceptance rate for 1993, after adjustments, is approximately 75 pmp according to EDTA, significantly higher than the 65 pmp reported in the Department of Health Review. There are a number of possible explanations for this. First, the adjustment made to the EDTA data presented in this article may have overestimated the true figure. In other words, the non-responding centres may have been small and therefore not have increased the aggregate patient numbers by a significant degree. Second, the timing of the two sets of data collection was slightly different: EDTA surveyed in 1993, whilst the Department of Health Review was based on an average from calendar years 1991 and 1992 for Thames region units, and financial years 1991/2 and 1992/3 for non-Thames region units. Acceptance rates are steadily rising and so it would be surprising if the Department of Health Review figure were not lower. Finally, the Department of Health Review data were based on a survey of English units (from which they had 100 per cent response rate), whereas EDTA surveyed the whole of the UK. Wales, for example, has a significantly higher acceptance rate than England.[8]

Notwithstanding these difficulties of data collection and interpretation, the UK estimates appear to be converging on the 80 pmp figure estimated by the Department of Health Review and the Renal Association as necessary to match 'need'. Furthermore, because the latest published data were based on a survey which is now four years old, it is reasonable to assume that in 1997 the acceptance rate is closer to that 'ideal', or even exceeds it.[9] Nevertheless, the growing UK

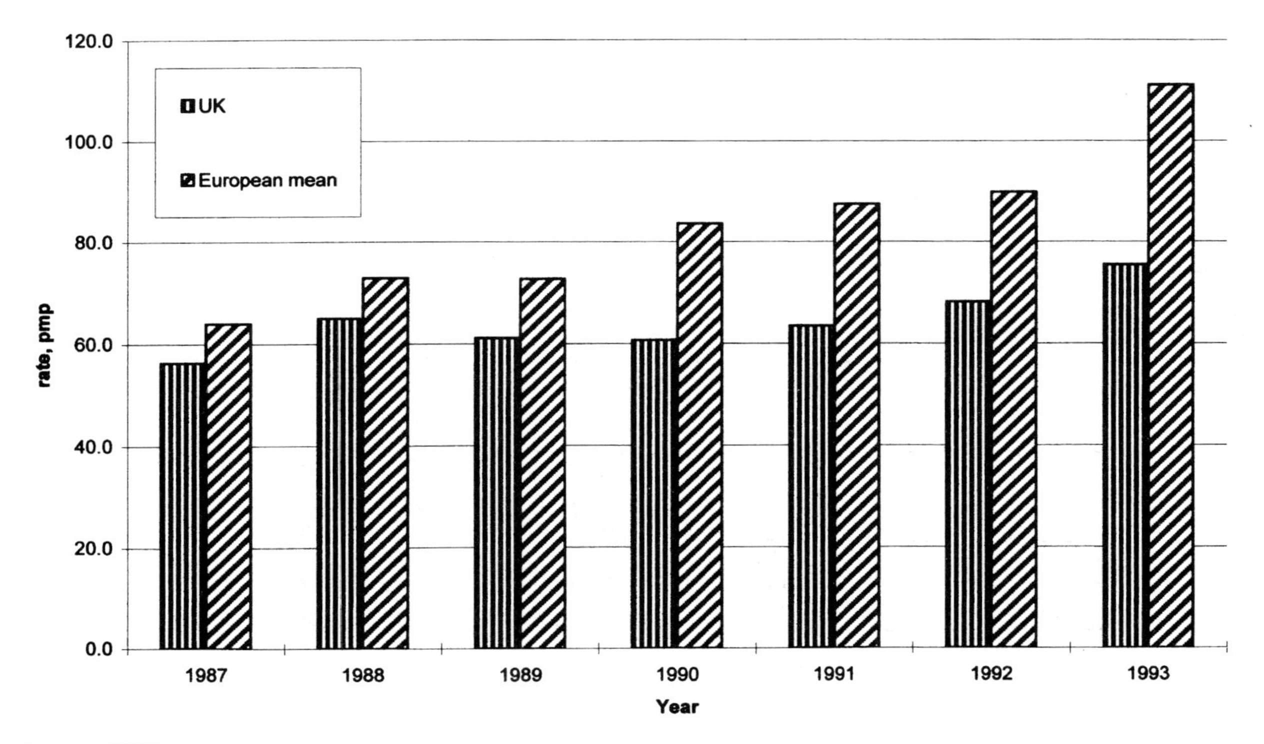

Source: EDTA

Figure 2 New patients accepted for RRT in the UK and Western Europe (pmp) adjusted for response rates from centres, 1987-93

acceptance rate does nothing to diminish the gap between UK and European levels of provision. Either this calls into question the calculation of the 80 pmp figure or the appropriateness of RRT in other European countries or both.[10]

The gap between the UK and Europe is also reflected in the proportion of people over 65 who are accepted for treatment. The UK treats relatively fewer people in this age range and, although we do not have hard evidence on incidence rates in other countries, there is little to suggest that this difference can be explained by significantly lower numbers of elderly people suffering from the disease in the UK. Figure 3 shows the percentage of each country's patients accepted for RRT who are aged over 65.

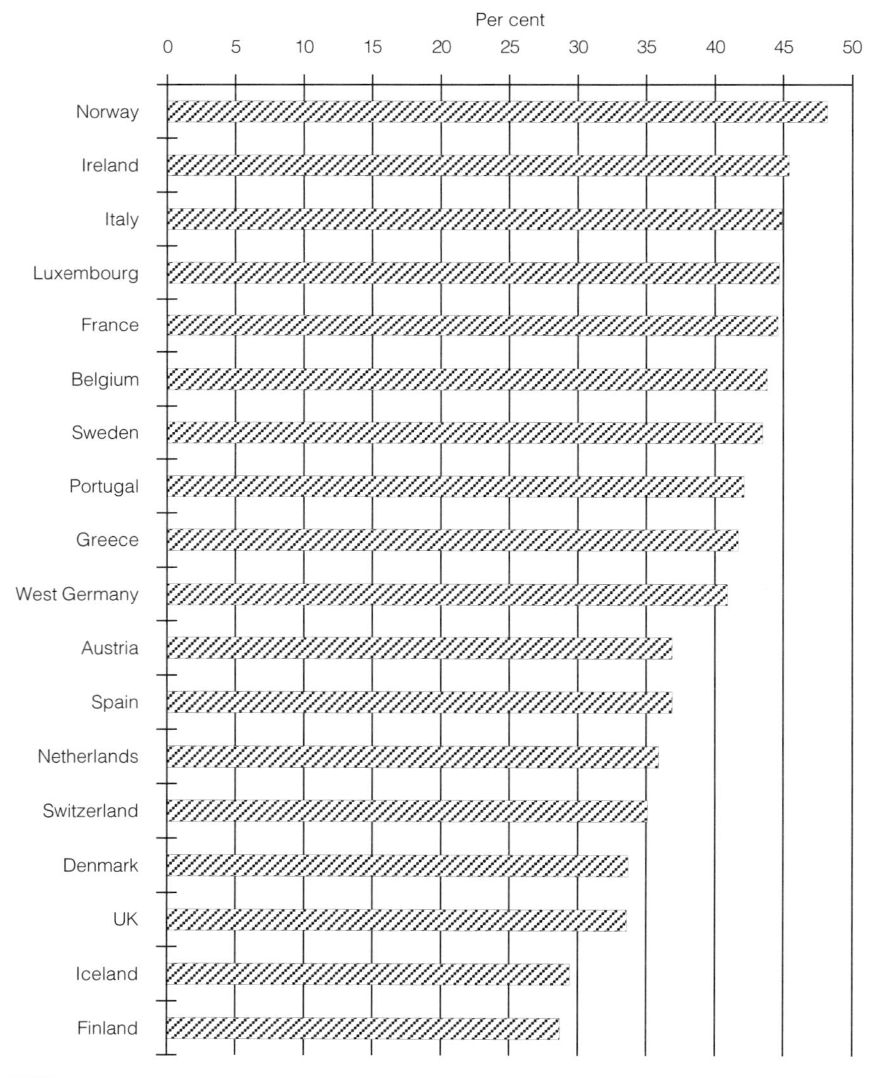

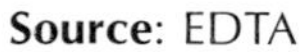
Source: EDTA

Figure 3 Percentage new patients accepted for renal replacement therapy, age > 65, Europe, 1993

One possible explanation for this pattern is that the proportion of elderly people treated rises as the total number of patients accepted rises. In other words, as a country accepts larger numbers of patients, the 'reservoir' of ill-health amongst younger age groups tends to be exhausted and a country will feel increasingly able to accept older patients. This hypothesis can be tested in a crude way by plotting the proportion of the population aged over 65 against overall acceptance rates on a scatterplot using the EDTA's (adjusted) data for 1993.

The results in Figure 4 are perhaps surprising – there is no clearly discernible link between these two factors. Norway, for example, has one of the lowest acceptance rates in Europe: 54.6 pmp on an adjusted basis. However, it has the highest proportion of over-65s accepted. Apparently, simple reference to life expectancy is not determining rationing decisions consistently across Europe. If it were, one would expect to see far fewer older patients treated in countries such as Norway, since life expectancy is significantly lower for 'high risk' (over 65, non-diabetic) than for 'standard risk' (under 55, non-diabetic) patients[11]. The former have a life-expectancy of 3.5 years after one year of treatment, the latter 14.3 years.

Unfortunately, this interpretation cannot be made with certainty; there may be other variations confounding the picture. For example, the case-mix of patients could vary across countries. ESRF is generally the product of other disease processes, especially in elderly people, and if these other diseases occur to different degrees in different countries a different age-

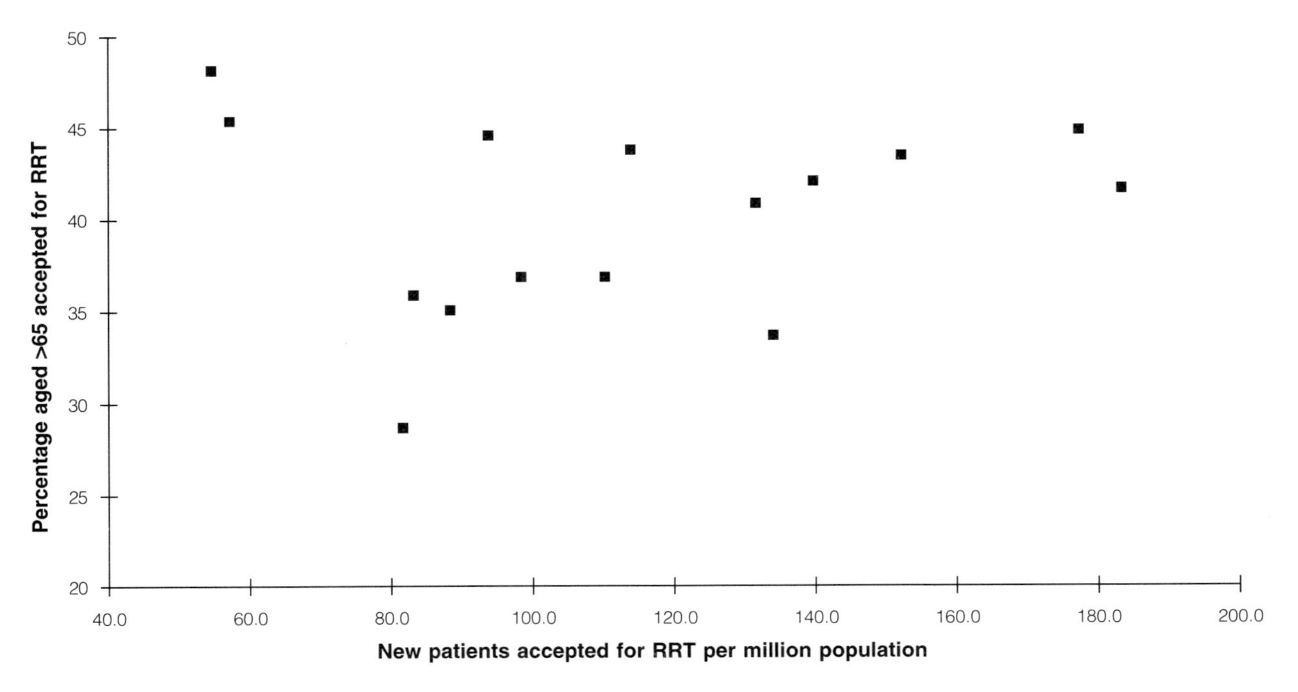

Source: EDTA

Figure 4 Scatterplot of proportion 65+ accepted for RRT and total accepted for RRT in 16 European countries, 1993

profile for incidence of ESRF would result. This in turn would be reflected in age-related acceptance rates.

Nevertheless, in the absence of evidence to the contrary, it does seem likely that countries such as Norway are sacrificing some overall benefit in terms of life expectancy in return for a more equal treatment of the generations. This may or may not be the result of conscious policy choices. Ireland, for example, has a strong commitment to inter-generational equity built into its welfare state legislation.[12] On the other hand it may simply be that implicit clinical practices differ. Whatever the explanation, groups such as Age Concern would like to see practice in the UK move toward the pattern observed in countries such as Norway. But would this more equal outcome be equitable?

Age and rationing

The preceding evidence inevitably leads one to ask whether it is appropriate for age to be taken into account when making the kind of rationing decisions necessary for RRT. Contrary to the impression in the news media, there is a small but well-established group of authors who firmly argue that it *is* reasonable to take age into account in favour of young people.

A few preliminary comments are necessary with respect to age and rationing before dealing with the substantive issues. First, it is extremely unusual for an author to suggest that age should be the *only* criterion for deciding on access to health care – although one, Callahan,[13] suggests that certain types of care should be restricted past a certain age. The central issue is whether age is *an* appropriate criterion for helping to make rationing decisions. In fact, other criteria are often accepted as having priority, with disagreement centring on whether age is relevant *other things being equal.* For example, some critics suggest that age is an inappropriate criterion because it may improperly discriminate against those elderly people who have a particularly good prognosis in favour of a younger person with a similar condition whose prognosis is poor. This would be a significant criticism if age were the only criterion, but typically those who support the use of age do so on the basis that it ought to be taken into account alongside, say, ability to respond to treatment. Age in this respect may be advocated as a 'tie-breaking' criterion.

The second contextual point is that 'age' does not necessarily refer to a particular category of person, but simply to a difference in a measurable feature of an individual. Thus the use of age could relate to the choice between a 25 and 35 year old as much as that between a 25 and 75 year old. In fact the nature of the priority could vary depending on the ages of those concerned (it might favour the younger person, for example[14]). In any event, it is rare for an author to specify a *particular category* of elderly person for differential treatment.

A third preliminary comment is that in many instances age is supported as a *proxy* for other criteria. Age *per se* is not usually the relevant variable, but the fact that age is a useful indicator of *other* factors which are considered appropriate to the rationing decision. For example, age might be used as an indicator of generally poorer responsiveness to treatment, or of smaller benefits in expected 'life-year' terms. In these cases, age is promoted as an easily identifiable guide to decision-making, but one which is morally grounded on the relevance of other factors. This makes age particularly difficult to remove entirely from rationing decisions as we see below.

A final preliminary comment is that those who oppose age as a criterion often cite 'ageism' in their critiques. 'Ageism' (as with 'sexism' or 'racism') implies that some unfair discrimination has been made on the basis of age (or sex or ethnic origin). But the fact that a discrimination has taken place is not sufficient to qualify a decision as unfair. As long as the need for rationing is accepted, and therefore that some choices have to be made, it will be necessary to find some way of 'discriminating' between the competing claims for resources. The question is whether the discrimination (the method of choosing) is fair or unfair. Using the phrase 'ageism' implies that it is unfair. However, moral reasoning requires more: good reasons must also be supplied as to *why* it is unfair.

The case against

Age is generally considered to be inappropriate as a rationing criterion.[15] The arguments tend to make use of three related points. The principal case against the use of age on ethical grounds is put by those who consider that there is a fundamental right to health care resources on the basis of equal moral worth of all people.[16] Such a position takes its principal criterion to be 'need', interpreted as the degree of ill-health and not necessarily ability to benefit from treatment. Such commentators reject 'maximising' theories of health care – which promote policies which produce the largest aggregate health gain for the whole community – as leading to unjust and inequitable distributions of benefits amongst those who need them. If resources are indeed limited, and if many people in the same degree of need cannot all be given equal access to resources or equal improvements in health status, then methods of discrimination such as a lottery are preferable to those relating to characteristics of people.

The focus on units of time as a component of benefit – central to some proponents of age-based rationing as we shall see below – has, in particular, been criticised as neglecting the ethical position of individuals.[17] For example, it is conceivable that the application of a principle which favoured maximising health benefits in life-year terms could favour saving the life of one young person rather than ten elderly people. This, it is argued, is fundamentally unjust in a health system (or society) which believes that the life and health of each person matters, and matters as much as any other.

The second category of objection to the use of age in rationing decisions relates to the heterogeneity of patients. If it is accepted that in general terms elderly people respond less well to treatment, cost more to treat and have a lower life expectancy,[18] there will nevertheless be many individuals for whom these attributes do not apply. Under these circumstances, explicit application of criteria such as age – particularly in the way advocated by Callahan[13] – will be inflexible and will militate against the fair treatment of individuals.[19] Such criticisms are echoed in more general critiques which argue that any activity which is as dependent on individual circumstances as health care must not be subject to specific, explicit criteria.[20] Instead we should 'muddle through elegantly' whilst developing mechanisms of accountability to monitor how decisions are taken.

The final set of ethical criticisms argues that the specific use of age as a criterion risks damaging social relations in society at large. In particular, 'solidarity' and the doctor-patient relationship could suffer. Solidarity requires that all individuals and groups are treated with respect, particularly those whose needs are greatest and who may be less able to articulate their rights or needs.[21] Arguably, elderly people fall into this category: explicit acknowledgement that such a group has a weaker claim on resources could damage social cohesion. This may lead to less respect and increased prejudice toward those who already suffer a degree of unfair discrimination and prejudice in other areas of life. Relations in the doctor's surgery or at the bedside could also suffer.[22] If the use of age were encouraged as a means of assisting rationing decisions it could provoke suspicion and mistrust in the elderly patient who is confronted with a clinician apparently withholding treatment.

This rejection of the use of age as a criterion lies behind many other specific critiques which oppose the use of criteria which appear to preclude identifiable sections of the population from equal consideration.[23] By specifically reducing the claims of particular groups, the danger is that the hard-to-quantify 'external benefits' which the NHS provides – reassurance, or 'tranquillity' – could be lessened. We may *all* suffer some reduction of welfare if there is the explicit acknowledgement that some are less eligible than others.

A final concern in this category is that support for tax-based welfare provision in general could suffer if those who perceive that they have contributed to the state all their lives fail to derive benefit from it when needed.

The case for

The first defence of age as an appropriate criterion for rationing decisions requires some acceptance that there is a statistical association between age and ability to benefit clinically. Age acts as a proxy for individuals' ability to benefit from treatment, if only in general terms, and this can be helpful in making difficult or 'borderline' decisions. Indeed, it may be supported by those who consider that clinical effectiveness should be the over-riding criterion relevant to rationing decisions. There is some evidence from sociological studies that clinicians do, in fact, make subtle and implicit use of a patient's age when deciding whether or not they are indicated for coronary surgery.[24] It appears that these clinicians took account of age when the judgement on whether surgery was suitable was a marginal one. In general, age used in this way will favour the young. However, if one believed that the extent of ill-health (rather than 'ability to benefit') should dominate rationing decisions, the reverse may be true since the older an individual is, other things being equal, the greater the degree of 'need' in this sense.[25]

The second principal rationale for supporting age as a criterion in rationing is an extension of the first. This school of thought argues that resources ought to be allocated such that they provide the most benefit measured in (quality-adjusted) life-year terms.[26] Utilitarian in spirit, such theories support the maximisation of *life-time* benefit as the principal objective of health care systems. Given a choice between two otherwise identical individuals, priority should be given to the younger. To do otherwise implies that the length of time in which one may derive benefit from a health improvement is unimportant. A generalisation of this position would systematically give lower priority to elderly groups in their claim for resources, even if their ability to respond to treatment is quite as good as that of younger groups. However, it is not suggested that treatment should be denied to elderly people altogether.

The central insight of this position is that an improvement in health status, and the benefit thereby derived, is not relevant to a single point in time. People continue to enjoy health improvements as long as they live (assuming the improvement is sustainable). This is true even if the prognosis is poor – as long as there is some chance of an improvement in health, this chance will be combined with a greater expectation of life in the younger patient. Only when life expectancy is identical for younger and older patients – when biological age is identical – will this rationale be redundant.

The third argument in favour of using an age criterion is offered by Callahan.[27] He emphasises the relatively high cost of treating elderly people as a group: 'for public policy purposes there is no generalisation that is more solid than the following: health care for the elderly is significantly more expensive than for younger age groups'.[28] Callahan predicts that the specific costs due to high-tech life-extending care will rise at unsustainable levels, and for very little gain in terms of length and quality of life. These comments reinforce the arguments of those who, like Williams, promote cost-effectiveness as the principal criterion for deciding on health care priorities.

However, Callahan has a rather different agenda. His thesis is that society must radically rethink its attitude to death, such that after a certain age – 'the late 70s or early 80s' – individuals should no longer have a claim on life-extending health care from public resources, and should rely instead on palliative and other 'caring' interventions. Callahan's argument for accepting age as a criterion is therefore not merely concerned with cost considerations, but has a sociological and philosophical component which criticises modern societies for continually striving to extend life. Modern theories on growing old have all but 'banished ageing as a meaningful human condition'[29] and threaten to 'turn old age into a permanent middle age'.[30] He is also unique, at least in the context of this review, in specifying a cut-off point beyond which certain forms of care are withheld.

The final basis for supporting the use of an age criterion is often referred to as the 'fair innings argument'. This is subtly different to that relating to maximising benefit described above. For example, take two individuals of different ages who nevertheless have identical life expectancies (their 'biological' ages are the same). If the cost of treating both individuals, and the benefit derived from that treatment, is the same for both, the fair innings argument would nevertheless favour the younger person (in chronological terms). This is because he or she has not yet had the *opportunity* to flourish and enjoy all the other benefits which life offers. Some economists have reformulated this type of argument as one of inter-generational equity.[31] In order to equalise the lifetime experience of health, it will tend to be necessary to favour the young because the old will already have experienced enough good health to reach old(er) age.

It should be noted that this kind of argument does not always favour the young: an older person with a lifetime of chronic and debilitating disease would be an example of a *bad* innings! It has also been suggested that an individual in early adulthood should be favoured over an infant because the former had invested in their future life but not yet had a chance to reap the dividend, whereas the infant had not yet invested to the same extent.[32]

Age, rationing and RRT

It is not possible to resolve these ethical debates here. Nevertheless, there is clearly a strong moral argument in favour of age-based rationing in the literature, as well as the expected arguments against. How do these two opposing points of view help us interpret the data for RRT? We will undertake the analysis in two steps. First, we will consider these issues in the context of a fixed level of resources, and for ease of exposition we will assume they are fixed at the level which existed at the time that the current evidence on provision was collected. In the second stage we will consider the implications of increasing the overall level of funding for RRT, and this will lead on to a discussion of how 'need' has been calculated in the past.

But first let us assume a fixed level of resources and take each of the arguments against age-based rationing in turn. The first is that the UK evidence on acceptance rates by age reflects a poor understanding of the clinical appropriateness of older patients for RRT – a failure to properly accommodate the heterogeneity of patients. Clinicians are inappropriately importing age as a factor in decision-making in order to simplify bewildering choices between candidates who are in other respects similar. Such decisions may be taken even when the best clinical evidence indicates that old age is not necessarily a bar to a good response to treatment. It takes time and energy to remain on top of the latest clinical thought and it is perhaps understandable that certain expedients are occasionally introduced to aid decision-making. Nevertheless, such decisions are inappropriate, argue the opponents of the use of age, and should be rectified by better dissemination of good practice and the latest scientific evidence. Each patient should be judged on his or her merits with full information on their likely prognosis to hand.

But can age really be taken out of the equation quite so easily? Even if life expectancy is ignored, some patients will be judged likely to respond less well to treatment than others. Sometimes this will be because the passage of time has meant that their recuperative powers have diminished, or because other age-related illnesses are present. This will not always be the case: some 90-year-olds are physiologically fit and suitable for dialysis. However, older patients will *tend* to display characteristics which mean that they are not so well indicated for treatment. We are mortal and the passing of time reduces the functioning of our bodies. A perfectly 'unbiased' decision not to treat on the basis of ineffectiveness[33] may, in fact, be based on a consequence of ageing. To argue that age should *never* form part of clinical judgement is a semantic sleight of hand. Although one should not refer *exclusively* to age, it is difficult to ignore its consequences.

It is also difficult to disentangle life-expectancy from these judgements. In the case of RRT, survival is an important clinical consideration. As noted above, patients are typically categorised by risk group, with 'standard' risk including those aged less than 55; 'medium' aged 55-64; and 'high' aged over 65 (all non-diabetic). Life expectancy is higher in the first two groups than in the last. If it is accepted, from a clinical point of view, that life expectancy is an indicator of success, then in order to make more successful treatment decisions a doctor will have to choose rather more younger people than older. This is not to claim an end to the moral debate. However, it does suggest that those who believe that clinical effectiveness is a relevant criterion, but who also argue that age should have no part in these decisions, are dangerously close to contradicting themselves. In short, if ability to benefit is considered an important part of clinical decision-making, then it will be difficult to avoid considerations of age even if these considerations are only indirectly related to clinical outcome.

The second rejection of age as an appropriate criterion is more uncompromising. It argues that ability to benefit is not a relevant criterion; rather, 'need', understood in terms of the degree of ill-health, is what should guide rationing decisions. Elderly people are just as much in need in this sense as are the young, so their moral claim to limited resources is as great. Whether the individual can be said to have had a 'fair innings', or whatever, is irrelevant.

We cannot say for sure if clinicians make decisions on these grounds. But such decisions are certainly less easy to entwine with 'purely' clinical judgements than decisions which use age as a proxy for responsiveness or life-expectancy. Consider two patients, both of whom are suffering from ESRF, have the same life expectancy, and are equally clinically indicated for RRT, but one is 55 years old and the other 25. In this case a decision to treat the younger patient could not be made on purely clinical grounds. It has to be based on a social judgement of some kind, such as the younger person having had fewer opportunities to enjoy the benefits life offers.

Even if we cannot resolve the complex theoretical and moral debate, we can note the consequences of this uncompromising anti-age rationing position. The views of some ethicists imply that age should be removed entirely from playing any part in the decision-making process.[16] In terms of Figure 1, and leaving aside the difficulties in ensuring that such a policy is effected, the outcome required by this policy would be equal acceptance rates as a proportion of incidence in each age range. In fact, it is not quite that simple: if many of those in the older age groups could not benefit *at all* from treatment, then not even the pure anti-ageists would advocate the use of resources which were providing *no* benefit. Nevertheless, it is important to note that this camp would not accept that 'trivial' benefit, or benefit with a low probability of success, are sufficient reasons to withhold treatment. A small chance of success, they argue, may be every bit as important to the elderly patient as the greater chance of success to the young. Precisely equal acceptance rates as a proportion of incidence may not be required for each age group; nevertheless, entirely removing age-related rationing would require a significant change in current practice.

Looking at the issue from a different perspective, let us return to Figure 3 which shows those aged over 65 as a proportion of the total accepted for RRT across Europe. Unless the incidence of ESRF is drastically different in other countries, the majority of the incidence of RRT occurs in the over 65s. And yet no country (including Norway) accepts more than 50 per cent of the over 65s. A massive change in practice across Europe would be necessary to remove age-based decision-making entirely from RRT.

On the other hand, those who advocate greater – or more explicit – reliance on age would probably not significantly change current practice if their position were accepted. Acceptance for RRT would continue to favour the young. In other words, those who advocate age-based rationing are, at least in part, defending the *status quo* rather than proposing a radical shift in current practice.

Perhaps the explicitness of the age-based rationers is their most radical characteristic, and this introduces the third case against this form of rationing. The outcome of rationing decisions in RRT has long been known to favour the young. Many have challenged this outcome, but in defence clinicians have been able to cite their use of clinical effectiveness criteria when faced with limited resources. There was no need for them to make explicit reference to age; it was enough simply to refer to life expectancy or clinical indications for treatment. However, more recently some commentators decided that it was necessary to respond to the arguments of Age Concern for fear, in their eyes, that resources might be redirected to less 'productive' uses. That is, small benefits for elderly people might be substituted for larger ones for the young. The time had come to be explicit about why age-based rationing is appropriate.

The final case against age-based rationing argues that this explicitness could damage social relations. If identifiable groups are openly cited as having lower claims, this may cause concern and widespread lessening of the reassurance that the NHS provides. Elsewhere this has been referred to as the 'disutility of denial'.[34] It is not just the articulation of age which is relevant – simply specifying the clinical criteria for acceptance to RRT could make it clear that the elderly people get lower priority.[35] If the veil of benign deceit is lifted, would this do more harm than good?

In one sense, this is not a case against age-based rationing *per se*; it is an argument for *implicitness*, whatever the basis for rationing decisions. As long as no one publicly advocates age-related rationing, and the outcome is simply the result of disinterested clinical decisions, the NHS' 'reassurance factor' may be retained. However, it is worth asking how such decisions are to be concealed from an increasingly well-informed and well-educated public without offending democratic principles.

At this point, however, we must turn to the second part of the context in which this debate is conducted. For clarity we have so far assumed that the level of resources is fixed: the question is simply how to distribute the available benefits fairly. But this is not how many of those who oppose age-based rationing view the set of available policy options. Those who argue against 'ageism' are often making the point that elderly people who are not now treated could benefit from treatment if more resources were made available.[36] Treatment should not be taken away from the young; rather, more should be done for the old. A significant step in this direction could be made by providing sufficient resources to meet the 80 pmp acceptance rate cited earlier.

However, whereas it might be *possible* to treat more people in older age groups if more resources were devoted to RRT, this does not imply that we *ought* to increase the overall acceptance rate. Those resources have other uses where they also provide benefits. To investigate this matter further we must analyse how the 80 pmp figure has been calculated.

Establishing 'need' for renal replacement therapy

Assessing the level of 'need' for RRT objectively is not straightforward. Estimates since the mid-1960s in the UK have risen over time, followed on each occasion by rises in the acceptance rates for treatment as indications for treatment have widened. This process suggests that a considerable degree of judgement enters into needs assessments in this field. The reasons for this are not hard to find when the steps in needs assessment are unpacked.

In order to assess the 'need' for RRT, two steps are necessary. First, a robust estimate is needed of the number of new cases of chronic or advanced renal failure over a specified period in a defined population (which requires an agreed definition of 'advanced' or 'chronic' renal failure and some relatively straightforward way of operationalising it at patient level in different age, sex, ethnic and co-morbidity groups such as patients with high blood pressure and diabetes). Second, an estimate must be made of the proportion of these patients which should be treated (that is, are genuinely in 'need' of RRT). For the latter stage, the analyst should ideally deploy some justified definition of 'need' in terms of either ability to benefit, defined again in terms of either length or quality (e.g. degree of restriction due to dialysis) of survival or some trade-off between the two, or the extent to which the renal disease is life threatening, or some other criterion (e.g. whether the patient has had a 'fair innings', random selection, or the relative cost-effectiveness of treating one group of renal patients versus another).

As we have seen above, deciding which definition of 'need' to use is far from uncontentious and, furthermore, advances in the effectiveness and alterations in the costs of treatment will affect decisions – for example, on the proportion of patients who stand a reasonable chance of benefiting from RRT over a specified period of time. Advances in the treatment and prevention of diseases which predispose patients to chronic renal failure, such as high blood pressure, cardiovascular disease and diabetes, will also affect incidence in complex ways. For example, recent advances in primary prevention are likely to have *reduced* the number of younger patients presenting because of diabetes, yet treatment improvements for these predisposing conditions are also likely to have *increased* the number of survivors among these patients at risk of chronic renal failure, thereby potentially *increasing* the number of patients presenting at a later date.

Hence, it is unsurprising that estimates of population need have increased over time and, in response to them, acceptance rates for RRT, as Table 1 shows. These increases are not simply the result of improvements in technology; they also reflect changing clinical judgements made in the light of changing financial circumstances. These factors interact in complex ways but nevertheless 'need' estimates are not simply uncontentious technical calculations. As we have seen, acceptance rates in a number of European countries have frequently exceeded estimates of UK 'need' at various points over the last 30 years. In fact, the European mean acceptance rate is currently approximately 110 pmp pa (Figure 2) while the current Renal Association estimate of average population need lags behind it at approximately 80 pmp per year. Paradoxically, perhaps, there have also been periods when renal physicians in UK reported spare capacity even when acceptance rates were substantially lower than they are today and lower than in most European systems at the time.[37] This suggests that in each country there is an element of clinical judgement in the estimates of both 'need' and of whom to refer and treat on a day-to-day basis, and that these judgements are exercised differently in different countries, as well as changing over time.

Table 1 Estimates of 'need' for RRT in the UK and acceptance rates

Year	*Estimate of 'need' for RRT pmp pa*	*Acceptance rate for RRT adjusted for response rates (EDTA)*
1968-70	38 (5-60 yrs)[38]	
	63 (5-80 yrs)[38]	
1982		30 (unadjusted)
1983		33 (unadjusted)
1984	40 (NHS target set)	
1985-86	77 (all ages 95% CI 63-91)[39]	
	59 (under 60 yrs 95% CI 64-90)[39]	
1986		47
1986-88	78 (under 80 yrs 95% CI 63-93)[5]	
	80 (all ages estimated)[5]	
1987		56
1988		65
1989		61
1990		61
1991	75-80[2]	63
1992		68
1993		75
1994		>80? (Unpublished and unvalidated estimate)

UK methodology for establishing the '80 pmp' estimate of need

A brief look at the methods used to produce the currently accepted UK level of 'need' of 80 pmp per year supports this contention. The latest estimates of 'need' for RRT in the UK are based on two studies carried out in the mid-1980s by renal physicians. The first study was carried out in Northern Ireland in 1985-86.[39] Over 12 months, all GPs and hospital consultants were asked to report all patients known to have a blood urea of more than or equal to 25 mmol/l or a serum creatinine concentration of more than or equal to 500 μmol/l. One hundred and twenty-two patients were identified. The estimate of 'need' was taken to be this annual incidence which produced a required acceptance rate of 77.3 pmp per year. Despite this all-inclusive definition of need based entirely on a measure of blood analytes, 23/122 (19%) of the patients identified survived for at least a year after ascertainment before dialysis became mandatory for their survival.

In this study, the annual incidence of chronic renal failure was assumed to equate to the number of patients 'needing' RRT without any consideration of patients' ability to benefit from the treatment or the relative cost of treating different patient sub-groups. Nonetheless, in the report of the study, the author stated that, in her view, eight of the 122 were 'unsuitable' for treatment (she does not explain on what basis this conclusion was reached) and eight had died before they could be treated (and were, therefore, probably too ill to be suitable for long term treatment). Excluding these patients would have reduced the level of need to 67.5 pmp per year.

The Northern Ireland study was a repeat of an earlier survey carried out in the late 1960s.[38] It produced a higher level of need or incidence than the earlier study, which is almost all attributable to the higher rate of notification of older cases (over 50 years). The author discusses the fact that these patients are more likely than younger patients to have other health problems, are less likely to be able to manage self-treatment modalities of RRT, are more likely to develop complications and to require hospital admissions and are less likely to be suitable for transplantation. However, none of these considerations is brought to bear on the assessment of the appropriate level of 'need' which remains based on the level of blood analytes. The paper concludes, 'There is an obvious need for a great increase in the resources devoted to the treatment of end stage renal failure.'

The second study used to support the current Renal Association recommendation of an acceptance rate of 80 pmp per year[4], which has been adopted by the NHS as a desirable target, employs a different method of case ascertainment and, to some degree, a different definition of 'need', but produces a similar conclusion.[5] It seems possible that this is a chance similarity since in both studies there are important weaknesses in methods. The second study was undertaken in three English health districts in 1986-1988 during which time laboratories reported on all new patients with creatinine results over 500 μmol/l irrespective of the reason for their blood tests. Two hundred and ten patients were identified, an incidence rate for chronic renal failure of 148 (95% CI 128-168) pmp per year. This increased steeply with age such that the rate in those 80 years or over was 588 pmp per year.Only two patients under 60 years of age had not been referred to a renal unit, but only 49% of the age group 60 to 80 years had been referred, indicating that more older patients could conceivably have been treated.

Unlike the Northern Ireland study, this study went on to adjust the incidence rate downwards to arrive at a separate estimate of 'need'. Again, however, there was no explicit statement of how the criteria and assumptions used to do so were arrived at or operationalised. Thus, the authors separated those in need from the total cases by adding together: all those who had received dialysis within one year of notification; those under 80 years who died but '*who* [sic] *we consider should have been referred*'; those alive after two years and '*in imminent need of referral*'; and those whom the authors judged to have been the victim of '*errors of judgement by renal unit staff*'. As a result of this process, the authors concluded that 78 (95% CI 63-93) pmp per year needed acceptance onto the RRT programme under 80 years of age. Allowing for the over 80s who were judged suitable for treatment increased this figure to an estimate of 80 pmp per year which was reassuringly close to the conclusions of the Northern Ireland study.

Both the studies used to assess the current UK 'need' for acceptance onto RRT[5,39] depend on large amounts of implicit clinical judgement. Both studies started from the clinical judgement that there was insufficient RRT available, particularly for elderly people, perhaps because of conservative referral behaviour by non-nephrologists. Both ascertained prevalence using an arbitrary cut-off for a so called 'objective' indicator of renal function, namely persistent serum creatinine levels over 500 μmol/l, but used different methods for case identification. The Northern Ireland study appeared to assume that all those with creatinine levels above the defined point were in some sense also 'in need' of RRT without further justification, while the English study proceeded to make a series of implicit judgements about 'need' as against incidence, but without articulating any clear definition or criteria for patient inclusion. The only clearly discernible notion underlying the specific judgements in the English study appeared to relate to the imminence of death without RRT rather than any assessment of ability to benefit or cost-effectiveness of treatment, although even this was contradicted to some extent in the discussion section of the report which stated, '*These figures suggest that … treatment is still not offered to all who would benefit from it*'. There is then an element of circularity in the logic underlying the assessment of need in both cases. The fact that both studies yielded similar average estimates of 'need' may be more a reflection of a shared clinical culture than valid methods of estimation.

A final note of caution concerning both studies relates to the representativeness of the populations surveyed. Both study teams were sanguine about the generalisability of their findings, but without a great deal of introspection. Bearing in mind the significantly higher incidence of chronic renal failure among the black and South Asian population,[40,41] a survey in Northern Ireland, for example, which has a very low proportion of Asian residents, is highly likely to underestimate the need for RRT experienced in many other districts elsewhere. Similarly, the English study was based on three districts (Exeter, North Devon and Blackburn) chosen arbitrarily. Although Blackburn has a sizeable Asian population, no consideration was given to whether or not the three districts together provided an adequate basis for planning services elsewhere.

This detour into the detail of assessments of the 'need' for RRT shows that establishing 'need' unequivocally is far from straightforward. It is equally, if not more, difficult to decide how to use estimates of 'need' for decision making concerning the allocation of resources. Neither of the UK studies offers any assistance on this point; indeed, the English study makes no reference to the fact that RRT is costly and that it has to compete with other claims on NHS resources. The Northern Ireland author briefly mentions the fact that resources have to be divided between competing claims, but simply states that an accurate estimate of the extent of 'need' will suffice for planning purposes.

Conclusions

The currently accepted figure of 'need' for RRT in the UK is 80 pmp per annum and, given the time lag since the latest published acceptance rates were estimated and the difficulties with under-reporting, it is likely that UK acceptance rates in 1997 are near to that figure on average. Nevertheless, as we have seen, the current assessment of 'need' will almost certainly be revised upward if history is any guide (see Table 1), and, as a result, further calls for increased resources to enable new estimates of 'need' to be met will be made. It will be claimed that elderly people in particular are unfairly denied care; more generally, the experience of our European partners will be cited as evidence of how the UK is failing its renal patients.

However, the preceding discussion has made it clear that no estimate of 'need' is straightforward. Published figures do not represent the level of provision which would provide every last drop of benefit to every patient with ESRF. What they *do* constitute is a judgement by clinician-researchers, made more or less implicitly, about where to draw the line for RRT in the light of technological potential and financial constraints. Whether this judgement is appropriate is a complex matter. It must involve an assessment of the costs of providing further renal services against the often small benefits to be gained from them, particularly for elderly people. Life expectancy for those currently not treated may be short and quality of life poor once placed on RRT.[42] Many of our European partners exercise this judgement differently from the UK, whether the result of conscious policy-making or not. The question of who is right cannot be answered simply by reference to estimates of need in one country, nor by comparing one country's treatment rate to the international average. At the very least we require improved information about the costs and benefits of RRT, and a better understanding of how the general public view the moral status of age in rationing decisions.

But whatever the outcome of further research, it will be very difficult to remove entirely age-related rationing decisions from RRT. They are intimately tied up with judgements of a clinical nature, and even those judgements which are entirely 'social' have well-understood moral foundations. Describing the outcome of such decisions as 'ageist', as Age Concern does, cannot be justified by simple reference to the data.

Furthermore, even if it were possible to achieve an entirely non-age-related provision of RRT, the consequence would be a massive shift in clinical practice. This is simply an empirical observation, even for countries with very high take-on rates: current patterns of provision reflect judgements about where the most benefit can be derived, and these judgements tend to favour younger patients. Completely removing age from these decisions would result in a radical shift from the status quo. The only alternative – increasing expenditure so that more elderly people can be treated – cannot be justified simply by reference to estimates of 'need', particularly when these are based on implicit criteria. We have to look at how much benefit would be provided by doing so, and, uncomfortable as it sounds, how much that would cost those who might benefit from other forms of NHS care.

References and Notes

1 A Williams, 'Rationing health care by age: the case for', *BMJ* 1997, 314: 820-822.
2 Health Care Strategy Unit, *Report of the Health Care Strategy Unit review of renal services*, Department of Health: London 1996.
3 Age Concern, *Age discrimination in kidney services: the renal review*, Press Release, 4 June 1996.
4 Working Group of the Renal Association Subcommittee on Provision of Treatment for Chronic Renal Failure, *Provision of services for adult patients with renal disease in the United Kingdom*. Report on behalf of the Royal College of Physicians and the Renal Association. Unpublished, mimeo, October 1991.
5 TG Feest, CD Mistry, DS Grimes and NP Mallick, 'Incidence of advanced chronic renal failure and the need for end stage renal replacement treatment', *BMJ* 1990, 301:897-900.
6 Countries included in the mean are: Austria, Belgium, Denmark, Finland, France, (West) Germany, Greece, Ireland, Italy, Netherlands, Norway, Portugal, Spain, Sweden, Switzerland, UK.
7 The data in Figure 2 are an estimate, adjusted for the variable response rate from certain countries. Published figures from EDTA up to 1993 simply presented the RRT acceptance rate as the national estimate, regardless of the number of centres

which returned the data. For this article a very simple adjustment was made, increasing the raw data by a proportion so as to approximate a 100 per cent response rate. The accuracy of this adjustment depends on there being consistency amongst RRT centres in acceptance rates within a country, and on the non-responding centres being of a similar size to those that did respond. The result is to smooth the upward trend, which showed erratic fluctuations year on year using the raw data. The substance of the argument in this article, however, is unaltered by this adjustment.

The European mean is weighted to take account of population size.

8 Wales accepted 135.4 pmp in 1994 compared with England's 76.2 pmp – personal communication from the EDTA.

9 Unpublished data for 1994 gives an adjusted acceptance rate for the UK at over 80 pmp – personal communication from the EDTA.

10 An alternative explanation is that incidence rates are higher in other countries. There is unfortunately no hard evidence to support or refute this hypothesis, and in the absence of such evidence the assumption in this paper is that incidence rates do not vary significantly across European countries.

11 R Beech, M Gulliford, N Mays, J Melia and P Roderick, 'Renal Disease', in A Stevens and J Raftery (eds.) *Health Care Needs Assessment*, Oxford: Radcliffe Medical Press 1994.

12 We are grateful to Don Light for this personal communication.

13 D Callahan, *Setting Limits*, Simon and Schuster, New York 1987.

14 PA Lewis and M Charny, 'Which of two individuals do you treat when only their ages are different and you can't treat both?', *Journal of Medical Ethics* 1989, 15, 28-32.

15 see, for example, Shawcross, 'A soft target for rationing', editorial, *British Journal of Health Care Management* 1997, 3(4): 180.

16 J Harris, 'QALYfying the value of life', *Journal of Medical Ethics* 1987, 13, 117-123; L Doyal, 'Needs, rights, and equity: moral quality in healthcare rationing', *Quality in Health Care* 1995, 4, 273-283.

17 J Harris op cit.

18 It should be noted that many of these general assumptions are questioned on empirical grounds, including the true extent of cost savings by limiting care for the old in Callahan's proposals – see NG Levinsky, 'Age as a criterion for rationing health care', *The New England Journal of Medicine* 1990, 322, 1813-1816.

19 J Grimley Evans, 'Health care rationing and elderly people', in M Tunbridge (ed.) *Rationing of Health Care in Medicine*, Royal College of Physicians of London 1993; J Grimley Evans, 'This patient or that patient?', in Smith (ed.) *Rationing in Action*, BMJ Publishing Group, London 1993; MM Rivlin, 'Protecting elderly people: flaws in ageist arguments', *BMJ* 1995, 310, 1179-1182; RW Hunt, 'A critique of using age to ration health care', *Journal of Medical Ethics* 1993, 19, 19-23.

20 See D Hunter, 'Rationing health care: the political perspective', in R Maxwell (ed.) *Rationing Health Care*, Churchill Livingstone, London 1995; and R Klein, 'Rationing in the NHS: the dance of the seven veils in reverse', in R Maxwell (ed.) *Rationing Health Care*, Churchill Livingstone, London 1995.

21 See the approach of the Swedish government in M McKee and J Figueras, 'Setting priorities: can Britain learn from Sweden?', *BMJ* 1996, 312, 691-4.

22 Hunt (1993) op cit.

23 ibid.

24 D Hughes and L Griffiths, ' "But if you look at the coronary anatomy…": risk and rationing in cardiac surgery', *Sociology of Health and Illness* 1996, 18, 172-197.

25 An interesting aside on this issue relates to the

use of age as a proxy for need in national resource allocation decisions. Areas with a high number of elderly people are favoured in resource allocation formulae – age is therefore formally accepted as an appropriate criterion *in favour of elderly people*. In this use, however, age is a proxy for the incidence of ill-health, not for need in the sense of ability to benefit. But after receiving their spending allocation, there is no requirement for health authorities to devote commensurate resources to elderly people if it is believed their priority should be low following the arguments in this section.

26 A Williams, 'Cost-effectiveness analysis: is it ethical?', *Journal of Medical Ethics* 1992, 18: 7-11.

27 See D Callahan, 'Response to Roger W Hunt', *Journal of Medical Ethics* 1993, 19: 24-27; D Callahan, *What Kind of Life: The limits of medical progress*, Georgetown University Press, Washington DC 1994.

28 Callahan 1993 op cit., p. 23

29 ibid. p. 25

30 ibid. p. 24

31 A Williams, 'Intergenerational equity: an exploration of the "fair innings" argument', *Health Economics* 1997, 6:117-132.

32 See Lewis and Charny, 1989 op cit.

33 In this discussion, an 'effective' treatment is one where there is some 'ability to benefit' taking all things into account. Dialysis is an unpleasant procedure in itself, and can be associated with other unpleasant side-effects and complications. Quality of life may be poor, particularly for elderly people. So, even if extensions to life expectancy are possible, the reduced quality of life might lead some patients, in partnership with their clinician, to decide that the *net effect* is negative (i.e. that there is no overall benefit) and to refuse treatment. However, as long as the decision is that overall net benefit is positive (i.e. the patient, all things considered, desires treatment), then withholding treatment must be considered an act of rationing, regardless of how justified this may be because of limited resources.

34 J Coast 'Rationing within the NHS should be explicit: the case against', *BMJ* 1997, 314: 1118-22; see also L Doyal 'Rationing within the NHS should be explicit: the case for' *BMJ* 1997, 314: 1114-8.

35 E. Farmery and P. Milner, *Renal Replacement Therapy: Purchasing review and recommendations*, Wiltshire Health Authority, Paper WHA/97/64, 19 May 1997.

36 NP Mallick, 'End-stage renal failure' in M Turnbridge (ed.) *Rationing of Health Care in Medicine*, Royal College of Physicians of London 1993.

37 M McCarthy, 'A decision-maker's guide to renal failure', in A Harrison and J Gretton (eds.) *Health Care UK 1985*, CIPFA: London 1985.

38 McGeown MG. Chronic renal failure in Northern Ireland 1968-70. *Lancet* 1972; I: 307-10.

39 McGeown MG. Prevalence of advanced renal failure in Northern Ireland. *British Medical Journal* 1990; 301: 900-3.

40 SG Rostand, KA Kirk, EA Rutsky and BA Pate, 'Racial differences in the incidence of treatment for end-stage renal disease', *New England Journal of Medicine* 1982, 306: 1276-9.

41 AC Burden, P McNally, J Feehally and J Walls, 'Increased incidence of end stage renal failure secondary to diabetes mellitus in Asian ethnic groups in the United Kingdom', *Diabetic Medicine* 1992, 9: 641-5.

42 C Byrne, P Vernon and JJ Cohen, 'Effect of age and diagnosis on survival of older patients beginning chronic dialysis', *JAMA* 1994, 271(1): 34-36.

The European Union and health: past, present and future

Elias Mossialos and Martin McKee

The European Union does not have a comprehensive health policy. Unlike other international organisations, it is essentially an economic entity, so health continues to come low in the policy agenda, unless it is related to the needs of the Single Market, such as product safety, health and safety at work, pharmaceuticals and medical devices and the free movement of professionals.[1]

The consequences of a failure to develop such a policy have long been commented on by the public health community. The creation of a Directorate General (DG) for Health has been advocated since the early 1970s but without success. The new institutional and legal framework introduced by the treaty establishing the European Union in 1991 raised hopes that such a development might come about but, although new legislation and some additional programmes were initiated, these did not add up to a coherent policy.

It is, therefore, important to establish a framework to define European Community public health priorities. An analysis of the legal, institutional and decision-making framework may help to better understand how policy has evolved and how policy development may evolve in the near future.

Despite the absence of a comprehensive policy, many aspects of European Union activity have an impact on health. This chapter examines the European legal and institutional framework within which decisions are taken, describes the decision-making process and examines some of the areas where European developments have had or will soon have consequences for national policy. It concludes with a discussion of how possible changes in the European Union might affect health policy in the future.

Before Maastricht

The legal framework within which the European Union may take action in the field of health policy has evolved consistently since the founding of the Community in 1956, when its health concerns were limited to those related to occupational health in the coal and steel industries.

The 1986 Single European Act amended the earlier treaties (Treaty of Rome, the Euratom and the European Coal and Steel Treaties) and, in Article 100A(3), required the Commission to take, as a base, a high level of protection in its proposals concerning health, safety and environmental and consumer protection, as they relate to the working of the Single European Market.

The most significant provision in the field of health was introduced in the 1991 Treaty on

European Union (the Maastricht Treaty). The Treaty gave the Union a new competence in public health with the insertion of Articles 3(o) and 129. Article 3(o) stipulates that the Community should contribute to the attainment of a high level of health protection. Article 129 identifies two areas for Community action: disease prevention and health protection. There are three means through which these objectives can be achieved: research, health information and education, and the incorporation of health protection requirements in the Community's other policies. However, harmonisation of the laws and regulations of the Member States is specifically excluded.

Article 129 is somewhat vague concerning the responsibilities of the Member States and the Commission. The obligation to achieve a high level of human health protection is for the Community as a whole. The Community is also responsible for directing actions towards the prevention of diseases, in particular the major health scourges. It is not clear, however, what are the major health scourges are although the one mentioned, drug dependence, is arguably not primarily a health matter or a major health scourge.

It is equally unclear what is meant by co-ordination of activities: the same or similar policy objectives, common programmes, or just exchange of information on policy initiatives? The role of the Council is more specific. The Council may adopt recommendations, and, together with the European Parliament, decide on incentive measures. What an incentive measure is, is not defined in the Treaty. It is also worth noting that a recommendation is not a legally binding instrument for the Member States.

A further complication was the introduction by the Treaty of the principle of subsidiarity. As set out in Article 3(b), the Community will act only where it has exclusive competence or where it shares competence with Member States, only where it can be more successful in achieving a particular objective than can an individual Member State. This concept is rather more political than legal and the different priorities of the Member States often make it difficult to reach agreement on how action at Community level can offer greater added value.

The decision-making process in the EU

EU decision-making resists simplification. The Commission is responsible for initiating policies (often encouraged by the Member States, the EU Presidencies or the European Parliament). The Commission can implement the provisions of the Treaty by different methods, including adoption of and proposals for regulations, directives, and decisions (which are binding) and recommendations and opinions (which are not binding). The regulations and directives then become part of the *acquis communautaire*. When making proposals the Commission has to consult with a range of bodies, including the Economic and Social Committee (consisting mainly of representatives of employers' and employees' organisations of the Member States) and the Committee of Regions (bringing together regional and local representatives from the Member States). Then the proposal is forwarded to both the Council of Ministers and the European Parliament. In the case of the so-called co-operation procedure, the Council is the final decision-making point but the European Parliament is involved in the legislative process and may propose amendments to the Council's common position. The Treaty on European Union increased the powers of the European Parliament. Under the Maastricht Treaty, the European Parliament has considerable powers in decision-making but its views are not always taken seriously by the Council. It is also worth noting that there is no accountability of the Council to the European Parliament.

The most important change was the introduction of the co-decision procedure. Under this procedure, the European Parliament and the Council adopt legislative agreements by joint agreement. If the European Parliament rejects the proposal by an absolute majority after two readings of a proposal and, if necessary, invoking a conciliation procedure between the Council and the Parliament, the proposal cannot become law. This procedure has failed to produce a decision twice so far, in cases related to voice telephony and biotechnology.

The Treaty introduced qualified majority voting to the Council in many fields of health-related activities but unanimity is still required in others. A problem may arise where there is ambiguity about which procedure to use. The European Court has usually upheld the choice of legal bases made by the Commission, even when their scope is extended to the extreme boundaries of particular legislation. Examples, discussed later, include the directive on working time, initiated under articles covering health and safety of workers, and proposals to ban most tobacco advertising, under articles on the free movement of goods.[2]

There are more than twenty combinations of procedures and voting rules that could be followed in creating health-related policies. The lack of logic in the choice of the various procedures and the different fields of activity where they apply, as well as the complex combination of powers and voting procedures in the Parliament and the Council and the involvement of large numbers of Commission services in initiating policies, makes the development of a coherent health policy difficult.

A further complication is that currently thirteen of the twenty-four Directorates General of the Commission headed by different Commissioners are involved in shaping health-related policies. Examples include the Common Agricultural Policy and VAT policy. Furthermore, the fragmentation of power leaves much scope for action by organised interests. Finally, the pattern of policy-making reflects national political realities with few long-term strategies and with incremental measures and short-term policies that do not always address the main challenges.

Current and forthcoming issues

The following sections address a selection of topics where European policies have had, or may yet have, an impact on national policies. They are not exhaustive but do illustrate the necessity for health policy makers to take into account the European dimension when making decisions.

Cross-frontier health care

In principle, most citizens of the European Union are entitled to medical treatment throughout the Union, but only in some circumstances, set out in a series of regulations dating from 1971. Coverage includes employed and self-employed European Union nationals who have coverage in one Member State, pensioners who are European Union nationals, and members of families of these groups, irrespective of nationality. Students and disabled or unemployed persons who are not members of the family of someone who is covered, are excluded, as are civil servants in those countries in which they have a separate insurance scheme that is not open to the rest of the population. The details of the schemes under which people can obtain treatment abroad have been described in detail elsewhere.[1]

In general, the focus of the legislation is on those who become ill while on temporary visits abroad. Patients may travel abroad to receive treatment for a pre-existing condition only in certain limited circumstances. This has, however, given rise to concern about the impact on attempts by national health care systems to ration care as part of a strategy of cost containment. In brief, patients have no automatic right to travel abroad for treatment paid for by the national health system. This does not, of course, preclude someone travelling abroad for treatment if they pay for it themselves or if a private insurer is willing to do so.

This legislation also provides a framework for health care funders to contract with a provider in another country. Some British health authorities have purchased non-urgent surgery in northern France and the Belgian health insurance scheme will pay for treatment of those living within 15 km of the national border in a foreign hospital that is no more than 25 km on the other side of the frontier.

The Working Time Directive

The Directive[3] obliges the UK to introduce legislation giving mandatory rest breaks after six consecutive hours, a minimum daily rest period of 11 hours, at least one day off a week, no more than eight hours a shift on average for night work and four weeks' annual paid holiday. The UK Government managed to achieve a number of exemptions for workers in rail, road, sea, air, inland waterways, lake transport services, priests and junior doctors, but the Directive does include nurses and health service administrative staff.

The British Government argued that the Directive should never have been tabled under the rubric of the EU's health and safety provisions where legislation requires qualified majority rather than unanimity. This allowed other Member States to overcome British reservations at the Council of Ministers, even though the UK had opted out from the Social Chapter of the Treaty on European Union.

In 1994 the UK Government unsuccessfully asked the Court to annul the Directive. The Court's decision[4] may trigger further legislation on work-related stress and other physiological aspects of ill health related to the working environment as the judges indicated that health and safety legislation should aim to protect the total well-being of all workers.[5]

There is likely to be continuing pressure to resolve what is seen by many as anomalous in that junior doctors in the UK are exempt from the Directive, even though they have much higher levels of stress than the general population,[6] which seems likely to have implications for patient safety.[7]

The BSE affair

It is now widely recognised the European Union played a major role in forcing the former British Government to address the BSE issue seriously. Following the announcement by the British

Government's Spongiform Encephalopathy Advisory Group that bovine spongiform encephalopathy (BSE) was the most likely explanation for the emergence of human cases of a new variant of Creutzfeld-Jakob Disease (nv-CJD), the introduction of a world-wide ban on the export of British beef placed the issue at the top of the national and European political agenda. The legal basis for the ban stems from the right of the European Union to restrict trade when an outbreak of infectious disease occurs.[8] The response to the emergence of BSE by both the Commission and the British Government has been highly criticised by a report of the European Parliament,[9] which catalogues a consistent failure to place public health concerns above those of industry. Furthermore, it raises fundamental questions about the impartiality of scientific experts from the UK and the extent to which the then British Government sought to subvert the development and implementation of policies to control the spread of the disease.

The action taken by the European Union has important implications for governments seeking to pursue deregulatory policies, on supposed grounds of competitiveness, where they adversely affect health.[10] The BSE affair has also had important implications for the Commission. The initial response of the European Commission President, Jaques Santer, was the announcement of several internal reforms of the European Commission to ensure that such problems would be better dealt with in the future. These measures include separation of responsibilities for food safety and agricultural policy. It was also reported that the Agriculture Commissioner, Mr Fischler, had backed the idea of a separate European Union Food Agency but Santer's initial proposal is only for a 30-strong inspection team responsible for food safety, within DG XXIV, that will be responsible for ensuring that the Member States enforce EU laws.[11] However, further pressure from the European Parliament, which has the power to censure the Commission, has led to new policy developments. It now seems that a new Directorate-General will be established but the plans are not at all clear and there is concern that the new DG might focus on consumer safety issues and free movement of goods.

Tobacco advertising

At the time of writing, five Member States – the UK, Germany, The Netherlands, Greece and Denmark – are effectively blocking proposals to ban tobacco advertising in the Council of Ministers, where a qualified majority is required. Five Member States have already banned tobacco advertising. These are France, Italy, Portugal, Finland and Belgium.[12] The former British Government believed that the best way to control tobacco advertising was by means of a voluntary agreement between the government and the industry. A new voluntary agreement came into effect on 1 January 1992 and, at that time, a health minister, Baroness Hooper, set out government policy to the House of Commons Health Committee as:

> *We are not convinced and have never been convinced that the total ban which we are currently talking about affecting posters and the newspaper advertising, is going to have the sort of impact that some countries believe it will.*[13]

The change of policy in the UK, following the election of a Labour government, seems likely to lead to a different approach at a European level and thus the introduction of a Europe-wide ban, which would include those countries that have, until now, resisted national action.

Medicines regulation

At present there is no single market in pharmaceuticals, as many aspects of pricing and reimbursement are controlled by national governments as part of their cost containment strategies. These include setting prices for products or, in the case of the UK, agreeing profit levels with industry. Industrial policy considerations also play an important role.

The European Commission has achieved agreement on directives on advertising, good manufacturing practice, on provisions relating to labelling and package inserts and on licensing of wholesalers. Nevertheless, existing divergent national policies combined with the inherent peculiarities of the pharmaceutical market and the structure of the industry make the completion of a Single European Market a particularly difficult task. For a Single Market to become a reality it would be necessary to remove the further barriers to trade by standardising pack sizes, dosages and the names of products marketed under different names in different countries. This should reduce costs and allow a pan-European wholesaler to stock fewer products.

Furthermore there is also a need to standardise the systems of regulation of prices and profits; to align costs of medicines to patients and to co-ordinate what drugs are covered by the health care system. In other words there is a need to standardise the present situation in which some countries have lists of drugs not covered (a 'negative list') and others have lists indicating what will be paid for (a 'positive list'). Progress has been uneven and the degree of harmonisation of national controls is by no means uniform across the many aspects of pharmaceutical regulation.

The concept of good manufacturing practice was adopted under a Directive in 1989[14] and took effect from the beginning of 1992. The aim is to ensure that all manufacturers have in place effective quality assurance and control of their manufacturing operations. The principles and guidelines include personnel, premises and equipment, documentation, production, quality control, complaints and product recall and self-inspection. Enforcement is by national authorities who should carry out regular inspections of production units. The marketing and distribution rules cover all aspects of the product's classification,[15] wholesale distribution[16] and labelling,[17] advertising and sales promotion.[18] Again, enforcement is left to the competent national authorities.

A new measure is the creation of a medicines licensing system for the EU as a whole. The European Medicines Evaluation Agency, based in London, will play an important role. All human medicines can be dealt with in one of three registration procedures. These are:

- a centralised procedure, reserved for innovatory products and leading to a single Community-wide authorisation valid for all 15 Member States. The use of the centralised procedure will be compulsory for all medicinal products derived from bio-technology but available only at the request of companies for other innovatory products. Under this procedure applications will be processed by the Agency in London. It is expected that one of the issues that will be raised in the near future will be the definition of what is an innovative product, with important policy implications for the future.

- a decentralised procedure, which will apply to the substantial majority of products, based upon the principle of mutual recognition, and covering a variable number of Member States.
- a national procedure, limited in principle to applications of local interest concerning a single Member State.

The number of pharmaceutical products marketed in different countries varies widely, from 4,900 brand-named products in Denmark to 23,000 in Germany,[19] and is largely determined by decisions by health services and insurance funds about what will be covered. Increasingly, these bodies are introducing criteria of effectiveness or cost-effectiveness into their decisions and, in some cases, as with Beta-Interferon in the UK, there are proposals that new treatments should only be made available within the context of clinical trials.

The question arises as to whether the law on free movement of goods precludes a national health system from restricting what it will purchase or reimburse. This was examined in a challenge to the imposition of a restricted list of pharmaceuticals in The Netherlands. The European Court of Justice took the view that a so-called 'negative list', excluding certain expensive products from reimbursement by health insurance institutions, may be compatible with Article 30, hence recognising that Member States had a legitimate interest in controlling drug budgets. Nevertheless in discussions prior to the introduction of the limited list in the UK, the Commission insisted that the list should not favour generic drugs over branded products which met the same criteria, as this could constitute a breach of Article 30 if imports were potentially disadvantaged. In the light of the Court's more recent judgment on Article 30, however, one might wonder whether the Commission would now take the same view.[20]

Pharmaceutical pricing

Pharmaceutical prices in the EU are not harmonised. The Transparency Directive[21] introduced in 1989 only regulates the process of setting prices in the Member States. In the UK there is no direct price control for pharmaceuticals and indirect regulation is exercised through the Pharmaceutical Price Regulation Scheme (PPRS). The banded profit control system of the PPRS is a version of rate of return regulation with capping elements. It has been argued that the UK Government's hand may be forced by developments in the EU, in particular in the Transparency Directive and that the European Commission is contemplating a legal scrutiny of the scheme.[22] In fact, Article 5 of the Transparency Directive specifically covers the PPRS. The Article specifies that where Member States adopt a system of direct or indirect control of profitability of persons responsible for placing medicinal products on the market, the Member State concerned should publish information on the methods used to define: profitability; the range of target profits; the criteria according to which target rates of profit are set and the criteria for granting permission to retain profits above targets; and finally the maximum percentage profit which a company is allowed to retain above the target. However, Article 30 of the EEC Treaty prohibits all measures having an effect equivalent to a quantitative restriction on trade between Member States. According to the Commission, freezing importers' margins on goods is compatible with Article 30 of the EEC Treaty only if it both allows importers to cover the costs and charges of importation and is accompanied by price freezes for domestic products.[23] The PPRS can thus only be challenged on the basis that it does not allow importers to cover costs and charges necessary to cover importation. The fact that the rate of return method employed is different for the locally produced and imported products may not constitute a legal problem.

Developments in the Transparency Directive are not expected since the Commission is currently developing an overall industrial policy for the European pharmaceutical sector. It is, however, questionable whether the Commission will achieve any consensus among national governments on harmonisation of pricing and reimbursement mechanisms in the foreseeable future. Unanimity in the Council is required and, given the current emphasis on subsidiarity, it will be a formidable task to achieve it. Standardising systems of prices, price liberalisation across the EU, or drug lists would be seen by Member States as a precedent-setting invasion by the Commission into the province of health care organisation, which Member States see as protected by the principle of 'subsidiarity' which they are keen to maintain.

It is also important to note that aspects of current systems of price controls and the lack of price liberalisation across the EU influence cross-border policy developments. Several countries set drug prices according to a comparison of drug prices in other countries. Two Member States (Italy and The Netherlands) use a system of average prices in which prices are linked to the average in four other countries. In both cases the UK prices are taken into account. Albeit less formally, many other countries also draw on information on prices elsewhere when establishing local prices.

While drug companies historically have charged higher prices in higher income countries, they are increasingly moving towards uniform prices to avoid the downward ratchet effect of cross-country comparisons, but with only limited success. UK prices are currently used as benchmark prices for exports to other countries. This becomes more important given the incomplete character of the EU market and cross-border policy developments. This may also be a reason why the UK regulators have not implemented price control systems.

The insurance market

Private health insurance is not yet significant in many States but it is growing in most of them. Developments were triggered by the Third Non-Life Insurance Directive,[25] which introduced important changes in the insurance market in the Union.

In the past there have been two main models for the supervision of insurance operations in the EU.[24] The first is known as material regulation and the second is based on financial regulation. The first is illustrated by Germany, where regulation is based on the idea that if insurers are sufficiently controlled in the type of business that they write and their level of premiums, then there can be no question of insolvency. The supervisory body considers the policies before they are offered for sale. Also, in Germany only insurers who have specialised in health care could operate in the field of private health insurance to protect policyholders from insolvency arising from failures in other sectors. Price competition is restricted or prohibited by the use of compulsory tariffs. The second model is seen in the UK. Here, the regulator must be satisfied with regard to solvency by means of detailed financial returns. The regulator is not concerned with consumer protection issues such as policy wording or prices.

The transposition into national law of the Third Non-Life Insurance Directive has had a significant effect on the so-called common insurance area. There is now, possibility of providing accident and health cover jointly with a life insurance contract and for accident and health insurers to offer life insurance contracts provided that different classes are administered separately. This may, however, have the effect that governments insist that life assurance rules and solvency standards also apply to health insurance operations. In addition there will be a single licence for insurers incorporated in a Member State to conduct operations anywhere within the EU, whether through branches or under the freedom to provide services, subject only to home state regulation. This raises the question of the regulatory ability of the domicile Member State to police and monitor activities of insurance firms in other Member States.[26] It also removes the right of the Member States to operate material supervision. Insurers will be able to fix freely the rates they wish to charge and this may lead to price competition. This might also be triggered by harmonisation of important elements of contract law to other forms of competition. Furthermore, movement of currency between any of the parties involved in transactions will be unrestricted. However, as long as private health insurance is a substitute for social insurance, the Member States can enforce their binding legal conditions and retain their right to prior notification of policy conditions, as has been done by Germany. In addition, Member States can enforce policies that ensure solidarity, such as the prohibition of age-related premiums, again as in Germany.

There is a possibility that the principle of home country control could introduce competition not only to providers but also national regulatory regimes. Strict regulatory regimes may discourage companies from investing in a specific Member State and this could induce Member States to reduce their regulatory constraints. Harmonisation could thus lead to the lowest common denominator. Table 1 presents the effectiveness of the Single Market in removing barriers to the free provision of insurance services. The main barrier remains the harmonisation of tax regimes.

Tax decisions require unanimity in the Council. The Single Market Programme introduced directives covering tax issues involving parent companies and their subsidiaries and also mergers. There is, however, no uniform treatment of interest and royalty payments and other related matters.

In July 1990 the European Community:[28]

- eliminated withholding taxes on distribution of profit from corporate subsidiaries to a parent corporation resident in a different Member State.
- provided tax relief for cross-border mergers and acquisitions.
- took steps to prevent double taxation arising from cross-border transfers within corporations, the so-called transfer pricing.

The parent subsidiary directive also prevents those distributions being taxed in the parent company's country without allowing a credit for taxes paid by the subsidiary. This puts the EU parent in an advantageous position over non-EU companies investing in EU subsidiaries.

Table 1 Effectiveness of the Single Market measures in removing barriers to the free provision of insurance services

Cross-border service restrictions	*	(Discriminatory conditions for cross-border sale of services
	†	(Restricting of marketing and services content
Restrictions on establishment	*	Discriminatory conditions for licensees
Restrictions on factor flows	*	Capital controls
Regulatory/technical barriers	†	Consumer protection
	†	Conditions for sales
Fiscal issues	●	Taxation of reserves
	●	Taxation of premiums
Other	●	Contract law

Note: * Barriers effectively removed; † Barriers partially removed; ● Remaining barrier

Source: European Commission (1996) [27]

Member States are finding it difficult to live with these new developments. One of the reasons is that the health ministries were not at all involved in the discussions concerning the harmonisation of private non-life insurance in Europe. Private health insurance was a small part of the insurance market and failed to attract specific attention. The fact that the Directive also covers health insurance may have escaped the attention of the relevant authorities. This can have untoward consequences, as illustrated by the recent dispute between the Irish Government and BUPA International.

BUPA launched its operation in Ireland in November 1996 by announcing its intention to differentiate itself from Voluntary Health Insurance (VHI) by offering two ranges of products,[29] the Essential Scheme and Cash Plans. The first scheme provides cover for essential medical care, while the latter offers the possibility to upgrade hospital accommodation according to four extra levels of payment. This has become a highly political issue and BUPA was accused of contravening the principle of Community rating since, unlike the prices of the Essential Scheme, the premiums for the Cash Plans vary according to the age of the insured. After lengthy negotiations with the Department of Health and public battles with the VHI, BUPA withdrew the Cash Plans but it is planning to launch a new scheme in late 1997.

Telemedicine and information society

The development of telemedicine in Europe is still embryonic but it is expanding very rapidly. This could lead to the provision of cross-border services in a number of medical fields. These include the development of computer-based patient records and administrative records which will facilitate all telemedicine potential applications at a very low cost.

Telemedicine applications which will facilitate cross-border care in the future include the development of radiology networks and applications in dermatology, pathology, mammography and, in the longer term, robotic surgery.[30] These developments will depend on the further liberalisation of telecommunication services in Europe and on reimbursement methods and regulations which are not yet established. The EC Information Society Program and new legislation on data transmission and data banks will also affect future developments. New developments related to the EC Information Society Programme may also facilitate further cross-border care. The Data Protection Directive,[31] due to be implemented in the Member States by July 1997, established a single regulatory framework for the free movement of personal data throughout the EU.

The proposed Directive for a Transparency Mechanism for Information Society Services,[32] put forward by the Commission in July 1996, if finally adopted, would extend the scope of Directive 83/189 (which covers national rules affecting free movement of goods) to include new Information Society services. The proposed Directive defines as 'Information Society Services' all existing or new services that will be provided at a distance, by electronic means and at the individual request of a service receiver including on-line health care services. However, the Directive would not require any harmonisation of the national rules but to ensure that the Single Market is not fragmented and that no new regulatory barriers appear. The Commission will seek to ensure that national initiatives are compatible with freedom of establishment or free movement of services. Since there is not yet free movement of services between Member States it may seem that the proposed Directive is irrelevant regarding the health care market. It may have, however, important implications in the case of cross-border care or private health insurance in the future.

The need to support the mobility of patients and citizens across the EU Member States has also raised the issue of compatibility and interoperability of initiatives using medical cards. In April 1996 the European Parliament passed a resolution to begin a legislative process to introduce in 1999 the card-based European Health Passport.[33] This is expected to be on a voluntary basis. This was not the first time that action on health cards was initiated. The Parliament adopted a resolution in 1981 on a European Health Card[34] and this was followed by a Council Resolution in 1986[35] concerning the adoption of a European emergency card. The Commission is currently funding a number of initiatives on the standardisation of patient record systems in Europe and several pilot projects have already been initiated.

New priorities

All of these issues could be affected by changes in the legal basis of the European Union that may arise as a result of the June 1997 Inter-Governmental Conference. At the time of writing the conclusions of these deliberations were not known. Following pressures from the European Parliament and a number of Member States, the Commission developed a proposal to revise Article 129 of the Treaty. As we have already mentioned, the Commission has in the past used a number of other Articles to propose legislation on health issues but it seems that without a revision of Article 129 there will be no possibility of integrating a number of currently scattered activities and preparing a comprehensive European public health policy. The Commission's proposal to revise Article 129 is shown in Box 1. As this article was going to press the final version of the new article 129 was published. It is rather more complex than the version proposed by the Commission and fails to address many key issues.

It is obvious that the proposals address the

Box 1 Commission Proposal to Revise Article 129

1) As part of its powers the Community shall ensure a high level of human health protection. It shall, in addition, encourage co-operation between Member States in this field by lending support, if necessary, to their action.

   Community action shall be directed towards any measure liable to prevent human illness or to obviate sources of danger to public health, the action shall cover the fight against the major health scourges, including drug dependence, by promoting research into their causes and their transmission, as well as health confirmation and education.

   Health protection requirements must be integrated into the definition and implementation of the Community's other policies.

2) Member States shall, in liaison with the Commission, co-ordinate amongst themselves their policies and programmes in the areas referred to in paragraph 1. The Commission may, in close contact with Member States, take any useful initiative to promote such co-ordination.

   The Council shall, on the basis of a report from the Commission, undertake a comprehensive annual evaluation of the results of such co-ordination.

3) The Community and the Member States shall foster co-operation with third countries and the competent international organisations in the sphere of public health.

4) In order to contribute to the achievement of the objectives referred to in this Article, the Council:

   – acting in accordance with the procedure referred to in Article 189b, shall adopt measures regarding the approximation of the Member States' laws, regulations and administrative actions designed to protect public health, especially in the veterinary and phytosanitary fields;

   – acting in accordance with the procedure referred to in Article 189b, after consulting the Economic and Social Committee and Committee of the Regions, shall adopt any incentive measures capable of lending support to efforts made by Member States in context of co-ordinating their policies;

   - acting by a qualified majority on a proposal from the Commission, shall adopt recommendations.

immediate problems of BSE and food safety and they are not the result of a careful and considered review of health policy developments at EU level. The emphasis on veterinary and phytosanitary fields is evidence of how a redrafting has bowed to immediate political concerns.[36] There is, however, a significant change concerning the introduction of a proposal to approximate laws, regulations and administrative actions designed to protect public health, especially in the veterinary and phytosanitary fields. Although the emphasis is again on veterinary and phytosanitary policies, the proposal opens the way for a broader discussion of what should be approximated and how it should be done. But this requires a definition of what is public health, which is still missing.

Developments at the IGC seem likely to lead to reorganisation of the Commission's functions and responsibilities. The establishment of a new Commission department with responsibility for health could play a significant role in co-ordinating currently scattered activities and programmes. A new department could incorporate units from DGV (responsible for Social Affairs and Employment) and other DGs as well as the whole DG XXIV (Consumer Policy). An indicative regrouping of areas of responsibility is presented in Box 2 based on current needs and anticipated developments.

The first task for such an entity should be to develop a coherent strategy to integrate public health into other Union policies. The new DG should also define, in co-operation with the Member States and the scientific community, where the European Union can act in public health and which areas should remain the preserve of the Member States, as the present lack of clarity is a recipe for disputes over the Union's role.[37] The significant powers of the European Parliament and the Council that may accrue from a revamped Treaty will ensure that elected representatives and authorities in the Member States have an important role in policy formation and implementation.

There are many tasks that a new DG could undertake at a European level. They include:

- development, in collaboration with WHO and other international organisations, common standards and definitions so that comparative studies can be undertaken to assess possible variations in health needs, utilisation, health expenditure and outcome;
- development of a Europe-wide system of surveillance of the incidence of communicable diseases;
- development of co-operative arrangements for the evaluation of methods of treatment and technology assessment;
- investigation of the aetiology of some of the major causes of mortality and morbidity to identify possible preventive strategies and evaluate different approaches to the control

Box 2 Proposed regrouping of the European Commission's health and health-related dossiers

Public Health
Environmental health and chemical substances, radiation protection, disease prevention, health promotion, health monitoring and health telematics, research and G7 health projects, epidemiology and surveillance of diseases, actions on specific risks, combatting drug dependence, programmes for the disabled, medical ethics;

Medical Care and the Internal Market
Medicinal products (orphan drugs, vaccines, consumption, pricing and reimbursement), technology assessment, effects of other Community policies on health systems, health professions, health economics and policy analysis, priority setting and policy evaluation;

Safety and Standards Regulation and Consumer Protection
Occupational safety and health, medical devices, veterinary and phytosanitary regulations and controls, nutrition and food safety, biotechnology, relations with and information to consumers, pricing, marketing and liability issues;

Health Developments in Other Countries and Humanitarian Aid
PHARE, ACE and TACIS programmes on health, Euro-Mediterranean projects, health planning in developing countries, humanitarian aid;

of diseases for which preventive measures are known.

However, until a political consensus is reached over all potential areas for action, policies may develop merely as a series of individual responses and not as a coherent strategy with clear objectives. The current institutional and legal conditions are unfortunately not the most appropriate for the development of a coherent EU public health framework.

References

1. McKee M, Mossialos E, Belcher P. The influence of European Community law on national health policy. *Journal of European Social Policy* 1996; 6(4):263–286.
2. Council Directive 89/662, 1989.
3. Directive 93/104, 1993, *Official Journal of the European Communities*, No 307, p 18.
4. European Court of Justice, Judgment of the Court of 12 November 1996 in case C–84/94: United Kingdom of Great Britain and Northern Ireland V. Council of the European Union, *Official Journal of the European Communities*, C9/10, 11.1.1997.
5. Hughes S. Healthy, Wealthy and Wise: The Aim for European Workers. *Eurohealth* 1996; 3(1):18–19.
6. McKevitt C, Morgan M, Simpson J, Holland WW. *Doctors' health and needs for services*. London: Nuffield Provincial Hospitals Trust, 1996.
7. McKee CM, Black N. Does the current use of junior doctors in the United Kingdom affect the quality of medical care? *Social Science and Medicine* 1992; 34:549–558.
8. McKee M, Steyger E. When can the European Union restrict trade on grounds of public health? *Journal of Public Health Medicine* 1997; 19:85–6.
9. European Parliament. Report on alleged contraventions or maladministration in the implementation of Community law in relation to BSE, without prejudice to the jurisdiction of the Community and national courts (Rapporteur: Medina Ortega M). Strasbourg, European Parliament, 1997.
10. McKee M, Lang T, Roberts J. Deregulating health: policy lessons of the BSE affair. *Journal of the Royal Society of Medicine* 1996; 89:424–6.
11. Anon. *BSE/Commission*. Reuter Edition 3; 15 January 1997.
12. Seldon T. Total weed killer. *Health Service Journal*. January 1997:16.
13. House of Commons Health Committee. *The European Community and Health Policy*, Health Committee Third Report, London: HMSO, 1992.
14. Directive 89/341 of May 1989, *Official Journal of the European Communities*, No. 142.
15. Directive 92/26, 1992, *Official Journal of the European Communities*, Vol. 113, 1992, p.5.
16. Directive 92/25, 1992, *Official Journal of the European Communities*, Vol. 113, 1992, p.1.
17. Directive 92/27, 1992, *Official Journal of the European Communities*, Vol. 113, 1992, p. 8.
18. Directive 92/28, 1992, *Official Journal of the European Communities*, Vol. 113, 1992, p.13.
19. Abel-Smith B., Mossialos E., Cost containment and health care reform: a study of the European Union, *Health Policy* 1994; 28(2):89–134.
20. Abel-Smith B, Mossialos E, Hancher L. *Regulation in Question: A Study of Regulating Expenditure on Medicines in Europe*. London: LSE Health, 1996.
21. Council Directive of 21 December 1988 relating to the transparency of measures regulating the pricing of medicinal products for human use and their inclusion in the scope of national health insurance systems, *Official Journal of the European Communities*, L40/8, 12.2.1989.
22. Earl-Slater A. Regulating the price of the UK's drugs: second thoughts after the government's first report. *BMJ* 1997; 314: 365–8.

23. European Commission, Communication from the Commission on the compatibility with article 30 of the EEC Treaty of measures taken by Member States relating to price controls and reimbursement of medicinal products, *Official Journal of the European Communities*, C310/7, 4.12.19986.
24. Freeman S, Health Care Provision in the EC, *AIDA Information Bulletin*. 1994; 47:120–122.
25. 92/49/EEC Third Council Directive on the coordination of laws, regulations and administrative provisions relating to direct insurance other than life insurance and amending Directives 73/239/EEC and 88/357/EEC.
26. Mossialos E, Le Grand J. (Eds) *Health Expenditure in the European Union: Cost and Control*, Ashgate, Aldershot, (forthcoming 1998).
27. European Commission, The impact and effectiveness of the Single Market. Communication from the Commission to the European Parliament and the Council. European Commission, COM(96) 520 final of 30 October 1996, Luxembourg, 1996.
28. Blouet J.F., Barnes S. The EU Makes (Slow) Progress on Harmonising Taxes. *The Wall Street Journal* 1994; April 7:8.
29. Kurunmaki, L. *Cost Containment and Health Care Reform in Ireland*. London: LSE Working Paper, 1997.
30. Coles SFS. *Telemedicine: The Rise of Digital Healthcare*. London Financial Times Report, London: 1995.
31. Directive of the European Parliament and the Council 95/46/EC of 24.10.95.
32. COM (96) 392 final of 30.08.96.
33. *Official Journal of the European Communities* C141, 13.05.1996.
34. *Official Journal of the European Communities* C 287, 09.11.1981.
35. *Official Journal of the European Communities* C 184, 23.07.1986.
36. Belcher P. EU Wakes Up to Public Health as a Public Issue. *Eurohealth* 1997; 3(1):1.
37. Belcher. P. Mossialos E. Health priorities for the European Intergovernmental Conference, *BMJ* 1997; 314:1637–8.

A view from the touch line: health services policy and management 1967–1997

Robert J Maxwell

My first working encounter with the National Health Service (NHS) was at the United Oxford Hospitals, as Oxford's main teaching hospitals were then known, in 1968. It began a preoccupation with health policy and health services management that has been more or less unbroken since then. As I retire from the King's Fund, it seems worth reflecting on what I have found fascinating and rewarding about the NHS: on what has changed and what has stayed the same.

The United Oxford Hospitals

In 1968 the Chairman of the Oxford Board of Governors was Eric Towler, a remarkable man, son of a Yorkshire miner who made a fortune in an oil and fuel supply company called Cawoods and also owned and farmed an estate at Glympton Park, near Woodstock. He was not only a man of great energy and determination, but also of considerable sensitivity, with a lifelong interest in medicine. The fundamental question he asked about the United Oxford Hospitals was why it was constantly short of money. Was it inefficient or was it underfunded? Himself coming from a commercial background, he turned to McKinsey and Company, management consultants, for advice. I had joined them 18 months previously, after eight years in a large international mining company, and was asked to manage the Oxford assignment.

We set out to learn everything we could about the group of hospitals that included the Radcliffe Infirmary, the Churchill, Cowley Road and the Slade, with the new John Radcliffe under construction. McKinsey was strong analytically and we compared Oxford's performance with other NHS hospitals, particularly the other provincial teaching centres.

We listened to the opinions of any staff who wanted to talk to us, which turned out to be very large numbers. We set up joint, inter-professional analytic teams, rather along the lines of today's process re-engineering teams, with the aim of improving value, whether by saving money through hospital closures (the Slade Hospital went as a result) or by rationalising the medical teams 'on take'.

Our conclusion, in answer to Eric Towler's question, was that Oxford was in some ways inefficient. Nevertheless it was also seriously underfunded for the work that it was trying to do. The reasons were partly historical: Oxford had developed relatively recently from a bread-and-butter district general hospital into a major teaching, research and referral centre. Moreover, it was still developing. Eric Towler's instinct when any medical or nursing post became vacant was to attract the strongest candidate he could find, provided that he or she would put collective interests before personal ones. That is a marvellous formula for developing an institution, but within the constraints of NHS funding it is one that is bound to lead to chronic financial crisis. The resulting arguments were taken to the national level, where Richard Crossman, then Secretary of State, was receptive. Change was also needed on the ground, to strengthen the management of the institution and to bring together into an effective team the whole body of its professional staff. We established a rudimentary form of clinical budgets and resource management, and the management structure that we introduced went beyond the later idea of clinical directorates, by bringing into the leadership of the whole institution a small group of four doctors, chosen jointly by their peers and by the institution, along with the Director of Nursing, a newly recruited Administrator (John Spencer from the Royal Marsden), the Finance Officer and the Chairman of the Board. For the next ten years, until overtaken by various reorganisations of the NHS and changes of people, it was a formula of institutional management that really worked.

What I took out of this experience was respect for the people involved, a fascination with medicine and nursing, a strong commitment to the NHS and what it was trying to do, and a sense that management in this field was weak. Better management, working in partnership with the health care professionals and the public interest, could transform the situation and this seemed immensely worthwhile. The sensation was as dramatic as catching a big wave and being swept along by its power.

One side-effect of all this was an article *How Sick are the Hospitals?*[1] that I wrote for Gordon Westerman, then Editor of the *British Journal of Hospital Medicine*. It achieved considerable notoriety at the time, with my being pursued by the media to a holiday cottage on Minorca. In it I said that we were spending too little on the NHS, wasting too much of what we did spend and changing our thinking methods too slowly. To my great regret, I had not cleared the text with Eric Towler, not expecting anything remotely like the impact that the piece briefly had. Fortunately, he forgave me and we remained lifelong friends, but not without some alarms in the upper reaches of McKinsey, which in general dislikes the intense glare of publicity that can arise in work for politically sensitive public services.

The New York Health and Hospitals Corporation

New York's public hospitals, about 18 of them at the time, were the providers of last resort for New York's poorer citizens. Some of them – for example, Bellevue – also had deservedly high reputations as teaching institutions: to have served your time in them and to have survived was a guarantee of clinical experience and human maturity.

The hospitals suffered from a number of problems familiar to the NHS, yet in even worse measure. They were under-funded. In financial management, personnel controls and supplies, they were subject to centralised city bureaucracy, and they were a political football.

In 1970 under Mayor Lindsay's reforming administration, these hospitals were to be taken out from direct government by the city into what today one might call an agency arrangement. There would be an independent board to run them, and they would be freed from detailed interference by the city.

Our job in McKinsey was to make this transformation happen. Eight or so large consultancy projects were established, with considerable dollar sums attached to them. We were responsible for one of the detailed assignments – to design a management information system – and for the overall co-ordination of them all. The nine months or so that I spent in New York were among the hardest of my working life, but the lessons were as much about what not to do as about what to do.

In the end, the appointed day for the Corporation's independence came and went, not because anyone was ready for it, but because that was the date set by the legislation. Much of the project work was of relatively limited value, not because it was bad work, but because the timing was wrong. With virtually no executive team in place for the new Corporation there was no effective client, except for the impressive Robert Derzon, Number 2 in the old New York City Department of Hospitals, who ultimately did not stay with the new organisation.

The danger of that combination of massive consultancy activity without an effective client was one lesson to take away. Another was that the new organisation came into being and survived, though it was never as independent of the City as its architects had intended: I was influenced by this later when Sir Richard Meyjes argued for an independent NHS agency, which never seemed to me feasible so long as its finance came from general taxation. A point of personal satisfaction was around the new Corporation's response to a change in the abortion laws. While I have grave misgivings about abortion on demand, it was necessary when the law changed on the first day of the new Health & Hospitals Corporation's existence, that the poorest citizens of New York should have the same access to terminations of pregnancy as those who could afford to pay. This we achieved by agreeing with the chiefs of gynaecology in each hospital what limited financial support they needed to offer the service required by law. They kept their side of the bargain and the service was provided.

The Republic of Ireland: The Health Act 1970

Next came Dublin, where the Irish Government was in process of implementing the Health Act 1970, establishing eight health boards, to be responsible for securing the provision of all health and social services, along with three regional hospital boards and Comhairle nan-Ospideal, a national hospital council. Our function was to assist the Department of Health to set up the detailed management arrangements for the new bodies. Curiously enough these remain today largely unchanged. We recommended for each health board a straightforward general management structure with one person in overall charge and then – depending on the size of the health board – two or three programme managers responsible for acute, long stay and community services. Gaining understanding and acceptance of the recommendations involved getting to know each part of Ireland, the personalities within it and their views.

One difficulty for us, I recall, was that we quickly concluded that the legislation involved one layer too many. Faced with local political backing for health boards, and professional backing for regional hospital boards, the Government had decided to have both. After one long meeting with the then Minister for Health (later President) Erskine Childers, he asked, with quiet amusement, whether we were telling him that the regional hospital boards were redundant. We were. The difficulty was finessed by establishing all the regional hospital boards and the National Hospital Council with a single staff. When it became obvious that one body could do the work, the change was relatively easy to make.

The Netherlands: A Protestant Association of Psychiatric Hospitals

In this instance the work involved advising a non-profit chain of half a dozen or so psychiatric hospitals on the mission of their association as a whole, as distinct from that of the individual hospitals, which were dispersed geographically and had strong individual identities. At the time I was struck by the strong thrust to community-based services in some of the hospitals, the deliberate use of change agents, i.e. people with special training in change management, and – compared with the UK – the relatively generous levels of funding. One dynamic hospital director took the view that a psychiatric hospital ought to be in a state of continuous change. To ensure that this was so, he was prepared to see that no building stood for more than ten years. It would have been hard to conceive of such boldness in the National Health Service.

The DHSS and the NHS Management Arrangements (The Grey Book)

In 1972, the Department of Health and Social Security, as it then was, set up a joint civil service and McKinsey team to examine its internal management arrangements. The team was jointly managed by Ron Matthews (later a Deputy Secretary) and myself, with Henry Strage of McKinsey as engagement director. Six months or so into the assignment, McKinsey was also appointed to work with a team from Brunel University, under Professor Elliott Jacques, in support of a joint DHSS/NHS Steering Committee, charged with developing the NHS management structures and processes for the 1974 reorganisation of the NHS. So the 'Grey Book' was born.[2]

It was felt that the two McKinsey teams should work independently of one another. So my influence on the Grey Book was minimal, although I often attended meetings of the Steering Committee and could follow the lines of thinking that emerged. The Grey Book has had a poor press and I would not want to defend it. To a degree it represents a high-water mark of a particular type of management thinking in the NHS. It is almost botanical in its obsession with definitions and relationships – the fruits of Brunel's NHS researches – and mechanistic in its prescriptions of how management must function in the new order. For its most criticised weakness, however, the reliance on consensus decisions in multi-disciplinary teams of equals, the DHS/NHS Steering Committee was much more responsible than either Brunel or McKinsey. The Steering

Committee was itself composed on the Noah's Ark principle (two of each kind of animal) and the idea of professional consensus was deeply ingrained in it.

Sir Keith Joseph who, as Secretary of State, was responsible for the 1974 NHS reorganisation, later came to recant. As so often with structural re-engineering, the aim was admirable: to draw upon management experience elsewhere and to unite the strands of the NHS (family practitioner services, community health services, and hospitals, including the teaching hospitals) into a single coherent whole. Unfortunately, the ends do not always justify the means. With hindsight, Sir Keith's recantation seems right. The prescribed management arrangements seem too prescriptive, too mechanistic and too 'closed'. It would have been better to propose some objectives and principles and encourage the learning to begin.

Health Care: The Growing Dilemma, 1974

My Oxford experiences of 1968/69 had committed me to health services in general and the NHS in particular. I believed – and still believe – this to be an enormously important field of human endeavour, in which management has a distinctive contribution to make, provided that it recognises good management to mean working with the health professions, not against them, and putting the public interest – patient and community – first.

International experience quickly persuaded me that the characteristics that had attracted me to the NHS were shared in some measure by health services elsewhere. I was more inclined than I should have been to believe that the NHS 'had it right'. I ranked UK medical and nursing standards high. I believed – and still believe – in the NHS that Nye Bevan and the post-war Attlee Government sought to create in Britain, based on the view that society is 'more serene, and spiritually healthier, if it knows that all its citizens have at the back of their consciousness the knowledge that not only themselves, but all their fellows, have access, when ill, to the best that medical skill can provide.'[3] I viewed as special virtues of the NHS the relative strength of British general practice – not so much as gatekeeper, but as a flexible medical resource, knowing the patient, the family and the paths into the health care system. And I was a firm believer (remember that I am, among other things, a management accountant) in the virtues of a capped budget to concentrate everyone's minds on issues of choice. As Lord Rutherford, the British physicist put it, 'We haven't the money, so we've got to think.'[4] Or, to put it another way, to recognise that public money is limited should lead to an acceptance that our collective duty is to use that money as best we can for the maximum number of patients. This is a stark (if not universally accepted) truth in the NHS. To focus the mind even more strongly, think about the same issues in a much poorer country, like Zambia. It has to be right to concentrate limited resources where they can do most good.

In 1974 I wrote a brief international study entitled *Health Care: The Growing Dilemma*.[5] It used the health statistics available to show variations between countries in death rates and disease patterns. While the trends over time were encouraging, in that health generally had improved, there was no evidence that higher health care spending guaranteed better health. Rather, what stood out forcibly was that health care spending was everywhere rising inexorably somewhat faster than Gross National Product. A law of diminishing returns almost certainly meant that each increase in spending produced smaller absolute gains. Where, I wondered, would this trend lead? Would there come a time when Governments were no longer prepared to contemplate substantially higher public spending on health care year by year, taking the view that they simply could not afford it?

The question was both obvious and timely. Even as I was writing and publishing the study, the oil crises of the mid-1970s were administering shocks to the economies of all the developed countries. By the late 1970s (by which time I had left McKinsey and was working at St Thomas' Hospital as Administrator to the Special Trustees) the international trends in health care spending were changing. Except in the United States, where expenditure trends continued to defy the laws of gravity, most governments had shown by 1980 that they could and would limit public expenditures on health. The next question was substantially more interesting. Granted that they knew how to limit medical care spending, where would they set the limits and why? How would they secure value from what they spent? How would they take the public and the health care professions along with them?

The Early Thatcher Years

Mrs Thatcher's election as Prime Minister of Britain in 1979 might have been expected to have immediate and dramatic implications for the NHS. But this was not so. Under Patrick Jenkin as Secretary of State for Social Services, one tier of the 1974 NHS structure was removed, the little-lamented Area tier. Norman Fowler's long rule as Secretary of State then began. He was pretty successful at fighting expenditure battles with the Treasury and at keeping the NHS out of the political limelight. Not only in the 1979 Conservative Party Election Manifesto, but again in 1983 and 1987, the NHS is not mentioned. Mrs Thatcher assured the electorate that 'The NHS is safe with us' and appeared to have no radical plans for it.

In NHS management terms, however, there was one development in these years that would prove radical and enduring, even though its beginning was low profile, even humdrum. In 1983 Norman Fowler asked Roy Griffiths, Managing Director of Sainsbury and an adviser to Mrs Thatcher, to conduct a review of resource management in the NHS. The result was a short, hard-hitting report, including the phrase that if Florence Nightingale were to enter the wards today she would make her way around them trying to find out who was in charge. His report – immediately accepted by Norman Fowler – laid the foundations for general management in the NHS. There was to be at any level one person in charge, no matter what professional discipline that person might come from. Throughout the Service, from the ward or its community equivalent to the Secretary of State, there was to be a general management spine committed to a common agenda.

By this time (1983) I was at the King's Fund and we had appointed Tom Evans from the London Business School as Director of the King's Fund College. Tom (brilliant, charismatic, brave) died all too soon from cancer. Before his death he had a dramatic influence on a generation of NHS managers and – reflecting a distinction that Roy Griffiths would have recognised – on NHS management, meaning the way that the Service in all its complexity is run. Roy Griffiths, at the suggestion of Cliff Graham, an unconventional civil servant who was working with him, asked

Tom and me to organise a dinner at the King's Fund to discuss his conclusions. Although ostensibly this was to enable him to take our views into account, it was soon clear that it was more an occasion for Roy Griffiths to explain and persuade.

The initial reactions in the NHS and the universities to Roy Griffiths' report were hostile. Tom and I by contrast took the view that it was up to the NHS to take hold of these ideas and to make good use of them. Tom seemed driven by an unconscious awareness of himself having limited time, and of how much there was to do in the management of the NHS. I felt that Roy Griffiths had underestimated the extent to which managing a professional enterprise is different: in my view consensus management had in many places worked much better than people now recognise. Nevertheless what he said deserved to be taken seriously and the Government had a right to listen to him. I therefore agreed wholeheartedly with Tom that our line must be to influence the NHS to use the Griffiths Report imaginatively and creatively – and I believe that this has in general been what has happened. Today I would never want to go back to the complexity and muddle of NHS management prior to the Griffiths Report and I would propagate the essence of its conclusions to any government anywhere in the world that is trying to incorporate into its health care system a capacity to get things done within resource constraints.

The 1987 Expenditure Crisis and Mrs Thatcher's NHS Review

The fundamental review of the NHS conducted by Mrs Thatcher and a small team of ministers in 1988 was not planned and deliberate, but was precipitated by events. 1987/88 was a particularly bad year for NHS funding. In the late autumn the presidents of the three premier Royal Colleges (Physicians, Surgeons and Obstetricians) put out a public statement condemning the Government and saying that the NHS was in imminent danger of collapse. Government denials failed to convince the public. Day by day the news headlines took up, echoed and extended the presidents' concerns, until Mrs Thatcher, in a television interview and in considerable anger, responded to their request for a Royal Commission by committing the Government to a Review to be led by herself.

Although triggered by public and professional concerns on financing, that turned out not to be the central focus of the Review. A look was taken at social insurance as an alternative to general taxation, but the idea appeared to be discarded relatively quickly. Thereafter the Review moved into more ideologically charged territory about the creation of a market in some form, using managed competition as a spur to efficiency.

When the Government's report appeared – as *Working for Patients*[6] – roughly twelve months after the Review had begun, it was about as unlike the Royal Commission report requested by the College presidents as one could imagine. To begin with, it made no commitments about funding, appearing to rest on the assumption that funding was not the issue, but rather the efficiency with which available funds used. Moreover the report, although commendably short, was not homogeneous. Among its seven key proposals were some that were certainly not new and were of limited importance – half an extra consultant post per health district, for example – and others that were potentially radical, but not necessarily compatible with one another. Among the radical ideas were much increased management autonomy for NHS providers, along with potential competition within and outside the NHS, a split between provision and purchasing, and the concept of GP fundholding. These last two ideas came from different intellectual parentages from one another – the health authority as the instrument of collective procurement of health care for the whole community within its boundaries, versus the GP as the proxy for the patients on his or her list. The two ideas seemed bound to prove incompatible with one another in the long run.

The Government (with, by now, Ken Clarke as Secretary of State for Health) was robustly against any form of piloting of its ideas, although there would in effect be some form of natural experiment, since the new NHS provider trusts and GP fundholders were to proceed in waves, based on an assessment of the readiness of willing volunteers. More arrogantly, the Government were also against systematic evaluation of the Reforms in practice – at least until Howard Glennester's research began to suggest some evidence of early gains for patients in fundholding practices.[7]

What was the Government aiming to achieve through *Working for Patients* and the associated legislation, the NHS and Community Care Act 1990? One view is that its ultimate intention was to privatise the NHS. I do not believe that for a moment. Apart from anything else, nobody who knew Ken Clarke could doubt his commitment to the NHS. Far more plausible is the view that what the Thatcher government was trying to do – based of course on its own assumptions and a Right Wing ideology – was to incorporate into the NHS market instruments that it believed would work better than those of the traditional Welfare State.

1997: the new Labour Government

Health featured surprisingly little in the 1997 General Election campaign. While the electorate – as judged by public opinion polls during the election period – trusted the Labour Party more than the Conservatives on health, Labour seemed reluctant to go on the attack and was also careful not to make any promises that would prove expensive to honour. Since the election, some strands of the new Government's health policy are emerging, but as yet these are at the level of statements of intent: what some of the statements mean is as yet unclear, and one has the impression that this is because the Government's health team is still working out the meaning. For example, the Government is committed to dismantling the internal market, but what does that actually mean and how will it be achieved?

The appointment for the first time of a Minister of State for Public Health, Tessa Jowell, indicates one policy thrust that is new. Other changes will include locality commissioning as an alternative to GP fundholding; a change in language – and perhaps in behaviour, though time will tell – from competition to co-operation in the relationships among providers; a shift from annual contracting by health authorities to longer-term service agreements; and an attempt to make all NHS authorities more democratic and more locally accountable. More ominously, the Secretary of State's call for fewer health authorities and trusts seems likely to set off yet another round of reorganisation: structural change in the NHS has so often proved to be a diversion, rather than a means of getting something done.

1967 to 1997: some personal reflections

I became fascinated by health care in 1967 and have remained so. I have no regrets about that. But what progress have we made in 30 years?

It seemed to me in 1967 – viewing the NHS with untutored eyes – that British medicine and nursing were of high quality, that the NHS provided a sound framework, but that its management was rather pedestrian. We ought to be able to do even better, and that ought not to be unduly difficult. My Oxford experience confirmed these views. At its best the NHS could be superb, and proving that it could be so was both enormously satisfying and worth devoting one's life to doing.

What is depressing 30 years later is to recognise that, despite much more sophisticated management now than then, my confidence in the NHS is in some ways less. It is not that standards of medical and nursing skill are lower or that the inefficiencies of the NHS are greater. Rather it is, I think, that because of the dramatic expansion of what is medically possible – expansion at a pace much greater than the increases in NHS funding – the job we are trying to do has become harder. There is a widening gap between Nye Bevan's benchmark that everyone should 'have access, when ill, to the best that medical skill can provide,'[8] and the service actually being provided. Nobody is more aware of this gap than the doctors and nurses working in the NHS. The public suspects it. In the main, governments deny it.

The NHS when established was a pacesetter in the provision of health care in a modern society. Other countries since then have sought the same ends by different means. The ends, however, are pretty universal. They are – see Box below – that health care should be available to all – an equity criterion; that it should include everything that is worth doing – a comprehensiveness criterion; and that it should be of high quality – a quality criterion. The problem may now be – as Professor Albert Weale has suggested[9] – that it is no longer possible to achieve these three ends simultaneously. If we are willing to put up with an inequitable system, there is no problem about the second and third ends. But if all three ends are crucial, then we do have a problem. Ignoring it, will not make it go away. Indeed, unless the trends of the past 30 years change, and there is no reason why they should, the situation will steadily worsen.

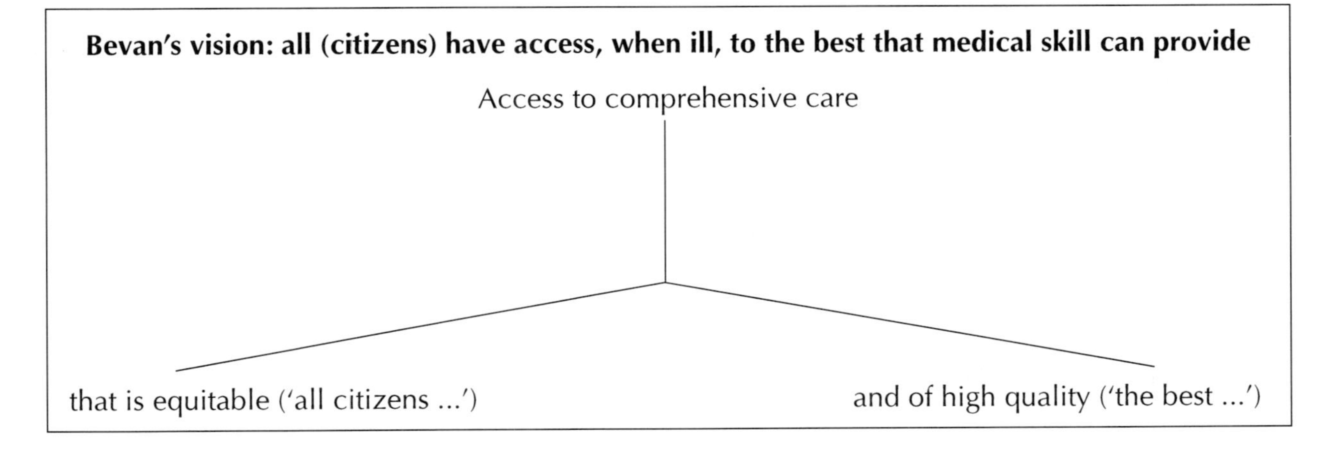

While this analysis may seem abstract and theoretical, it helps to explain why the malaise that currently afflicts the NHS is not a national but an international phenomenon. Even countries like Sweden, Canada, Germany, that for a while have had very stable health care systems, seem much less complacent now than 20 years ago that they have all the answers.

If the analysis is correct, then what is to be done? After four major reorganisations of the NHS in the past 25 years, I am extremely resistant to any ideas of a heroic quick fix. But the NHS must be run as well as we collectively can run it, and the health of Britons must be as good as we can make it. Any step towards making easier the simultaneous achievement of our three fundamental ends is worth taking, even though its contribution is limited. In this spirit seven themes are worth pursuing. There may, of course, be others – the list is not necessarily comprehensive and complete.

1. *Leadership is crucial. It must involve the clinicians and be publicly accountable.* Sir Roy Griffiths was right: strong general management is a necessary requirement, but it is not sufficient. As a Malay proverb has it, 'Clapping with the right hand only will not produce a noise'. It is essential that the clinicians trust the leadership of the enterprise, and that the leadership understands the current experiences of patients and the dilemmas facing those treating them. It is also essential that there is enough public voice in the leadership to satisfy accountability requirements and to make the enterprise and the community responsive to one another.

   This is absolutely not a matter of adopting a particular structure (clinical directorates, for example) and assuming all will be well. Structures do not by themselves deliver trust and responsiveness, though they may help. The point is not to try to dump the intensely difficult problems of health care management on the clinicians, but to secure their insight, commitment and creative energy, and to weld the individual institution and the NHS as a whole to the community.

2. *Evidence will not resolve all our dilemmas, but it will help.* Evidence-based medicine has a substantial contribution to make to sharpening the therapeutic focus and reducing activity that is of low benefit. 'What is the evidence for this?' is a good question to ask, even though we must avoid assuming that the answers are simple. Moreover, the request for evidence should go broader than simply a procedure or a therapeutic programme. It can apply – as, for example, the Rand health insurance studies[10] demonstrated in the USA – to financing and organisational questions also. Not only medicine, but also management, should answer the call for actions to be based on evidence.

3. *People should be more involved in their own health and health care than has generally been the case in the NHS, and better informed. We also need more citizen involvement (reflecting an increasingly heterogeneous society) in broader health and health care issues.* This is not just political correctness. While some clinicians will rightly quote many instances where patients respond to information about treatment choices by saying, 'Whatever you think best, doctor', the fact is that practice has already changed perceptibly and will

continue to change. Many patients are less passive than they once were, and many clinicians are less paternalistic (or maternalistic, as the case may be). The change strikes me forcibly when I sit in on clinical consultations now, compared with 30 years ago. There are some shining examples of talking through with patients how to monitor their health, how to look after themselves, what the treatment choices are. But there is still a long way to go.

There has been less progress on citizen involvement, though techniques like focus groups, citizens' juries and 'open space' events are beginning to make a contribution. The point is that as ordinary citizens, with enormously diverse points of view, we need to influence and understand what the NHS is doing, the constraints under which it is working at current funding levels, and the choices that are open.

Neither at the individual nor at the collective level will the NHS work satisfactorily on the analogy of car maintenance and repair. We have to take more responsibility than that for our own health, and for the way in which the NHS is run. Moreover, the NHS has to move on from the Henry Ford concept of popular choice – you can have any car so long as it is black – to one that recognises the profoundly different views about health and health care that are held within a culturally diverse society.

4. *We have to tackle inequalities.* Health inequalities are extreme and have increased in Britain in the Thatcher years. They are related to income, education and race. To be true to Bevan's vision we must tackle health inequalities seriously and systematically.

5. *The new Government's emphasis on public health is correct.* One of the themes that will not go away is a tension between the view that the NHS is about health care and the view that it is about health. National policy has to be about both. Housing, employment, education, transport, food, the environment, all have profound influences on the nation's health – including inequalities in health. At last this is recognised through the appointment of a Minister of State for Public Health, which creates the opportunity to pursue health through other routes besides health care, and to monitor the impact of other policies on health. Just as the Treasury has a responsibility to oversee and protect the economic well-being in Britain, so the Minister of Public Health has a parallel responsibility for human well-being. This surely is appropriate in what Bevan would have envisaged as a healthy society.

6. *At all levels in the NHS there should be a systematic pursuit of value for money.* In the days when I first worked for the NHS we called this value improvement. Today it is, I would argue, what process re-engineering at its best is about.[11] What it calls for is a multi-disciplinary, evidence-based approach to working out how to do better what we are trying to do, not merely (nor even mainly) in support services, but also in mainline clinical activities.

7. *Rationing is inescapable in the NHS, and is often done secretively, even without knowing that it is happening. That it happens should be understood, and how best to do it requires more, and better informed, public discussion.*

Envoi

The NHS is nearly 50, whereas when I first became involved it was only 20. On its tenth anniversary, speaking in the House of Commons, Bevan described the NHS as 'the most civilised achievement of modern Government.'[12] I agree with that, but the challenges that face us now and in the future are such that we must not for one moment be complacent. Nor, on the other hand, should we be defeatist. There are several ways forward that offer the opportunity to strengthen the NHS. We should take some of them, learning as we go along and maintaining our commitment to the vision of a service that is ambitious to deliver for all, when sick, the best that medical care can provide.

References

1 Maxwell R. How sick are the hospitals? *British Journal of Hospital Medicine* 1969, April pp. 895–9

2 DHSS. *Management Arrangements for the Reorganised National Health Service*. London: HMSO, 1972

3 Foot M. *Aneurin Bevan 1945–1960*. Paladin Books, 1975, p103

4 Rutherford E, quoted in Mackay AL. *The Harvest of a Quite Eye: A Selection of Scientific Quotations*. The Institute of Physics, 1977, p131

5 Maxwell R. *Health Care: The Growing Dilemma*. McKinsey and Company, New York, 1974

6 Secretaries of State for Health, Wales, Northern Ireland and Scotland. *Working for Patients*. London: HMSO, Jan 1989

7 Glennerster H, Matsaganis M, Owens P. A *Foothold for Fundholding*. Research Report No. 12, London: King's Fund Institute, 1992

8. See 3

9 Weale A, paper on *What should be rationed?* at a Royal College of Physicians Conference on 'Choosing Priorities in the NHS', 19 May 1997

10 Newhouse J P, Manning W G, Morris C N *et al*. Some Interim Results from a controlled trial of cost sharing in health insurance. *New England Journal of Medicine* 1981; 305:1501–7

11 Homa P. *Re-engineering the Leicester Royal Infirmary Healthcare Process*. Doctoral thesis, unpublished, 1997